Precalculus

A Functional Approach with Applications

Precalculus

A Functional Approach with Applications

SALVATORE BARBASSO

State University of New York, Farmingdale

JOHN IMPAGLIAZZO

State University of New York, Farmingdale

HARCOURT BRACE JOVANOVICH, INC.

New York   Chicago   San Francisco   Atlanta

To my wife Annamaria, and my children Loretta and Stelio   J. I.

To my sons Adam, Eric, David and a new tomorrow   S. B.

ISBN: 0-15-571050-8

Library of Congress Catalog Card Number: 77-70575

Printed in the United States of America

PREFACE

This book is designed for a one- or two-semester precalculus course taken by both mathematics and nonmathematics majors. Although the text is primarily intended to provide a background in elementary functions for students who will eventually pursue a calculus sequence, it can also be used effectively by students engaged in a noncalculus, applications-oriented field of study.

A course of this nature has two fundamental objectives. First, it consolidates many of the mathematical concepts and skills to which the student has already been exposed. Second, it builds on these concepts in order to improve the student's ability to cope with more advanced concepts in both pure and applied mathematics. For these reasons, the student should be prepared with a minimum background of intermediate algebra or its equivalent.

The text is organized in a conventional sequence of topic development, except for three instances. To allow for early treatment, the circular/trigonometric functions are introduced prior to exponential and logarithmic functions; hence, discussion on polynomial zeros and rational functions appears later in the text. Also, to allow the instructor greater flexibility, sequences, induction, and series are discussed in a separate chapter.

The exercises are usually presented in three levels of difficulty—Set A, Set B, and Set C. Set A exercises are of a basic nature and within the ability of all students. Set B exercises are more challenging, and Set C exercises require some mathematical sophistication and are intended for the better student. In addition, the text includes examples and exercises of a numerical character designed to reinforce one or more of the mathematical concepts presented. Such examples and exercises, denoted by the symbol ●, help illustrate how the accuracy and speed of the electronic calculator are used to evaluate problems whose entries are not necessarily of the integer type. Important equations are highlighted by the symbol ▶.

The text also provides special features and topics not usually found in texts of a similar nature. These include: the direct sum of sets and its use in defining the set of complex numbers, accuracy and precision of approximate numbers, the use of contemporary mathematical notation, an in-depth discussion of composite and inverse functions, implicit functions, functional symmetry, the step, signum, and ramp functions, and planar translation. Furthermore, it includes a lucid development of circular/trigonometric functions by the consolidation of geometric angle with the real-valued argument of these functions, a discussion and development of the exponential function base conditions, the complex number use of Euler's Identity, and logarithms with negative arguments.

We wish to thank our editor, Marilyn Davis, for undaunted faith and encouragement in the development of this text. In addition, special thanks to our manuscript editor, Judith Burke, and our copy editor, Karen Bierstedt, for their outstanding efforts and attention to detail.

We wish to thank C. F. Blakemore of the University of New Orleans, Ben Bockstege of Broward Community College, Charles Murray of Chabot College, Gerald Ludden of Michigan State University, Greg McNeil of Foothill College, Robert Nowlan of Southern Connecticut State College, Frank Salzmann of Florida Technological University, and Erik A. Schreiner of Western Michigan University for their comments and reviews.

We also wish to thank our colleagues Joan Gardner, Nicholas Harding, Emmanuel Kondopirakis, Michael Laudante, and Philip Reichmeider of SUNY Farmingdale for their assistance with the manuscript and exercises. Lastly, thanks to Barbara Golden of SUNY Farmingdale and William Kane of Adelphi University who read and class tested the manuscript.

SALVATORE BARBASSO
JOHN IMPAGLIAZZO

CONTENTS

Functions and Relations

Linear Functions

Quadratic Relations

Circular (Trigonometric) Functions

Properties of the Circular Functions

The Exponential and Logarithmic Functions

Complex Numbers

Polynomial and Rational Functions

Induction—Sequences and Series

Precalculus

A Functional Approach with Applications

Sets and Numbers

1-1 ELEMENTARY SET THEORY

In mathematics, it is often necessary to classify or collect objects. The concept used to accomplish this is called a *set*. This concept is too basic for formal definition, but we can say that a set is any collection of distinct objects, which are usually (but not necessarily) related in some manner. A set is *well defined* if, given any object, it is clear whether the object belongs to the set or not. It is not necessary that a set consist solely of mathematically oriented objects. However, the sets that will be of the most interest to us will be sets composed of numerical quantities related in some manner.

Set Notation

Sets are symbolized by capital letters (*A*, *B*, and so on). The objects contained within a set, called *elements*, are listed with commas between them and are enclosed by braces. The order in which the elements are listed is of no importance, but every distinct element of the set must be listed. For example, the elements of set *A* might be the brand names of the first five cars passing a tollbooth on a particular day. If these cars are a Ford, a Rambler, a Chevrolet, a Dodge, and a Ford, then set A would be written

$$A = \{\text{Ford, Rambler, Chevrolet, Dodge}\}$$

Note that even though two Fords passed the tollbooth, the name "Ford" is considered one element, since no information is given (such as model or style) to enable us to distinguish between the two Fords.

In order to indicate that an object is an element of a set, we use the symbol $\in$. Thus, we can write Ford $\in A$, read "Ford is an element of A." The symbol $\notin$ means "is *not* an element of," so we can also write Plymouth $\notin A$, read "Plymouth is not an element of A."

As another example, consider the set B of whole numbers from 1 to 9, which can be written

$$B = \{1, 2, 3, 4, 5, 6, 7, 8, 9\}$$

Another way of writing this set is by the use of *set builder notation*:

$$B = \{x \mid x \text{ is a whole number and } x \text{ is between 1 and 9 inclusive}\}$$

This notation is read "B is the set of elements x such that x is a whole number and x is between 1 and 9 inclusive." As an example of the usefulness of set-builder notation, consider the set E composed of all positive even numbers. To list every positive even number would be impossible, since there exist an infinite number of them. However, in set-builder notation, the set can be easily written as

$$E = \{x \mid x \text{ is a positive even number}\}$$

Set-builder notation enables us to write, in a concise form, complicated sets that may even contain an infinite number of elements.

Sets containing a finite number of elements are called *finite sets*, and sets containing an infinite number of elements are called *infinite sets*. Although infinite sets are used extensively in this book, we will not discuss them, because the set concepts and operations encountered do not depend on the distinction between finite and infinite sets.

Special Sets

Certain special sets are quite useful in the analysis of complex problems. Suppose a researcher is exclusively studying the population of an island. Then all the elements of any set considered by the researcher would come from the island's population, and as far as the researcher is concerned, the external world does not exist for the problem being studied. The island's population is said to be the *universal set* for the problem under study.

> **DEFINITION** The **universal set** for any problem, denoted U, is the most general set from which the elements of all other sets under consideration are drawn.

As a numerical example, suppose a problem arose in which the only numbers under consideration were the whole numbers from 21 through 30. (For instance, these numbers might be the ages of the students at a particular graduate school.) Then this set would be the universal set for the problem and would be denoted

$$U = \{21, 22, 23, 24, 25, 26, 27, 28, 29, 30\}$$

Another special set that arises often is the set containing no elements. For example, what is the set of all numbers x such that $x = x + 1$? Obviously, there are no such numbers, so this set contains no elements and is said to be *empty* or *null*.

> **DEFINITION** A set containing no elements is called a **null set** or **empty set** and is symbolized by $\varnothing$.

This set can also be expressed as $\varnothing = \{\ \}$. Note that this is different from the set $\{0\}$, which is the set containing only the number 0 (zero).

Set Relationships

Sometimes we wish to consider only part of a set. Suppose the universal set for a problem was all the letters of the English alphabet and we wished to consider only the vowels. In this case, we could form a set consisting of the elements a, e, i, o, and u, which are all members of the original alphabet. The collection of vowels can thus be considered a part, or *subset*, of the original alphabet.

> **DEFINITION** If A and B are two sets and if all the elements of B are also elements of A, then B is a **subset** of A. Symbolically, this is written $B \subseteq A$.

If it happens that all the elements of B are elements of A but not all the elements of A are elements of B, then B is called a *proper subset* of A. Symbolically, this is written

$$B \subset A$$

For example, the set of vowels is a proper subset of the alphabet, because there exists at least one letter of the alphabet (say, q) that is not a vowel. Note that the null set, $\varnothing$, is a subset of every set. This is easily seen, because if $\varnothing$ were not a subset of some set A, then $\varnothing$ would contain at least one element that was not in A. But $\varnothing$ has no elements at all. Thus, it must be true that $\varnothing \subseteq A$.

Two otherwise unrelated sets may have the same number of distinct elements. For example, $R = \{a, 1, v, 3\}$ and $S = \{\#, \$, 7, g\}$ each have four elements. We say that set R is *equivalent* to set S.

DEFINITION   Two sets A and B are **equivalent** if they contain the same number of distinct elements. This is denoted $A \sim B$.

For the sets R and S described above, we have $R \sim S$. Note that the set $T = \{a, q, v, a\}$ is *not* equivalent to R, because T contains only three distinct elements.

In order to measure the "size" of a set, the concept of *cardinality*, or *cardinal number*, is often employed.

DEFINITION   The **cardinality** of a set A, denoted $N(A)$, is the number of distinct elements in A.

The notation $N(A)$ is read "N of A." For the three sets R, S, and T above, we have

$$N(R) = 4 \qquad N(S) = 4 \qquad N(T) = 3$$

The concept of cardinality can be used to give an alternative definition for equivalence.

DEFINITION   Two sets are **equivalent** if they have the same cardinality.

For the sets R and S previously mentioned, since $N(R) = N(S) = 4$, then $R \sim S$.

A special case of equivalence occurs when two sets have not only the same number of elements but also *identical* elements. In this instance, the sets are said to be *equal*. The subset concept can be used to state the definition of equality.

DEFINITION   Two sets A and B are said to be **equal** if both $A \subseteq B$ and $B \subseteq A$.

Thus, if $F = \{4, \$, q\}$ and $G = \{q, 4, \$\}$, then set F is equal to set G, or simply $F = G$. However, if $H = \{q, 5, \$\}$, then $H \neq F$, even though $H \sim F$.

EXAMPLE 1-1   Consider the sets

$$A = \{1, 3, 5\} \qquad B = \{5, 7, 2\} \qquad C = \{5, 4\}$$
$$D = \varnothing \qquad\qquad E = \{5, 1, 3\}$$

Find the cardinality of each set. Determine which sets are equivalent and which sets are equal.

The cardinalities of these sets are $N(A) = 3$, $N(B) = 3$, $N(C) = 2$, $N(D) = 0$, and $N(E) = 3$.

Equivalent sets: $A \sim B \sim E$.

Equal sets: $A = E$.

Venn Diagrams—Set Operations

A pictorial representation of a mathematical system is often helpful in interpreting and solving problems relating to the system. In set theory, *Venn diagrams* are used to help develop solutions to complex problems. These diagrams serve to show the relationships among the various sets contained within some specified universal set. For example, let U be the set of letters of the English alphabet; then, as previously noted, the set V of vowels is a proper subset of U. The set $T = \{a, u\}$ is a proper subset of V, so we have $T \subset V \subset U$. Figure 1-1 is the Venn diagram illustrating this relationship. The universal set U is usually represented by a rectangle, and the sets contained in U are usually represented by simple closed curves such as circles.

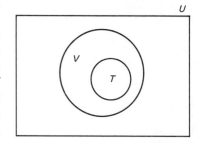

FIGURE 1-1

One might ask, What is the region outside set V but still within set U? Clearly, this region represents the set of consonants. We call it the *complement* of V.

> **DEFINITION** Let $A \subseteq U$. The **complement** of A, denoted A', is the set composed of all elements of U that are not elements of A.

Hence, the set of consonants can be represented by V'. Figure 1-2 shows the relationship between V, V', and U.

Let $U = \{1, 2, 3, 4, 5, 6, 7, 8, 9, 10\}$, $A = \{1, 2, 3, 4, 5\}$, and $B = \{3, 5, 7, 9\}$. Figure 1-3 shows the Venn diagram for these sets. Notice that A and B overlap; the overlapping portion is called the *intersection* of A and B.

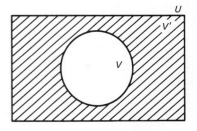

FIGURE 1-2

> **DEFINITION** If A and B are two sets, the **intersection** of A and B, denoted $A \cap B$, is the set of all elements common to both A *and* B.

From Figure 1-3, we can see that $A \cap B = \{3, 5\}$.

Figure 1-3 also suggests that two sets A and B can be joined to form a new set, called their *union*.

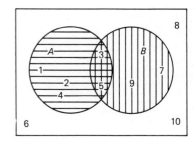

FIGURE 1-3

> **DEFINITION** If A and B are two sets, the **union** of set A with set B, denoted $A \cup B$, is the set of elements that belong to set A *or* to set B (or to both A and B).

In Figure 1-3, we see that $A \cup B = \{1, 2, 3, 4, 5, 7, 9\}$. Note that the elements common to A and B (3 and 5) are listed only once. In summary, for the sets shown in Figure 1-3,

$$A \cap B = \{3, 5\} \quad \text{and} \quad A \cup B = \{1, 2, 3, 4, 5, 7, 9\}$$

Two sets that have no elements in common are said to be *disjoint*. Figure 1-4 shows two disjoint sets. Here, $U = \{1, 2, 3, 4, 5, 6, 7, 8, 9, 10\}$, $A = \{2, 4, 6\}$, and $B = \{1, 7, 9\}$. Clearly, $A \cap B = \varnothing$.

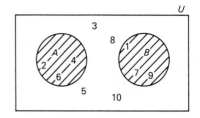

FIGURE 1-4

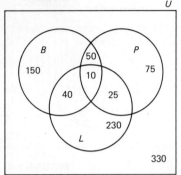

FIGURE 1-5

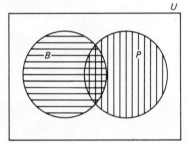

$B \cup P$ (lined regions)

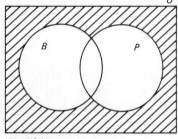

$(B \cup P)'$ (lined regions)

FIGURE 1-6

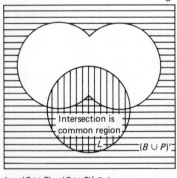

$L - (B \cup P) = (B \cup P)' \cap L$

FIGURE 1-7

DEFINITION Two nonempty sets A and B are **disjoint** if $A \cap B = \varnothing$.

In constructing Venn diagrams, it is important that the set relationships be clearly indicated (e.g., which sets intersect, which do not, which are contained within others). The geometric shapes used to represent sets are unimportant. Some additional examples will show how Venn diagrams are used to solve problems. First, however, we define a few more terms.

The complement defined earlier was with respect to the universal set; that is, we considered the set of elements in U but not in A. Sometimes, however, it is necessary to take the complement of a set relative to another set contained in the universal set.

DEFINITION Let $A \subseteq U$ and $B \subseteq U$. Then the **difference** between sets B and A, denoted $B - A$, is the set

$$B - A = \{x \mid x \in B \text{ and } x \notin A\}$$
$$= B \cap A'$$

The set $B - A$ is the complement of A relative to B.

EXAMPLE 1-2 Let

$$U = \{1, 2, 3, \ldots, 10\} \qquad A = \{1, 2, 3\} \qquad B = \{1, 2, 4, 5, 8\}$$

Then $B - A = \{4, 5, 8\}$, and $A - B = \{3\}$.

EXAMPLE 1-3 Figure 1-5 shows the Venn diagram for a college course survey taken by the dean. Set B represents the students taking biology, P the students taking physics, and L the students taking literature. The universal set, U, represents the sophomore student body for which the analysis was taken. (Note that there are students taking one or more of the courses and students taking none of the courses.) Find the number of students contained in each of the following sets:

(a) $(B \cup P)' \cap L = L - (B \cup P)$
(b) $P' \cap (B \cap L') = (B \cap L') - P = (B - L) - P$

These problems have similar methods of solution, which will be carried out in two parts. The sets contained within the parentheses must be found first. Consider problem (a). The sets involved in the parentheses are B and P. The required sequence is first to form the union of these sets and then to take the complement of this union. Figure 1-6 shows these two steps. The problem calls next for the intersection of the set $(B \cup P)'$ with set L. The cross-hatched region in Figure 1-7 is the resulting set. From Figure 1-5, we see that the number of students contained in this region is 230. Note that this region represents those students registered for literature but not for biology or physics.

In problem (b), the sequence is different. First, we must find the intersection of set B with the complement of L, and then the intersection of the resulting set with the complement of P. Figure 1-8 shows the set $B \cap L'$, and Figure 1-9 shows the final result. Note that this region represents those students registered in biology but not in physics or literature. From Figure 1-5, we see that the number of students contained in this region is 150.

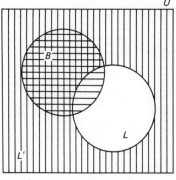

$(B \cap L') = B - L$ is common region

The student should note the technique used in these examples. First, the sets in the parentheses were found as if they were separate problems. Then these sets were used in the remaining parts of the problem. If such problems are done in steps, there is much less confusion, and the regions to be identified are not obscured.

Set Summation   don't have to know

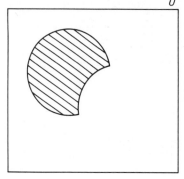

$(B \cap L)' = B - L$

It is natural to ask whether there is any significance to the *sum* of two sets A and B. If the elements of A and B are numbers, we can construct a new set by summing elements of A and elements of B.

> **DEFINITION**   Let A and B be sets. Then the **sum** of A and B, denoted by $A + B$, is the set
>
> $$A + B = \{x + y \mid x \in A \text{ and } y \in B\}$$

EXAMPLE 1-4   Let $A = \{a, b, c\}$ and $B = \{g, h\}$. Then $b + h \in A + B$.

FIGURE 1-8

EXAMPLE 1-5   Let $A = \{a, b, c\}$ and $B = \{b, c, d\}$. Then $a + d \in A + B$, but we also have $a + b \in A + B$ and $b + c \in A + B$.

Note that in the first example, A and B are disjoint, so elements of $A + B$ could be constructed only as one from A plus one from B. In the second example, an element such as $a + b$ could be constructed from elements of A alone as well as from A and B. To avoid this confusion, a special sum of sets, called the *direct sum*, is defined.

> **DEFINITION**   Let A and B be sets such that $A \cap B = \{0\}$. Then the **direct sum** of A and B, denoted $A \oplus B$, is the set
>
> $$A \oplus B = \{x + y \mid x \in A \text{ and } y \in B \text{ where } A \cap B = \{0\}\}.$$

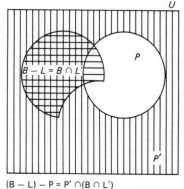

$(B - L) - P = P' \cap (B \cap L')$
is common region

Note that A and B *must* have exactly one element, 0, in common; otherwise, $A \oplus B$ is not defined.

EXAMPLE 1-6   Let $A = \{0, 3, 5\}$ and $B = \{0, 2, 4\}$; then $7 = 3 + 4 \in A \oplus B$, but $14 \notin A \oplus B$ and $8 = 3 + 5 \notin A \oplus B$.

FIGURE 1-9

EXERCISES 1-1

Set A

1. Let $U = \{2, 3, 4, 5, 6\}$, and let $A = \{2, 3\}$, $B = \{3, 4, 5\}$, and $C = \{5, 6\}$. Find the following sets:
    (a) A' (b) C' (c) $A \cup B$ (d) $B \cup C$
    (e) $A \cap B$ (f) $A \cap C$ (g) $A \cup \varnothing$ (h) $A \cap U$
    (i) $(B \cap \varnothing)'$ (j) $(B \cap C)'$

2. Let $U = \{1, 2, 3, 4, 5, 6, 7, 8, 9, 10\}$ and $A = \{1, 3, 5, 7, 9\}$.
    (a) Find A'.
    (b) Find $A \cap A'$ and $A \cup A'$.
    (c) Let $B = \{1, 2, 3, 4, 5, 6\}$ and $C = \{2, 3, 4\}$. Find $B \cap C$ and $B \cup C$.

3. Exercises 2(b) and 2(c) illustrate two of the general properties of sets, namely, that
    (a) if $A \subseteq U$, then $A \cup A' = U$ and $A \cap A' = \varnothing$.
    (b) if $C \subseteq B$, then $C \cup B = B$ and $C \cap B = C$.
    Draw Venn diagrams showing these properties.

4. Let $A = \{1, 2, 3, 4, 5, 6\}$, $B = \{2, 3, 4, 9\}$, $C = \{1, 4, 5, 7, 9\}$, and $D = \{2, 3, 4, 9\}$. Find the sets $A \cap B$, $A \cap C$, $B \cup C$, $D \cup C$, $B \cap D$, and $A \cup B$.

5. For the sets described in Exercise 4, find
    (a) $N(A \cap B)$ (b) $N(A \cap C)$
    (c) $N(B \cup C)$ (d) $N(D \cup C)$
    (e) $N(B \cap D)$ (f) $N(A \cup B)$

6. (a) From the results of Exercises 4 and 5, which sets are equivalent?
    (b) Which sets are equal?

7. For the Venn diagram shown in Figure 1-10, find the following:
    (a) A (b) B
    (c) $A \cup B$ (d) $N(A)$
    (e) $N(B)$ (f) $N(A \cap B)$

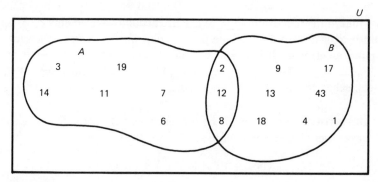

FIGURE 1-10

Set B

8. De Morgan's Theorem for sets states the two following properties:
    (a) $(A \cup B)' = A' \cap B'$
    (b) $(A \cap B)' = A' \cup B'$

Use Venn diagrams like the one in Figure 1-11 to illustrate these properties. (*Hint*: For each equation, draw two Venn diagrams, one representing each side of the equation, and show that the resulting regions
are the same.)

9. Use Venn diagrams like the one in Figure 1-11 to show that for any
   sets A and B,
   $A \cap B \subseteq A \cup B$.

10. Use the Venn diagram in Figure 1-10 to illustrate the following formula:
    $N(A \cup B) = N(A) + N(B) - N(A \cap B)$

11. By definition, the set $A - B = \{x \mid x \in A, \text{ and } x \notin B\}$.
    (a) Illustrate $A - B$ using a Venn diagram.
    (b) Illustrate $B - A$ using a Venn diagram.
    (c) Using Venn diagrams, show that the statement $A - B = A \cap B'$
        is true for any sets A and B.
    (d) What conditions must be placed on sets A and B for the following
        statement to be true?
        $$[(A - B) \cup (B - A)]' = A \cap B$$

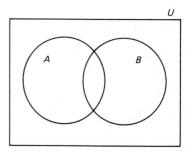

FIGURE 1-11

12. Let $A = \{0, 1, 2\}$, $B = \{0, 3\}$, and $C = \{2, 5\}$. Find, if possible, the
    elements of the following sets:
    (a) $B - A$ (b) $A - B$
    (c) $A + B$ (d) $B + C$
    (e) $A \oplus B$ (f) $B \oplus C$
    (g) $A \oplus C$ (h) $A + C$

13. Prove the following statements:
    (a) $A + B = B + A$ for any sets A and B.
    (b) $A \oplus B = B \oplus A$ for any sets A and B such that $A \cap B = \{0\}$.

Set C

14. A blood bank classifies blood received from its donors according to the
    presence or absence of the antigens A, B, and Rh, as shown in Table 1-1.
    The number of donors of each type of blood during a particular week is
    also shown.

TABLE 1-1

A	B	Rh	Blood type	Number of donors
Yes	No	Yes	A+	70
Yes	No	No	A−	10
Yes	Yes	Yes	AB+	7
Yes	Yes	No	AB−	1
No	Yes	Yes	B+	18
No	Yes	No	B−	3
No	No	Yes	O+	80
No	No	No	O−	11

(a) Using Figure 1-12 as a guide, label each of the subregions according to blood type.
(b) How many donors had a positive Rh factor?
(c) How many donors had at least an A antigen present in their blood?
(d) How many donors had at least a B antigen present in their blood?
(e) How many donors gave blood to the blood bank that week?

U = Blood types

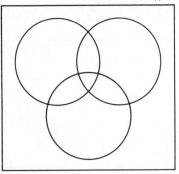

FIGURE 1-12

1-2 HIERARCHY OF NUMBERS

We have all been familiar, since childhood, with the use of different types of numbers. Children first use numbers when they learn to count individual objects. Later, the concepts of fractional parts of an object and negative amounts become familiar and are used, for example, in connection with monetary transactions. In mathematics, these concepts are formally incorporated into the *hierarchy of numbers*. This section discusses the various sets of numbers that make up this hierarchy and the relationships between them.

Subsets of Real Numbers

The most fundamental set of numbers is the set of *natural numbers* or *counting numbers*, defined as

$$\mathbb{N} = \{1, 2, 3, 4, \ldots\}$$

Here, the three dots indicate that the pattern of numbers continues indefinitely, that is, that there is no last element. If the set of counting numbers is extended to include the number 0, then the set $\mathbb{W}$ of *whole numbers* is formed:

$$\mathbb{W} = \{0, 1, 2, 3, 4, \ldots\} = \mathbb{N} \cup \{0\}$$

Every whole number except 0 has a distinct negative counterpart. The set $\mathbb{J}$ consisting of the whole numbers and their negatives, is called the set of *integers*.

$$\mathbb{J} = \{\ldots, -3, -2, -1, 0, 1, 2, 3, \ldots\}$$

Now consider the situation where a 6-acre plot of land is to be divided among three people so that one person receives twice as much land as each of the others. Then the first person receives 3 acres, and each of the others receives $1\frac{1}{2}$ acres, or 3/2 acres. The number 3/2 is not an integer but the ratio of two integers. Such numbers are called *rational numbers*. Other examples of rational numbers are 1/2, $-7/9$, 0/2, 13/6, 3/8, and $6/-3$. The set of rational numbers is defined as

$$\mathbb{Q} = \left\{ \frac{a}{b} \,\middle|\, b \neq 0 \text{ and } a, b \in \mathbb{J} \right\}$$

DEFINITION The number x is a **rational number** if it can be represented as a ratio of two integers, a/b, with $b \neq 0$.

Note that such numbers as 2/1, −3/1, and 4/1 are both integers and rational numbers. Since every integer a can also be written in the form of the rational number $a/1$, we see that $\mathbb{J} \subset \mathbb{Q}$. Clearly, then, there are an infinite number of rational numbers. The rational numbers can also be characterized by the fact that they have *terminating* or *repeating* *decimal representations*.

EXAMPLE 1-7 The number 2.1 is a rational number because it can be represented by the ratio $\frac{21}{10}$. Similarly, the number 0.002 can be rewritten as $\frac{2}{1000}$, 300.68 as $\frac{30068}{100}$, and 0.04109 as $\frac{4109}{100000}$.

EXAMPLE 1-8 Consider the number 3.45252525252..., which by convention is represented as $3.4\overline{52}$ (where the bar means that the digits 52 repeat indefinitely). This is a rational number. We can see this by letting $n = 3.4\overline{52}$. Then $1000n = 3452.\overline{52}$ and $10n = 34.\overline{52}$. Subtracting, we obtain

$$1000n - 10n = 3452.\overline{52} - 34.\overline{52}$$
$$990n = 3418$$
$$n = \frac{3418}{990} = \frac{1709}{495}$$

Thus, $n = 3.4\overline{52}$ can be expressed as a ratio of two integers.

However, there are some numbers that cannot be represented as a ratio of two integers. Such numbers are called *irrational numbers,* and we denote the set of irrational numbers by $\mathbb{H}$.

DEFINITION The number x is **irrational** if the decimal representation of x is nonterminating and nonrepeating.

For example, the number π, which is the ratio of the circumference of a circle to its diameter, cannot be represented as a ratio of two integers. (The value $\frac{22}{7}$, often used for π in numerical calculations, is only an approximation.) Its decimal representation, $\pi = 3.14159\ 26535\ 89793\ldots$, is nonterminating and nonrepeating. As another example, $\sqrt{2}$ is an irrational number because it has a nonterminating, nonrepeating decimal expansion. In fact, square roots of all positive numbers except perfect squares are irrational.

The union of the set of rational numbers and the set of irrational numbers forms the set of *real numbers,* designated $\mathbb{R} = \{x \mid x \in \mathbb{Q} \cup \mathbb{H}\}$. Much of the work done in mathematics uses only the real numbers. When real numbers are taken to be the universal set, then $\mathbb{H} = \mathbb{Q}'$, that is, the complement of the set of rational numbers is the set of irrational numbers.

The Set of Pure Imaginary Numbers

The expression "real number" leads one to wonder whether there might be another classification of numbers that in some sense are "not real." It is possible to solve the equation

$$x^2 - 1 = 0$$

by rewriting it as

$$x^2 = 1$$

and noting that there are two real numbers whose square is 1, namely, $x = \pm 1$. However, the equation $x^2 + 1 = 0$ cannot be solved in this way. If we rewrite it as $x^2 = -1$, we see that we are looking for a number whose square is -1. Since $(+1)\cdot(+1) = 1$ and $(-1)\cdot(-1) = 1$, there seems to be no real number with this characteristic. In fact, since the product of two real numbers of the same sign (both positive or both negative) is always positive, we conclude that the square of a real number can never be -1. This difficulty puzzled mathematicians for centuries. The best that can be done is to use a symbol that we treat in our calculations as if it yielded -1 when multiplied by itself. The letter i is chosen for this purpose.

DEFINITION i is the number such that $i^2 = -1$.

That is, $i = \sqrt{-1}$. Hence, a solution to the equation $x^2 + 1 = 0$ is $x = i$. The product of a real number and i (that is, a number of the form xi where x is a real number) is called a *pure imaginary number*. The set of pure imaginary numbers is denoted $\mathbb{I}$. Note that $\mathbb{I} \cap \mathbb{R} = \{0\}$, since $0 \in \mathbb{R}$ and $0i = 0 \in \mathbb{I}$.

EXAMPLE 1-9 The pure imaginary number $(-1)i$ is another solution to the equation $x^2 + 1 = 0$, because

$$\begin{aligned}
[(-1)i]^2 &= (-1)^2 i^2 \\
&= 1(-1) \\
&= -1
\end{aligned}$$

EXAMPLE 1-10 Find a number whose square is -9.

$$\begin{aligned}
\sqrt{-9} &= \sqrt{9 \cdot (-1)} \\
&= \sqrt{9} \cdot \sqrt{-1} \\
&= 3\sqrt{-1} \\
&= 3i
\end{aligned}$$

EXAMPLE 1-11 Find a number whose square is -0.25.

$$\begin{aligned}
\sqrt{-0.25} &= \sqrt{0.25(-1)} \\
&= \sqrt{0.25}\sqrt{-1} \\
&= 0.5i
\end{aligned}$$

The Set of Complex Numbers

The introduction of pure imaginary numbers was motivated by the need to find a solution to the equation $x^2 + 1 = 0$. If we are looking for a solution to the equation

$$x^2 - 2x + 10 = 0$$

we will find that no real or pure imaginary number satisfies it. To find a solution, we must resort to a combination of real and pure imaginary numbers, such as

$$x = 1 + 3i$$

We can see whether this number is a solution by substituting it in the equation:

$$x^2 - 2x + 10 = 0$$
$$(1 + 3i)^2 - 2(1 + 3i) + 10 = 0$$
$$(1 + 3i) \cdot (1 + 3i) - 2 - 6i + 10 = 0$$
$$1 + 3i + 3i + 9i^2 - 6i + 8 = 0$$
$$9 + 9i^2 = 0$$

But by definition, $i^2 = -1$, so we have

$$9 + 9(-1) = 0$$

which simplifies to

$$0 = 0$$

Hence, $x = 1 + 3i$ is a solution.

The solution to this equation is the sum of a real number and a pure imaginary number; that is, it has the form

$$a + bi \quad \text{where} \quad a \in \mathbb{R}, b \in \mathbb{R}$$

Such numbers are called *complex numbers*, and the set of complex numbers is denoted $\mathbb{C}$. Note that if $a = 0$, then the number $a + bi$ is pure imaginary; if $b = 0$, then the number is real. Hence, $\mathbb{I} \subset \mathbb{C}$ and $\mathbb{R} \subset \mathbb{C}$. Since, as mentioned above, $\mathbb{I} \cap \mathbb{R} = \{0\}$, we have that

$$\mathbb{C} = \mathbb{R} \oplus \mathbb{I} = \{a + bi \mid a \in \mathbb{R}, b \in \mathbb{R}\}$$

To summarize, the most general set of numbers used here is the set of complex numbers, which has the set of real numbers and the set of pure imaginary numbers as proper subsets. In turn, the real numbers are composed of the rational and irrational numbers. The rational numbers contain the integers and fractions, and the integers contain the whole and natural numbers. In set notation,

$$\mathbb{N} \subset \mathbb{W} \subset \mathbb{J} \subset \mathbb{Q} \subset \left.\begin{array}{c} \mathbb{Q} \subset \\ \mathbb{H} \subset \end{array}\right\} \mathbb{R} \subset \left.\begin{array}{c} \mathbb{R} \subset \\ \mathbb{I} \subset \end{array}\right\} \mathbb{C}$$

These relations are shown in Figure 1-13. Note that the set of complex numbers and all the subsets of it discussed above are examples of infinite sets.

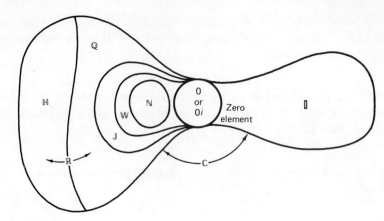

FIGURE 1-13

EXERCISES 1-2

Set A

1. For each of the following numbers, list all the sets defined in this section ($\mathbb{N}$, $\mathbb{W}$, $\mathbb{J}$, $\mathbb{Q}$, $\mathbb{H}$, $\mathbb{R}$, $\mathbb{I}$, $\mathbb{C}$) that contain it.

   (a) 17 (b) 20 (c) $3 - 4i$ (d) $5 + 0i$

   (e) 5 (f) $\dfrac{17}{6}$ (g) $-\dfrac{\pi}{2}$ (h) $3i$

   (i) $-6 + 2i$ (j) $\dfrac{1745}{21}$ (k) $0 - 12i$ (l) -17

2. Determine which of the following are true and which are false. Give reasons for your answers.

   (a) $\mathbb{J} \subset \mathbb{R}$ (b) $\mathbb{Q} \subset \mathbb{W}$
   (c) $\mathbb{Q} = \mathbb{H}'$ for $U = \mathbb{R}$ (d) $\mathbb{N} \cup \mathbb{J} = \mathbb{J}$
   (e) $\mathbb{J} \cap \mathbb{N} = \mathbb{N}$ (f) $\mathbb{C} \cap \mathbb{Q} = \mathbb{Q}'$
   (g) $\mathbb{C} \cup \mathbb{R} = \mathbb{R}$ (h) $\mathbb{Q} \cup \mathbb{H} = \mathbb{R}$
   (i) $\mathbb{Q} \cap \mathbb{H}' = \varnothing$ (j) $\mathbb{Q} \cap \mathbb{H} = \varnothing$
   (k) $\mathbb{I} \cap \mathbb{Q} = \mathbb{H}$ (l) $\mathbb{C} \cap \mathbb{I} = \mathbb{C}$

Set B

3. Find the smallest subset of the complex numbers to which the solutions of the following equations belong.

   (a) $3 + x = 4$ (b) $2x + 3 = -4$
   (c) $x^2 + 4 = 0$ (d) $3x + 4 = -6$

4. We sometimes use the rational number 22/7 as an approximation of the irrational number π. Divide 7 into 22 to show that $\pi \neq 22/7$. (The value of π is 3.141592653589793 . . . .)

5. A positive *prime number* is defined as a positive integer other than 1 that has no positive divisors other than 1 and itself. A *composite number* is a positive integer that is not a positive prime number. Determine which of the following are prime and which are composite:

(a) 39
(b) 41
(c) $x^2 - x$, $x \in \mathbb{J}$, x greater than 1
(d) 437
(e) 133
(f) $y + 2y$, $y \in \mathbb{J}$ and y greater than 0
(g) 119
(h) 221

1-3 IMPORTANT PROPERTIES OF REAL NUMBERS

Complex numbers are the most general type of number we will discuss. However, since most of our work will be with real numbers, we now present a brief review of some of their important properties.

Real Number Postulates

When we do arithmetic on real numbers, we use certain assumptions about the arithmetic properties of real numbers, perhaps without realizing that we are using them. These assumptions can be stated explicitly as *postulates* and used to prove further properties of the real numbers. First, we need the concept of a *binary operation*.

> DEFINITION A **binary operation** $*$ on $\mathbb{R}$ is a rule that assigns to each pair of real numbers a and b, taken in a definite order, a number c, denoted $a * b$.

For example, the operation of addition is a rule that assigns to the real numbers 2 and 3 their sum, $2 + 3 = 5$, whereas the operation of multiplication is a rule that assigns to these numbers their product, $2 \cdot 3 = 6$. Note that the order of the elements a and b is important; for instance, the operation of subtraction assigns the number 2 to the numbers 6 and 4 ($6 - 4 = 2$), but it assigns the number -2 to the numbers 4 and 6 ($4 - 6 = -2$).

We can now describe the basic postulates for the real numbers. The most fundamental postulate is that of *closure*.

> CLOSURE Let $*$ be an operation on a set S. The set S is **closed** under $*$ if, whenever $a \in S$ and $b \in S$, $a * b \in S$.

For example, the set of all real numbers, $\mathbb{R}$, is closed under addition and multiplication. On the other hand, the set of pure imaginary numbers is *not* closed under multiplication, since the product of the imaginary numbers $3i$ and $2i$ is $3i \cdot 2i = 6i^2 = 6(-1) = -6$, a real number.

If we want to add the numbers 2, 3, and 5, we can do this by adding 2 to the sum $3 + 5$ or by adding the sum $2 + 3$ to 5. Either grouping yields the same answer, 10. Similarly, we can calculate the product of the numbers 2, 3, and 5 either by multiplying 2 by the product $3 \cdot 5$ or by multiplying the product $2 \cdot 3$ by 5. The result of either approach is 30. This property of addition and multiplication of real numbers is called *associativity*.

> ASSOCIATIVITY If $a \in \mathbb{R}$, $b \in \mathbb{R}$, and $c \in \mathbb{R}$, then $(a + b) + c = a + (b + c)$ and $(a \cdot b) \cdot c = a \cdot (b \cdot c)$.

We are also familiar with the fact that the order in which two numbers are added or multiplied does not affect the result. For example, $9 + 3 = 3 + 9 = 12$, and $9 \cdot 3 = 3 \cdot 9 = 27$. This property is called *commutativity*.

> COMMUTATIVITY If $a \in \mathbb{R}$ and $b \in \mathbb{R}$, then $a + b = b + a$ and $a \cdot b = b \cdot a$.

The product of a real number a and a sum of real numbers $b + c$ can be rewritten with the use of the *distributivity* property.

> DISTRIBUTIVITY Let a, b, and c be any real numbers. Then $a \cdot (b + c) = (a \cdot b) + (a \cdot c)$.

For example,

$$9 \cdot (5 + 2) = (9 \cdot 5) + (9 \cdot 2)$$
$$9 \cdot 7 = 45 + 18$$
$$63 = 63$$

The number 0 has the property that

$$a + 0 = a$$

for every real number a. A number with this property is called an *additive identity*.

> ADDITIVE IDENTITY The number 0 is the **additive identity** element of $\mathbb{R}$.

We also know that the number 1 has the property that

$$a \cdot 1 = a$$

for every real number a. A number with this property is called a *multiplicative identity*.

MULTIPLICATIVE IDENTITY   The number 1 is the **multiplicative identity**
element of $\mathbb{R}$.

1-3 *Important*   **17**
Properties of
Real Numbers

If the sum $a + b$ of two real numbers is 0 (the additive identity element), we say that b is the *additive inverse* of a. The additive inverse of
a is usually denoted $-a$.

ADDITIVE INVERSE   Every real number a has an **additive inverse**,
denoted $-a$, in the set of real numbers. Symbolically, $a + (-a) = 0$.

Similarly, if the product $a \cdot b$ of two real numbers is 1 (the multiplicative
identity element), we say that b is the *multiplicative inverse* of a. The
multiplicative inverse of a is usually denoted $1/a$.

MULTIPLICATIVE INVERSE   Every real number a other than 0 has a
multiplicative inverse, denoted $1/a$, in the set of real numbers. Symbolically, $a \cdot (1/a) = 1$.

The postulates must also include the following properties of equality
of real numbers.

1. *Reflexivity*. Every real number is equal to itself; that is, for any
    real number a, $a = a$.
2. *Symmetry*. For any real numbers a and b, if $a = b$, then $b = a$.
3. *Transitivity*. For any real numbers a, b, and c, if $a = b$ and $b = c$,
    then $a = c$.
4. *Substitution Property of Equality*. For any real numbers a and b
    such that $a = b$, b may be substituted for a, or a for b, in any
    mathematical statement. The meaning of the statement is unaltered
    by the substitution.

The arithmetic postulates and equality properties of real numbers are
summarized as follows. For a, b, and $c \in \mathbb{R}$,

Closure
$$a + b \in \mathbb{R}$$
$$a \cdot b \in \mathbb{R}$$

Associativity
$$a + (b + c) = (a + b) + c$$
$$a \cdot (b \cdot c) = (a \cdot b) \cdot c$$

Commutativity
$$a + b = b + a$$
$$a \cdot b = b \cdot a$$

Distributivity
$$a \cdot (b + c) = (a \cdot b) + (a \cdot c)$$

Identity Elements
$$a + 0 = a$$
$$a \cdot 1 = a$$

Inverses

$$a + (-a) = 0$$
$$a \cdot (1/a) = 1, a \neq 0$$

Reflexivity

$$a = a$$

Symmetry

If $a = b$, then $b = a$

Transitivity

If $a = b$ and $b = c$, then $a = c$

Subtraction and Division

Suppose we have two real numbers, a and b, and we wish to determine what number must be added to a in order to obtain b. Since the quantity to be added to a is unknown, it may be represented by the symbol t. Then we are looking for a number t such that

$$a + t = b$$

The first step in finding t is to add the additive inverse of a to both sides of this equation. This can be done by virtue of the following theorem. (A *theorem* is a conditional statement that is proved by the use of postulates or prior theorems.)

THEOREM 1-1   For a, b, and $c \in \mathbb{R}$, if $a = b$, then $c + a = c + b$.

PROOF   Since $a \in \mathbb{R}$ and $b \in \mathbb{R}$, $c + a \in \mathbb{R}$. By the reflexive property of equality, $c + a = c + a$. But since $a = b$, the substitution property of equality gives $c + a = c + b$.   ∎

The symbol ∎ denotes the end of the proof.

The equation $a + t = b$ now reads

$$(-a) + (a + t) = (-a) + b$$

By the associative property of addition, this can be rewritten as

$$[(-a) + a] + t = (-a) + b$$

But by the commutative property of addition,

$$[a + (-a)] + t = b + (-a)$$

and since $a + (-a) = 0$, we have

$$0 + t = b + (-a)$$

But $0 + t = t$, so this equation becomes

$$t = b + (-a)$$

Therefore, the real number t that must be added to a to obtain b is $b + (-a)$.

Since the expression $b + (-a)$ is sometimes awkward to write, a new operation, called *subtraction*, is defined so that this expression can be written more concisely.

> **DEFINITION** The operation of **subtraction** symbolized $b - a$, is defined by the equation $b - a = b + (-a)$ for any real numbers a and b.

Although subtraction is nothing more than the addition of an additive inverse, it is often considered a separate operation. Note, however, that this operation is neither commutative nor associative.

We have seen that it is always possible to solve the equation $a + t = b$ for t (where a and b are any real numbers). Now suppose a and d are any real numbers and we wish to find a number that when multiplied by a yields d. That is, we wish to find a real number q satisfying the equation

$$a \cdot q = d$$

If $a \neq 0$, a has a multiplicative inverse, $1/a$. Then by the following theorem, we can multiply both sides of the equation by $1/a$.

THEOREM 1-2   If a, b, and c are real numbers and $a = b$, then $ca = cb$.

PROOF   The proof is left as an exercise.   ∎

The equation $a \cdot q = d$ $(a \neq 0)$ can now be rewritten as

$$(1/a) \cdot (a \cdot q) = (1/a) \cdot d$$

and then as

$$[(1/a) \cdot a] \cdot q = (1/a) \cdot d$$

or

$$1 \cdot q = (1/a) \cdot d$$

since $(1/a) \cdot a = 1$. Since $1 \cdot q = q$, the equation can now be rewritten again as

$$q = (1/a) \cdot d$$

or, by the commutative property of multiplication,

$$q = d \cdot (1/a)$$

Thus, q is found by multiplying d by the multiplicative inverse of a. Again, the expression $d \cdot (1/a)$ is awkward to write, so we define a new operation, called *division*.

> **DEFINITION** The operation of **division**, symbolized d/a or $d \div a$, is defined by the equation $d/a = d \cdot (1/a)$ for any real numbers a and d such that $a \neq 0$.

Division is nothing more than multiplication by a multiplicative inverse, but in practice it is sometimes considered an operation in its own right. Division, like subtraction, is neither associative nor commutative.

In summary,

$$b - a = b + (-a) \quad \text{and} \quad \frac{b}{a} = b \cdot (1/a)$$

Inequality and Absolute Value

We have considered the relationship of equality and some of its properties. If two real numbers a and b are not equal, we call the relationship between them *inequality*. A basic symbol used to denote inequality is $<$, read "is less than."

> **DEFINITION**   Let $a \in \mathbb{R}$ and $b \in \mathbb{R}$. Then a **is less than** b (symbolized $a < b$) if there exists a *positive* real number c such that $a + c = b$.

Conversely, if $a + c = b$ for c positive, then $a < b$.

Similar definitions can be written for "is greater than" $(>)$, "is less than or equal to" $(\leqslant)$, and "is greater than or equal to" $(\geqslant)$. The expression $a > b$ means that $b < a$; $a \leqslant b$ means that either $a < b$ or $a = b$; and $a \geqslant b$ means that either $a > b$ or $a = b$. Expressions such as these are called *inequalities*.

The most important postulate concerning inequality of real numbers is the Trichotomy Law.

> TRICHOTOMY LAW   Let a and b be real numbers. Then exactly one of the following is true: $a < b$, $a = b$, or $a > b$.

> **EXAMPLE 1-12**   Let $a = \pi$, $b = 4$. Then either $\pi < 4$, or $\pi = 4$, or $\pi > 4$. Since we know that $\pi = 3.1415\ldots$, we see that $\pi < 4$.

A complete list of inequality symbols follows.

$a < b$ a is less than b
$a \leqslant b$ a is less than or equal to b
$a > b$ a is greater than b
$a \geqslant b$ a is greater than or equal to b
$a \neq b$ a is not equal to b (either a is greater than b or a is less than b)
$a \not> b$ a is not greater than b (a is less than or equal to b)
$a \not\geqslant b$ a is not greater than or equal to b (a is less than b)
$a \not< b$ a is not less than b (a is greater than or equal to b)
$a \not\leqslant b$ a is not less than or equal to b (a is greater than b)

EXAMPLE 1-13

(a) The expression $x \leqslant 6$ means that x is less than or equal to 6.

(b) The expression $-8 > -9$ means that -8 is greater than -9.

(c) The expression $3 < x < 63$ means that x is greater than 3 but less than 63.

(d) The expression $7 < t \leqslant 10$ means that t is greater than 7 but less than or equal to 10.

(e) However, the expressions $7 > t < 10$ and $10 < t < 7$ have *no* meaning. Why?

Very often, the magnitude of a real number is required. The magnitude, or *absolute value*, of a number can be thought of as the value of the number without regard to its sign.

DEFINITION The **absolute value** of a real number a, denoted $|a|$, is given by

$$|a| = \begin{cases} a, & \text{if } a \geqslant 0 \\ -a, & \text{if } a < 0 \end{cases}$$

EXAMPLE 1-14

(a) $|74.3| = 74.3$

(b) $|-\sqrt{2}| = \sqrt{2}$

(c) $-|-\pi| = -\pi$

(d) $|\frac{10}{3}| = \frac{10}{3}$

(e) $|-14| = 14$

The absolute value of a real number can also be defined algebraically as the positive square root of the square of the number. That is, if $b \in \mathbb{R}$,

$$|b| = \sqrt{b^2}$$

EXAMPLE 1-15

$$|25| = \sqrt{25^2} = \sqrt{625} = 25$$
$$|-25| = \sqrt{(-25)^2} = \sqrt{625} = 25$$

Powers and Roots

Mathematical problems often involve powers and roots of a number. The expression

$$x^n, \quad \text{for} \quad x \in \mathbb{R}, n \in \mathbb{N}$$

means the product consisting of n factors of x. Here, x is called the *base*, n the *exponent*, and x^n the nth *power of x*.

EXAMPLE 1-16

(a) The third power of 2 is $2^3 = 2 \cdot 2 \cdot 2$. Here, 2 is the base and 3 is the exponent.

(b) $3^5 = 3 \cdot 3 \cdot 3 \cdot 3 \cdot 3$.

(c) $y^2 = y \cdot y$.

(d) $x^3 = x \cdot x \cdot x$.

An exponent can also be the reciprocal of a positive integer greater than 1. The expression

$$x^{1/n} \quad \text{where} \quad x \in \mathbb{R}, n \in \mathbb{N}, n > 1$$

means the nth root of x, that is, the real number a satisfying the equation

$$a^n = x$$

For example, 8 raised to the 1/3 power, or $8^{1/3}$, means the cube root of 8, which is sometimes also written in radical form as $\sqrt[3]{8}$. Since $2^3 = 2 \cdot 2 \cdot 2 = 8$, $8^{1/3} = 2$.

The expression "the fourth power of 3," refers unambiguously to one real number, namely

$$3^4 = 3 \cdot 3 \cdot 3 \cdot 3 = 81$$

On the other hand, the expression "the square root of 9" refers to a number that when multiplied by itself yields 9, and there are actually two such numbers, 3 and -3 (because $3 \cdot 3 = 9$ and $(-3)(-3) = 9$). Hence, there are two square roots of 9. This situation arises whenever one takes an even root of a positive real number. To eliminate the confusion, the positive real root is chosen and is called the *principal root*.

EXAMPLE 1-17

(a) $32^{1/5} = 2$, since $2^5 = 2 \cdot 2 \cdot 2 \cdot 2 \cdot 2 = 32$

(b) $27^{1/3} = 3$, since $3 \cdot 3 \cdot 3 = 27$

(c) $36^{1/2} = 6$, since $6 \cdot 6 = 36$

   Note that $(-6)(-6) = 36$ as well, but -6 is *not* the principal root.

(d) $16^{1/4} = 2$, since $2^4 = 16$

   Note that $(-2)^4 = 16$, but -2 is not the principal root.

Odd real roots of negative numbers are always negative.

EXAMPLE 1-18

(a) $(-8)^{1/3} = -2$ since $(-2)(-2)(-2) = -8$

(b) $(-32)^{1/5} = -2$ since $(-2)(-2)(-2)(-2)(-2) = -32$

In the last section, it was shown that the square root of a negative number is imaginary. In general, even roots of negative numbers are imaginary.

The following list summarizes the basic rules for exponents. In all cases, $m \in \mathbb{N}$, $n \in \mathbb{N}$, $x \in \mathbb{R}$, and $y \in \mathbb{R}$.

1. $x^n \cdot x^m = x^{n+m}$

2. $\dfrac{x^n}{x^m} = x^{n-m}, \qquad x \neq 0$

3. $(x^n)^m = x^{nm}$
4. $(x \cdot y)^n = x^n \cdot y^n$
5. $\left(\dfrac{x}{y}\right)^n = \dfrac{x^n}{y^n}, \quad y \neq 0$
6. $x^{n/m} = (x^{1/m})^n = (\sqrt[m]{x})^n, \quad x^{1/m} \in \mathbb{R}$
7. Special relationships:
$x^0 = 1$

$x^{-n/m} = \dfrac{1}{x^{n/m}} \quad \text{and} \quad x^{n/m} = \dfrac{1}{x^{-n/m}}$

Note that rule 6 allows us to use fractional exponents and rule 7 gives meaning to negative rational exponents.

EXAMPLE 1-19
(a) $2^3 \cdot 2^5 = 2^{3+5} = 2^8 = 256$
(b) $x^7/x^9 = x^{7-9} = x^{-2} = 1/x^2$
(c) $(2x)^4 = 2^4 \cdot x^4 = 16x^4$
(d) $64^{5/6} = (64^{1/6})^5 = (\sqrt[6]{64})^5 = 2^5 = 32$
(Note that $64^{5/6}$ can also be written as $(64^5)^{1/6}$, but this is more cumbersome to calculate, since 64^5 is a very large number.)
(e) $(3,548,741)^0 = 1$

EXAMPLE 1-20 Simplify:

$$\frac{x^3 y^4}{(\sqrt{y}x^{3/2})^8} = \frac{x^3 y^4}{(\sqrt{y})^8 (x^{3/2})^8} = \frac{x^3 y^4}{(y^{1/2})^8 (x^{3/2})^8}$$

$$= \frac{x^3 y^4}{y^4 x^{12}} = \frac{x^3 x^{-12}}{y^4 y^{-4}} = \frac{x^{3-12}}{y^{4-4}} = \frac{x^{-9}}{y^0} = \frac{1}{x^9}$$

EXAMPLE 1-21 Simplify:

$$\frac{t^{-5}\sqrt{s^3}}{\sqrt[5]{t^6 s^7}} = \frac{s^{3/2}}{t^5 (t^6 s^7)^{1/5}} = \frac{s^{3/2}}{t^5 t^{6/5} s^{7/5}} = \frac{s^{3/2} s^{-7/5}}{t^5 t^{6/5}}$$

$$= \frac{s^{3/2-7/5}}{t^{5+6/5}} = \frac{s^{15/10-14/10}}{t^{25/5+6/5}} = \frac{s^{1/10}}{t^{31/5}} = \frac{\sqrt[10]{s}}{\sqrt[5]{t^{31}}}$$

Additional Properties

Many other rules, or theorems, are used in solving mathematical problems. The following are those most often used in the solution of elementary problems; their proofs are based on prior theorems or postulates. (In all cases a, b, and c are real numbers.)

1. If $a + c = b + c$, then $a = b$
2. If $a \cdot c = b \cdot c$ and $c \neq 0$, then $a = b$

3. If $a + b = 0$, then $a = -b$
4. If $a \cdot b = 1$ and $b \neq 0$, then $a = 1/b$
5. $a \cdot 0 = 0$ for any a
6. $(-1) \cdot a = -a$
7. $(-1) \cdot (-a) = a$
8. If $a \cdot b = 0$, then $a=0$ or $b=0$ or both a and b are 0.

EXAMPLE 1-22

(a) Solve for s:

$$2s - 4 = -5$$
$$2s = 4 - 5 = -1$$
$$s = -\frac{1}{2}$$

(b) Solve for t:

$$3(4 - 3t) = 22$$
$$4 - 3t = \frac{22}{3}$$
$$-3t = \frac{22}{3} - 4 = \frac{22}{3} - \frac{12}{3} = \frac{10}{3}$$
$$t = -\frac{1}{3}\left(\frac{10}{3}\right) = -\frac{10}{9}$$

(c) Solve for y:

$$y^2 - 2y = 0$$
$$y(y - 2) = 0$$

Thus

$$y = 0 \quad \text{or} \quad y - 2 = 0$$

Therefore,

$$y = 0 \quad \text{or} \quad y = 2$$

EXAMPLE 1-23 Simplify and solve:

$$\frac{5 - 6x}{2} = 3x + 7$$

$5 - 6x = 2(3x + 7)$	Multiply both sides by 2
$5 - 6x = 6x + 14$	Distributive property
$-6x = 6x + 14 - 5$	Subtraction rule
$-6x - 6x = 14 - 5$	Subtraction rule
$-12x = 9$	
$x = -\frac{9}{12} = -\frac{3}{4}$	Division rule

EXAMPLE 1-24 The following is an illustration of the inconsistency

that results when the rules for arithmetic on real numbers are violated. Suppose $S \in \mathbb{R}$, $T \in \mathbb{R}$, and

$$S = T$$

then

$$S^2 = T^2$$
$$S^2 = T \cdot T$$

Since $T = S$, we can substitute S for T in this equation.

$$S^2 = ST$$

Subtracting T^2 from each side, we get

$$S^2 - T^2 = ST - T^2$$

Factoring yields

$$(S + T)(S - T) = T(S - T)$$

Dividing both sides by $(S - T)$ gives

$$S + T = T$$

Since $S = T$, then

$$T + T = T \quad \text{or} \quad 2T = T$$

Dividing both sides by T gives

$$2 = 1$$

What went wrong?

EXERCISES 1-3

Set A

1. Identify the property of real numbers illustrated by the following equations:

    (a) $3 + 4 = 7$ (b) $7 \cdot 2 = 14$
    (c) $6 \cdot 2 = 2 \cdot 6$ (d) $3 + 4 = 4 + 3$
    (e) $9(6 + 5) = 54 + 45$ (f) $6 + 8 = 2(3 + 4)$
    (g) $(9 + 2) + 3 = 9 + (2 + 3)$ (h) $(7 \cdot 3) \cdot 4 = 7(12)$
    (i) $3 = 3 + 0$ (j) $Q = Q \cdot 1$
    (k) $1 = (2 + 4)[1/(2 + 4)]$ (l) $0 = x + (-x)$
    (m) $6[4 + (\frac{1}{8})] = 24 + \frac{3}{4}$

2. Using the properties of real numbers, fill in the blanks for the following problems:

    (a) $(3 \cdot 2) \cdot \underline{\quad} = (3) \cdot (\underline{\quad} \cdot 7)$
    (b) $4 + \underline{\quad} = 4$
    (c) $3 \cdot \underline{\quad} = 1$
    (d) $2 \cdot (\underline{\quad} + 3) = (\underline{\quad} \cdot 4) + (2 \cdot \underline{\quad})$
    (e) $(6 \cdot 2) + (3 \cdot 4) = (3 \cdot 4) + (\underline{\quad} \cdot \underline{\quad})$

3. Consider the following table. Indicate by writing *yes* if the postulate is always true and *no* if it is not always true.

	Natural	Whole	Integer	Rational	Irrational
Closure under addition					
Closure under multiplication					
Additive identity					
Multiplicative identity					
Additive inverse					
Multiplicative inverse					
Closure under subtraction					
Closure under division					

4. Classify the following statements as always true, always false, or neither:
   (a) $7 < 9$
   (b) $6 \neq 4$
   (c) $5 = 4$
   (d) $9 < 11$
   (e) $8 \not> 6$
   (f) $4 \not> 5$
   (g) $x = 4$
   (h) $y \leq z$
   (i) $a > 4 + a$
   (j) $a = b + c$
   (k) $9 \leq \sqrt{x}$
   (l) $3 + 0 \neq 3$
   (m) $6 + (-6) = 0$
   (n) $\frac{1}{2}R < R$

5. In each of the following, solve for x using the methods developed in this section:
   (a) $x + 7 = 10$
   (b) $7 - 3x = 8$
   (c) $7x - 4 = 0$
   (d) $2x - 3 = x + 1$
   (e) $-\sqrt{x} + 3 = 0$
   (f) $6 - 2\sqrt{x} = 1$
   (g) $(x - 2)(x + 1) = 0$
   (h) $x(x - 1)(x + \pi) = 0$

6. In each of the following, let $a = 2$, $b = 3$, $c = 9$, and $d = 49$; evaluate the given expressions.
   (a) $a^3 + b^2$
   (b) $c^{1/2} + d^{1/2}$
   (c) $(a + b)c$
   (d) $\dfrac{a + c + d}{ab}$
   (e) $a + b(c + d)$
   (f) $a + b/c$
   (g) $(a + b)(c + d)$
   (h) $(a + b)/c$

Set B

7. Using the property that $x^n/x^m = x^{n-m}$, develop examples to show that the special relationships

$$x^0 = 1 \quad \text{and} \quad x^{-1} = \frac{1}{x}, \quad x \neq 0$$

are valid.

8. Do the operations of division and subtraction satisfy all of the real number postulates? Give a reason for your answer.

9. If possible, factor and simplify the following:
   (a) $6^{3a+2} - 6^{3a}$
   (b) $2^{6n+4} + 16$
      (*Hint:* Write 16 as a power of 2.)
   (c) $3^{-7n-2} \cdot 9$
      (*Hint:* Write 9 as a power of 3.)
   (d) $\left[c - \dfrac{b^2}{(2a)^2} \right]^{1/2}$
   (e) $\sqrt[2]{\sqrt[2]{256}} + 8x$

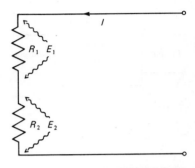

10. Part of an electric circuit is composed of two resistors, R_1 and R_2, in series, and a current, I, passing through them as shown in Figure 1-14. The voltage E across a resistor R is given by

$$E = I \cdot R$$

   Use the distributive property to show that the sum of the two voltages, $E_1 + E_2$, is equal to the current I times the total resistance sum.

FIGURE 1-14

11. A block of wood is suspended by two ropes, which in turn are attached to a common weight as shown in Figure 1-15. Which inverse property do the forces in the ropes illustrate?

12. A man travels to work by driving 6 miles by automobile and then riding a train for 30 miles. He returns home by traveling 30 miles by train and 6 miles by automobile. Which real number postulate does this activity illustrate?

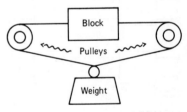

13. Prove that if $a \in \mathbb{R}$, $b \in \mathbb{R}$, $c \in \mathbb{R}$, and $a = b$, then $ca = cb$.

14. Supply the reasons in the proof of the following theorem. Let $a \in \mathbb{R}$, $b \in \mathbb{R}$, $c \in \mathbb{R}$ with $b \neq 0$. If $a/b = c$, then $a = bc$.

FIGURE 1-15

Statement	Reason
$\dfrac{a}{b} = c$	
$a \cdot \dfrac{1}{b} = c$	
$\dfrac{1}{b} \cdot a = c$	
$b \cdot \left(\dfrac{1}{b} \cdot a \right) = b \cdot c$	
$\left(b \cdot \dfrac{1}{b} \right) \cdot a = b \cdot c$	
$1 \cdot a = bc$	
$a = bc$	

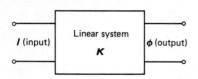

FIGURE 1-16

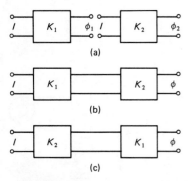

FIGURE 1-17

Set C

● 15. Use an electronic calculator to reevaluate the expressions in Exercise 6(a), 6(c), and 6(e) if $a = 2.776$, $b = 3.7841$, $c = 8.7792$, and $d = 50.003$.

16. In any linear system, the total output at any specified part of the system equals the sum of the outputs at that part due to each individual input. Let the black box in Figure 1-16 represent such a system, and let the output ϕ for each input I be $K \cdot I$.

    (a) Write the output if the input is

$$I_1 + I_2 + I_3$$

    (b) What real number postulate does this illustrate?

17. Now suppose there are two linear systems with the properties that

$$\phi_1 = K_1 \cdot I \quad \text{and} \quad \phi_2 = K_2 \cdot I$$

as shown in Figure 1-17(a). Let them be connected as shown in Figures 1-17(b) and (c). In each case, note that the output of the first system is the input of the second.

    (a) In each case, find the output ϕ in terms of the input I.
    (b) What real number postulate does this illustrate?

1-4 NUMERICAL APPROXIMATIONS

In the sciences, it is rare that a quantity is represented exactly. Since the tools used have only limited precision and possible human error is involved, measurements are only approximations of the quantity being measured. The approximation is characterized by the accuracy and the precision of the measurement.

Accuracy and Precision

Suppose a rock with an exact weight of twenty kilograms is placed on a scale. One should not expect the measured weight to be exactly twenty kilograms. The actual value obtained depends on the quality of the scale; this quality is reflected in the number of *significant digits* that can be read.

> **DEFINITION** A **significant digit** is any digit that is meaningful to the number, including any zero *not* used to indicate the location of the decimal point.

The exact weight of twenty kilograms is represented by 20.000 ... kilograms, which has an infinite number of significant digits. If the weight of the rock is measured as 20.1 kilograms, then the measurement involves three significant digits.

EXAMPLE 1-25 The approximate number 53,100 has only three significant digits, whereas the numbers 53,100. and 53,001 each have five. In the first case, the zeros were decimal point locators, but in the second and third cases, the zeros denote the values in their respective positions.

EXAMPLE 1-26 The approximate number 0.00523 has three significant digits, whereas 0.0052300 has five. The last two zeros are not decimal point locators, but rather give the numerical values of those positions and, therefore, are significant.

EXAMPLE 1-27 The approximate number 100.0 has four significant digits.

The immediate concern in measuring the weight of the rock is the *accuracy* of the measurement.

DEFINITION The **accuracy** of a number is determined by the number of significant digits in the number.

Thus, when the weight of the rock is measured as 20.1 kilograms, it can be said that the measurement is accurate to three significant digits. The degree of refinement of the accuracy is called *precision*.

DEFINITION The **precision** of a number is determined by the position of the last significant digit in relation to the decimal point.

Again, the measurement of 20.1 kilograms is precise to the nearest tenth, since the last significant digit, 1, is in the "tenths" place.

EXAMPLE 1-28 The approximate number 735.02 is accurate to five significant digits and is precise to the nearest hundredth.

The approximate number 0.00542 is accurate to three significant digits and is precise to the nearest hundred-thousandth.

The numbers 1.000 and 100.0 are equally accurate (to four significant digits), but 1.000 is more precise (to the nearest thousandth rather than to the nearest tenth).

The approximate measurements 56.2 centimeters and 56.2 kilometers are equally accurate, but the first is more precise, because a centimeter is more precise than a kilometer.

The approximate numbers 0.732 inches and 256.118 inches are equally precise (to the nearest thousandth), but 256.118 inches is more accurate.

Operations with Approximate Numbers

There are set rules for arithmetic on approximate numbers and the accuracy of the results.

Rule for Addition and Subtraction of Approximate Numbers When two numbers are added or subtracted, the result is only as precise as the least precise value.

Rule for Multiplication and Division of Approximate Numbers When two numbers are multiplied or divided, the result is only as accurate as the least accurate number.

> **EXAMPLE 1-29** If the approximate numbers 37.647 and 12.51 are added, the sum is precise only to the nearest hundredth.

> **EXAMPLE 1-30** If the approximate numbers 3.97 and 643.73821 are multiplied, the product is accurate only to three significant digits.

In order to perform the operations in these examples, we need a rule for rounding off. The following rule is generally accepted:

Rules for Rounding Off

1. Decide on the last decimal place (whether to the left or the right of the decimal point) to be retained.
2. If the group of digits being dropped begins with a value less than 5, the digit in the last decimal place being retained is left unchanged.
3. If the group of digits being dropped begins with a value greater than 5 or with a 5 followed by other nonzero digits, the digit in the last decimal place being retained is increased by 1.
4. If the group of digits being dropped is a succession of zeros preceded by 5, the digit in the last decimal place being retained is left unchanged if it is even and increased by 1 if it is odd.

> **EXAMPLE 1-31** The number 37.647 becomes 37.65 when rounded off to the nearest hundredth.
> The number 643.73821 becomes 644 when rounded off to the nearest unit.
> The number 78.45 becomes 78.4 when rounded off to the nearest tenth, 78.55 becomes 78.6 when rounded off to the nearest tenth.

The following examples illustrate how the rounding off rules are combined with the rule for addition and subtraction, as well as the rule for multiplication and division of approximate numbers.

$$37.647 + 12.51 = 50.157$$
$$= 50.16$$

when rounded to the nearest hundredth. For the product of 3.47 and 644.48, we obtain

$$3.47 \cdot 644.48 = 2236.3456$$
$$= 2240$$

when rounded to three significant digits.

Note that the rounding off rule is to be applied *after* the operations are performed. In these examples, if the rounding off were done first, the results would be

$$37.65 + 12.51 = 50.16$$

as before, but

$$3.47 \cdot 644 = 2234.68$$
$$= 2230$$

when rounded to three significant digits, which is *not* equal to 2240 because of the prior application of rounding off.

Now suppose 3.14159 is added to and multiplied by the integer 2. According to the rules for addition and multiplication of approximate numbers, the results would be

$$2 + 3.14159 = 5.14159$$

which must be rounded off to 5, and

$$2 \cdot 3.14159 = 6.28318$$

which must be rounded off to 6. Is this correct?

No. Since 2 is known to be exact (an integer), its decimal representation is actually $2.00000000\bar{0}$. Therefore the correct answers are 5.14159 and 6.28318.

Scientific Notation

In a previous example, the answer 2240 was obtained by rounding off to three significant digits due to the operation performed. If one did not know that this was the result of a multiplication involving a factor with three-digit accuracy, how would it be known whether this number was rounded off to 2240 or whether it was exactly 2240? A method used to eliminate this ambiguity, as well as to represent numbers in a manageable form, is scientific notation. As a general rule, a number in scientific notation is written as a number between 1 and 10 (including 1 but not 10) times a power of 10. Symbolically, a number is written as $P \cdot 10^k$ where $1 \leqslant P < 10$ and $k \in \mathbb{J}$.

In order to find the proper exponent when writing a number in scientific notation, simply begin at the decimal point and move either to the left (if there are nonzero digits to the left of the decimal point) or to the right (if there are no nonzero digits to the left of the decimal point) until a number between 1 and 10 is obtained. This number is the coefficient of the power of 10, and the number of places moved is the exponent of 10. If the movement is to the left, the exponent is positive; if the movement is to the right, the exponent is negative.

$$173000 = 1.73 \cdot 10^5$$
$$\underset{5\ 4\ 3\ 2\ 1}{}$$

$$0.00523 = 5.23 \cdot 10^{-3}$$
$$\underset{1\ 2\ 3}{}$$

$$403.2 = 4.032 \cdot 10^2$$
$$\underset{2\ 1}{}$$

FIGURE 1-18

EXAMPLE 1-33 Write 173,000, 0.00523, and 403.2 in scientific notation. (See Figure 1-18.)

$$173,000 = 1.73 \cdot 10^5$$
$$0.00523 = 5.23 \cdot 10^{-3}$$
$$403.2 = 4.032 \cdot 10^2$$

The number 25,600 can be written

$$2.56 \cdot 10,000 = 2.56 \cdot 10^4$$

This number is accurate to three significant digits. However, the number 25,600. is written as

$$2.5600 \cdot 10,000 = 2.5600 \cdot 10^4$$

which is accurate to five significant digits. How does the number $2.56 \cdot 10^4$ differ from the number $2.5600 \cdot 10^4$? Since $2.56 \cdot 10^4$ has only three significant digits, whereas $2.5600 \cdot 10^4$ has five significant digits, the first number could be interpreted as the value obtained after rounding off to three digits, whereas the second number could be interpreted either as exactly 25,600 or as a number rounded off to five significant digits. In this way, not only has a cumbersome number been written in a concise form, but the zeros that express the accuracy of the number are used in its representation.

The number 0.0000000765, which is rather awkward to write, would be $7.65 \cdot 10^{-8}$ in scientific notation. For large numbers (that is, numbers greater than 10), the exponent is positive; it is important to maintain the distinction between positive and negative exponents, since a mistake in the sign of the exponent could make an answer wrong by some large factor such as 10^3 or 10^6. For a scientist, it is just as important to get the correct power of 10 as to get a very precise coefficient of the power of 10. For example, suppose a result is 428,200, which in scientific notation is $4.282 \cdot 10^5$. If one inadvertently writes $4.282 \cdot 10^{-5}$, the answer is wrong by a factor of 10 billion. A precise result for the coefficient, 4.282, is valueless when the power of 10 is off by such a vast magnitude. Scientific notation is a great asset to scientific calculations, because it puts a number in perspective by showing its magnitude as a power of 10 and at the same time allows for proper representation of the number's accuracy.

EXAMPLE 1-34 Write the following quantities in scientific notation:

$$m = 0.00000000000000000000000000000911$$
$$e = 0.00000000000000000016$$
$$A = 600000000000000000000000$$

These are, respectively, the mass of an electron, the charge of an electron, and the approximate number of molecules in a mole substance.

$$m = 0.00000000000000000000000000000911 = 9.11 \cdot 10^{-28}$$
$$e = 0.00000000000000000016 = 1.6 \cdot 10^{-19}$$
$$A = 600000000000000000000000 = 6 \cdot 10^{23}$$

Clearly, these numbers are more useful when written in scientific notation than in decimal form. Errors can easily be made in counting the number of decimal places for such very large or very small quantities. The magnitudes of these numbers are clearly expressed by the power of 10; 10^{-28} is obviously an extremely small number, and 10^{+23} is very large. Since it is necessary to work with such numbers in science, their representation in scientific notation is invaluable.

EXAMPLE 1-35 As an example of the usefulness of scientific notation, consider the evaluation of the following expression:

$$P = \frac{746000 \cdot 0.000000435}{0.0000298}$$

Start by writing each of the numbers in scientific notation.

$$P = \frac{(7.46 \cdot 10^5) \cdot (4.35 \cdot 10^{-7})}{2.98 \cdot 10^{-5}}$$

This can be rewritten as

$$P = \frac{7.46 \cdot 4.35 \cdot 10^5 \cdot 10^{-7}}{2.98 \cdot 10^{-5}}$$

$$= \frac{32.5 \cdot 10^{-2}}{2.98 \cdot 10^{-5}}$$

$$= \frac{32.5}{2.98} \cdot \frac{10^{-2}}{10^{-5}}$$

$$= 10.9 \cdot 10^3$$

$$= 10,900$$

This example shows clearly that the use of scientific notation in the evaluation of expressions involving both large and small numbers makes the solution more tractable and minimizes the common difficulty of deciding on the position of the decimal point.

The electronic calculator can be used quite effectively to simplify calculations and to keep track of significant digits. The student should realize that even though the readout may indicate an eight- or twelve-digit result, all of these digits may not be significant.

● **EXAMPLE 1-36** Evaluate N for the given approximate numbers

$$N = \frac{1783000 \cdot 2870}{0.0000041723 \cdot 0.193887}$$

and give the answer with the proper number of significant digits.

Before we proceed with the calculations, some preliminary work is necessary. First, since the evaluation involves only multiplication and division, accuracy is the ruling factor, and the least accurate number (three significant digits) is $2.87 \cdot 10^3$. In scientific notation, the problem becomes

$$N = \frac{(1.783 \cdot 10^6) \cdot (2.87 \cdot 10^3)}{(4.1723 \cdot 10^{-6}) \cdot (1.93887 \cdot 10^{-1})}$$

Next, separate the powers of 10, so that the problem reads

$$N = \frac{(1.783 \cdot 2.87) \cdot (10^6 \cdot 10^3)}{(4.1723 \cdot 1.93887) \cdot (10^{-6} \cdot 10^{-1})}$$

Now, the power of 10 may be handled separately from the numerical coefficient. The exponent portion becomes

$$\frac{10^6 \cdot 10^3}{10^{-6} \cdot 10^{-1}} = \frac{10^9}{10^{-7}} = 10^{16}$$

The coefficient portion becomes

$$\frac{1.783 \cdot 2.87}{4.1723 \cdot 1.93887} = \frac{5.11721}{8.089547301} = 0.63257062$$

This *must* be rounded off to three significant digits and thus becomes

$$0.633$$

The final answer is

$$N = 0.633 \cdot 10^{16}$$

In proper scientific notation, the coefficient should be a number between 1 and 10, so the final answer becomes

$$N = 6.33 \cdot 10^{15}$$

Note: All numerical values in these exercises are approximate unless otherwise stated.

Set A

1. Find the number of significant digits in each of the following:
   (a) 123
   (b) 0.764
   (c) 7894.0
   (d) 10,453.2
   (e) 0.0038217
   (f) 12.00
   (g) 3.74173
   (h) 4.00032
   (i) 72040000
   (j) 72040010
   (k) 0.00004902
   (l) 0.004902
   (m) 17601
   (n) 17601.003
   (o) 0.00004900
   (p) 0.000049

2. Determine the accuracy of the numbers given in Exercise 1.

3. Determine the precision of the numbers given in Exercise 1.

4. Round off the numbers in Exercise 1 to two significant digits.

5. Convert each of the numbers in Exercise 1 to scientific notation.

6. In physics, the ratio e/m is often encountered. Using the values given in Example 1-34 for e and m, find this ratio to the proper number of significant digits.

7. Write the results of the following to the proper number of significant digits. Assume that the integers are precise to the nearest unit.
   (a) $2.4 + 0.639$
   (b) $8.41 \cdot 3$
   (c) $56 \cdot 0.400$
   (d) $88.8888 + 24$
   (e) $0.000003 \cdot 9642$
   (f) $0.4381 + 8972$

8. Round off the following numbers to three significant digits:
   (a) 63.77
   (b) 0.8124
   (c) 0.8888
   (d) 92.65
   (e) 83.15
   (f) 3334
   (g) 77.75
   (h) 0.3231
   (i) 0.07645
   (j) 0.9835

Set B

9. Table 1-2 shows the prefixes used with metric units and the powers of ten they represent. As an example, 1 kilometer = 10^3 meters = 1000 meters. Reexpress the following, first in decimal notation and then in scientific notation:
   (a) 7.1 kilometers in meters
   (b) 5.3 microfarads in farads
   (c) 3 gigahertz in hertz
   (d) 5.6 megohms in ohms
   (e) 73 millimeters in meters
   (f) 83 picofarads in farads
   (g) 92.6 milliliters in liters
   (h) 573 centimeters in meters
   (i) 10 nanoseconds in seconds
   (j) 35 milligrams in grams

TABLE 1-2

Power of ten	Prefix
10^{-12}	Pico
10^{-9}	Nano
10^{-6}	Micro
10^{-3}	Milli
10^{-2}	Centi
10^{-1}	Deci
10^{1}	Deka
10^{2}	Heckto
10^{3}	Kilo
10^{6}	Mega
10^{9}	Giga
10^{12}	Tera

10. Why is the metric system considered the most advantageous of all systems of units of measurement?

● 11. Express the results of the following in scientific notation. Determine the proper number of significant digits in the answer as well as the power of 10.

(a) $\dfrac{67 \cdot 823.468 \cdot 654}{0.000338172}$

(b) $\dfrac{0.00000011111111 \cdot 864}{3}$

(c) $\dfrac{99999 \cdot 66}{33} \cdot (777777 \cdot 10^{-20})$

Set C

12. Consult a table of conversion units and reexpress the following in meters, grams, or liters.

(a) 75 micrograms   (b) 12 angstroms
(c) 2 microns   (d) 27 tons
(e) 0.63 gallons   (f) 8 light years
(g) 9 grains   (h) 200 pounds (U.S.)
(i) 11 cubic feet   (j) 8 milli-inches

● 13. Use an electronic calculator to evaluate the following expressions to the proper number of significant digits, and express the answer with the correct power of 10.

(a) $\dfrac{(76280 + 94133)(0.00000071)}{0.00000000008}$

(b) $\dfrac{(0.00000777)(0.0941338)}{0.0005778139}$

REVIEW EXERCISES FOR CHAPTER 1

1. Given $U = \{a, b, c, d, e, f, g\}$, $A = \{a, c, e\}$, $B = \{c, d, e, f\}$, and $C = \{b, f, g\}$. Find
   - (a) $N(A)$
   - (b) $N(B)$
   - (c) A'
   - (d) C'
   - (e) $A \cup B$
   - (f) $C \cup A$
   - (g) $A \cap C$
   - (h) $B \cap C$
   - (i) $(A \cup C)'$
   - (j) $(A \cup B)'$

2. Which of sets A, B, and C in Exercise 1 are equivalent?

3. Simplify:
   - (a) $3^{6n+4} - 27$
   - (b) $x^{-2n} \cdot x^{3+4n}$
   - (c) $(2^{-7n+4})/32$

4. True or false?
   - (a) $\pi = 22/7$
   - (b) $\sqrt{2} = 1.414$
   - (c) $-7 < -8$
   - (d) $t^2 < -4$, if $t \in \mathbb{R}$
   - (e) $5 < x < 4$
   - (f) $-|-31| = 31$
   - (g) $i \in \mathbb{R} \cap \mathbb{I}$
   - (h) $(-3i)^2 \in \mathbb{N}$
   - (i) $\mathbb{Q} \cap \mathbb{H} = \mathbb{C}$
   - (j) $(\mathbb{Q} \cap \mathbb{H})' = \varnothing$

5. Do the following for the numbers 0.00492, 12345.67, $7.30 \cdot 10^9$, and 83.45:
   - (a) Find the number of significant digits.
   - (b) Determine the accuracy and precision.
   - (c) Round off to two significant digits.
   - (d) Convert to scientific notation.

6. Perform the indicated operations on the following approximate numbers:
   - (a) Add 43.7294 and 0.0003768
   - (b) Multiply 73.2482 and 6.3

Functions and Relations

2-1 RELATIONS AND GRAPHING

The use of mathematics is not restricted solely to simplifying algebraic expressions or writing these expressions in different ways. Mathematics is a tool for solving problems. Although it may be satisfying, as well as necessary, to master algebraic simplifications, it is also important to utilize this skill in finding solutions to scientific, social science, and business problems that can be represented by a mathematical model. The purpose of the following discussion is to develop models of mathematical reasoning that can be used to represent real situations.

Relations

Consider the problem of formulating a mathematical expression for a particular gear train, such as might be found in a washing machine, an automobile, or many other situations. Assume that when the drive wheel for this gear train is rotated at the speed of 100 revolutions per minute, the resulting speed at the end of the gear train is 20 revolutions per minute. The task is to establish a mathematical model that can be used to represent this gear train and to establish the output speed resulting from any speed of the drive wheel.

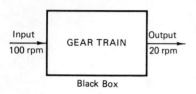

Black Box

FIGURE 2-1

One way to do this is to use the "black box" approach, that is, to ignore the exact gear formation and concentrate only on the input speed and the resulting output speed. A model of this type is shown in Figure 2-1; the entire gear train is represented as a black box, with no indication of how the input of 100 revolutions per minute gives rise to the output of 20 revolutions per minute. If the only input speed was 100 revolutions per minute, there would be no need for further discussion, because it is already known that the output would be 20 revolutions per minute; but we wish to investigate other possible input speeds and the corresponding output speeds. In this model, it should be clear that there are two distinct sets of values to consider, namely, the input values and the output values.

Thus far, only one input value (100 revolutions per minute) and one output value (20 revolutions per minute) are known. If the input were doubled to 200 revolutions per minute, what might be said of the output? From the information given, it is not possible to determine this new output value, because the composition of the gear train has not been established. Although it might seem reasonable that since the input is doubled, the output should also be doubled, this may or may not be the case. (For example, in the case of an automobile engine, a transmission gear shift might prevent the velocity from doubling when the input is doubled.) However, in order to simplify this problem, assume that for any change in the input, a proportional change will occur in the output. Thus, if the input is doubled, the output will also be doubled; and if the input is reduced by 20 percent, the output will also be reduced by 20 percent. Then it is possible to begin a tabulation of data. The three situations already mentioned are shown in Table 2-1.

TABLE 2-1

Information	Input (rpm)	Output (rpm)
Original	100	20
Double	200	40
20% reduction	80	16

There is no reason why the tabulation must cease with these three entries. There may be many possible input speeds; in fact, there may be an infinite number of them, since the input speed may vary continuously through the set of all real numbers. From the practical viewpoint, there must be some physical limitation on this mechanical gear train, so suppose the maximum input speed is 5000 revolutions per minute and the minimum input speed is 0 revolutions per minute. Then the maximum output would be 1000 revolutions per minute, and the minimum output would be 0 revolutions per minute.

The correspondence between input and output can be tabulated for input values between 0 and 5000 revolutions per minute. Of course, it is impossible to tabulate all such values, but it is not difficult to list representative ones that relate the same information, as is done in Table 2-2.

TABLE 2-2

Input (rpm)	Output (rpm)	Comment
0	0	Minimum rpm
10	2	
50	10	
80	16	Reduced 20%
100	20	Original
200	40	Twice original
400	80	
800	160	
1500	300	
2000	400	
3000	600	
4000	800	
5000	1000	Maximum rpm

From Table 2-2, it is clear that there are two distinct sets of numbers, one set corresponding to the input of the gear train, the other corresponding to the output. To each element of the input set there corresponds an element of the output set. For example, for the input element 400, Table 2-2 shows that the corresponding output element is 80. Thus, Table 2-2 lists pairs of numbers in which the first element represents a value from the input set and the second element represents the corresponding value from the output set. The set of these *pairs* of numbers is called a set of *ordered pairs*.

⋆ **DEFINITION** An **ordered pair** is a set of two elements in which the order of the elements has significance. An ordered pair is symbolized (x, y), where x is the **first component**, or **element**, and y is the **second component**, or **element**.

The model of the gear train can now be represented by a set of ordered pairs taken from Table 2-2. One representation of the gear train model is the set

$$\{(50, 10), (100, 20), (200, 40), \ldots\}$$

This set of ordered pairs describes a correspondence between elements of the input set and elements of the output set. Such a correspondence is called a *relation*.

⋆ **DEFINITION** A **relation** is a set of ordered pairs.

It is not necessary to consider only those values tabulated in Table 2-2, since these were selected only to illustrate the operation of the gear train.

An unlimited number of other input values could have been chosen to form additional members of the set of ordered pairs of input and output elements. The only restriction is that the input values must be between 0 and 5000. Similarly, there are an unlimited number of corresponding output values, all between 0 and 1000.

The set of all possible values of the first element (or component) of these ordered pairs is called the *domain* of the relation.

✱ **DEFINITION** The **domain** $\mathscr{D}$ of a relation is the set of all first components of the ordered pairs that belong to the relation.

Similarly, the set of all possible values of the second elements of these ordered pairs is called the *range* of the relation.

✱ **DEFINITION** The **range** $\mathscr{R}$ of a relation is the set of all second components of the ordered pairs that belong to the relation.

Rather than consider individual elements of a relation, it is more convenient to represent the relation symbolically. Since it is common to denote an ordered pair by (x, y), the relation can be represented as the set of ordered pairs (x, y) such that x is an element of the domain, $\mathscr{D}$, of the relation and y is the corresponding element of the range, $\mathscr{R}$.

The concepts of the preceding discussion are summarized in Figure 2-2. To each $x \in \mathscr{D}$ there corresponds a $y \in \mathscr{R}$. These correspondences (represented by arrows in Figure 2-2) form a set of ordered pairs, which defines the relation between the input set and the output set.

Since x and y can take on any values from the domain and range, respectively, these symbols are often called *variables*.

✱ **DEFINITION** A **variable** is a symbol that can be used to represent any element of a set.

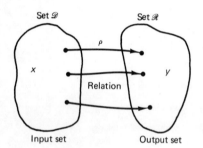

FIGURE 2-2

Since x is an element of the domain, which in our model is the set of input values, and y is an element of the range, which is the set of output values, the output element can be said to depend upon the input element. For this reason, x is called the *independent variable* (domain variable) and y the *dependent variable* (range variable), since the output elements *depend* on the *independent* choices of the input element. Note that any convenient symbols could have been used instead of the conventional x and y.

The relation for the gear train can also be represented by an equation (or rule or formula) showing the correspondence between the output and input values. The formula for this relation can be written as

$$\text{Output speed} = \tfrac{1}{5} \cdot \text{Input speed}$$

or

$$y = \tfrac{1}{5}x$$

This mathematical formulation can be tested for various values appearing in Table 2-2. For example, if an independent choice for x is made, say $x = 100$, then the formula yields

$$y = \tfrac{1}{5}(100)$$
$$y = 20$$

which corresponds to the tabulated value. It cannot be overstressed that the choice of the value 100 is an independent choice, whereas the corresponding value, 20, depends on this choice of x. Any value in the domain of the relation can be chosen for x, and the corresponding value of y is an element of the range of the relation.

These concepts can be generalized by the use of a more symbolic form. As has already been stated, a relation takes values from the domain and by some rule (formula or equation) converts these values into elements in the range. This may be written as

$$y = \rho(x)$$

where $\rho(x)$ stands for the operations that must be performed on the x values in order to obtain the y values. So in the expression

▶ $\rho = \{(x, y) \mid y = \rho(x),$ for $x \in \mathscr{D}, y \in \mathscr{R}\}$

the symbol ρ is the *name* of the relation and $y = \rho(x)$ describes the *rule* of correspondence between the values x and y. The range $\mathscr{R}$ is often called the *image* of the domain $\mathscr{D}$, since the relation *maps* (transforms, converts) values of $x \in \mathscr{D}$ into values of $y \in \mathscr{R}$. For an individual element x, this concept of mapping is expressed symbolically by

▶ $\rho : x \rightarrow \rho(x)$

In general, sets $\mathscr{D}$ and $\mathscr{R}$ will be subsets of some other sets A and B, respectively. Thus, the mapping ρ can be written symbolically in set form as

▶ $\rho : \mathscr{D} \rightarrow \mathscr{R}$

where $x \in \mathscr{D} \subseteq A, y \in \mathscr{R} \subseteq B$, and the rule of correspondence is $y = \rho(x)$. This situation is shown graphically in Figure 2-3.

It is usual to let $\mathscr{D} = A$ instead of just $\mathscr{D} \subseteq A$. In such an instance, the mapping is symbolically written in set form as

▶ $\rho : A \rightarrow B$

In this book, we will loosely refer to the rule

$$y = \rho(x)$$

as the relation itself. The same convention will be followed in the discussion on functions in later sections.

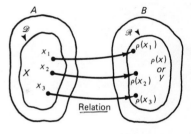

FIGURE 2-3

Graphing Concepts

It is often convenient to illustrate a relation graphically. It is as true in mathematics as in other areas that "A picture is worth a thousand words," and a graph is often very useful in understanding the behavior of a relation. This is especially true in higher analysis, where one encounters many relations that cannot be symbolized by a mathematical formula.

The results of scientific experiments are often represented by pictorial diagrams, called *graphs*.

> **DEFINITION** A **graph** is the spacial representation of a set of ordered pairs.

Before discussing the graph of a relation, we must develop the concept of the one-dimensional *real number line*, which is illustrated in Figure 2-4. It is customary to use a horizontal line for the real number line. On it, we arbitrarily identify a particular point as the number 0, which separates the positive real numbers (to the right of 0) from the negative real numbers (to the left). A convenient distance is selected to locate the value 1 (and thus all the integer values) on this line. Then any real number can be represented by some point on the line.

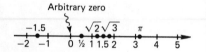

FIGURE 2-4

> **ASSUMPTION** (Cantor–Dedekind Axiom) It is possible to set up a correspondence between the points on a line and the real numbers such that every real number is represented uniquely by a point on a line and every point on a line is represented uniquely by a real number.

The real-line representation of numbers is not useful for representing relations, because the elements of a relation are ordered pairs rather than numbers. For this reason, it is necessary to have two reference lines. The method of setting up these reference lines is arbitrary; for example, in Figure 2-5, reference line L_1 is used to represent the elements of the domain of the relation, and reference line L_2 is used to represent the elements of the range. (Note that L_1 and L_2 are not straight lines.) The point where the two lines cross is chosen as the zero point on both lines. On line L_1, points to the right of 0 represent the positive elements of the domain, and points to the left of 0 represent the negative elements of the domain. On L_2, points above 0 represent the positive elements of the range, and points below 0 represent the negative elements of the range. Lines can be drawn from the integer points on L_1 parallel to L_2 and from the integer points on L_2 parallel to L_1, as shown in Figure 2-5. These lines now form curved "parallelograms," and each point on the two-dimensional plane can now be uniquely identified with a particular domain value and a particular range value. That is, any point in the plane is associated with an ordered pair, where the first component identifies a particular domain value and the second component identifies a particular range value.

The assumption given above for the one-dimensional case is now extended to the two-dimensional case.

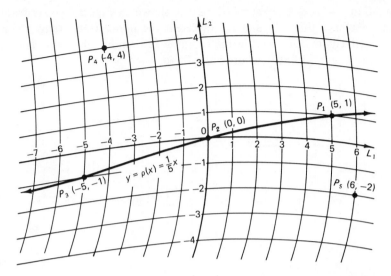

FIGURE 2-5

ASSUMPTION It is possible to set up a correspondence between the points in a plane and the ordered pairs of real numbers such that for each ordered pair of real numbers, there exists a unique point on the two-dimensional plane, and for each point on the two-dimensional plane, there exists a unique ordered pair of real numbers.

Figure 2-5 also shows five points labeled P_1 through P_5. For example, P_1 is obtained by moving 5 units to the right of 0 along L_1 and 1 unit up from 0 along L_2. The ordered pair corresponding to P_1 is (5, 1). Similarly, P_4 is represented by the ordered pair $(-4, 4)$.

Figure 2-5 also illustrates the graph of the relation

$$y = \rho(x) = \tfrac{1}{5}x$$

By substituting 5, 0, and -5 for the domain variable x in the relation ρ, we can generate corresponding range elements, 1, 0, and -1. Therefore, the ordered pairs (5, 1), (0, 0), and $(-5, -1)$ are elements of the set of ordered pairs determined by ρ. The graph of the relation contains these points, which are labeled P_1, P_2, and P_3, respectively. Points such as P_4 and P_5 are not on the graph of ρ, since the corresponding ordered pairs are not elements of the relation. It is important to bear in mind that the way in which the reference lines of a two-dimensional plane are constructed is completely arbitrary; any convenient reference lines can be used to graph a given relationship.

The most convenient representation for a two-dimensional plane is the *Cartesian*, or *rectangular*, *coordinate system*. In this system, the reference lines, L_1 and L_2, are straight lines perpendicular to each other, so the grid lines form rectangles. A rectangular coordinate system with the relation $y = \rho(x) = \frac{1}{5}x$ graphed on it is shown in Figure 2-6. As before, the reference lines, L_1 and L_2, represent the domain and range values, respectively, and intersect at the common zero point. This point is called the *origin* and has as its coordinates the ordered pair $(0, 0)$.

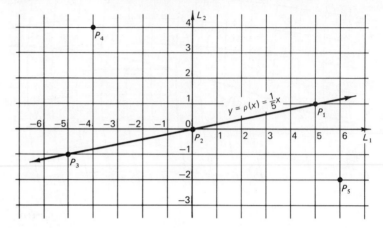

FIGURE 2-6

Note that the points P_1 through P_5 corresponding to those shown in Figure 2-5 are also shown in Figure 2-6. The points P_1, P_2, and P_3 are on the graph of the relation ρ.

In the rectangular coordinate system, the horizontal reference line, L_1, is called the *abscissa*, and the vertical reference line, L_2, is called the *ordinate*. More common expressions for the abscissa and the ordinate are *x* axis and *y* axis, respectively. However, since it is not necessarily the case that the domain elements are represented by *x* and the range elements by *y*, these two axes will be designated throughout this book as the *D* axis (for the domain values) and the *R* axis (for the range values). The *D* axis and *R* axis are also known as *coordinate axes*.

How to Graph a Relation

The following five steps will facilitate the graphing of a relation.

Step 1 *Write the Range Variable in Terms of the Domain Variable.*

This should be done whenever possible, so that for each value in the domain of the relation, one can compute the corresponding value in the range.

Step 2 *Tabulate Pairs of Corresponding Elements of the Range and Domain.*

The tabulation of a sufficient number of ordered pairs is a necessary part of the graphing procedure. Care must be taken to avoid substitution of values that are not in the domain of the relation; in particular, values that would force a *division by* 0 or result in *even roots of negative numbers* are *not* in the domain of any real relation and may not be substituted. Only real-valued ordered pairs are to be considered.

Among the values often considered when graphing a relation are the *intercepts* of the graph.

> **DEFINITION** An **intercept** is a point where the graph of the relation crosses a reference, or coordinate, axis.

Intercepts always occur when the domain element equals 0 or when the range element equals 0, provided that the value 0 is in the domain or range. The intercepts are usually the first choices made, because they generally simplify computations.

> **EXAMPLE 2-1** Find the intercepts of the relation $y = \rho(x) = 2x - 1$.
>
> By definition, the intercepts occur when an axis is crossed. On the D axis, all y values are 0, and on the R axis, all x values are 0. To find the D intercept, set $y = 0$. This yields
>
> $$0 = 2x - 1$$
>
> Solving for x yields $x = \frac{1}{2}$. Thus, the coordinates of the D axis intercept are $(\frac{1}{2}, 0)$. To get the R axis intercept, set $x = 0$. This yields
>
> $$y = 2(0) - 1 \quad \text{or} \quad y = -1$$
>
> The coordinates of the R axis intercept are $(0, -1)$.

Step 3 *Scale the Coordinate Axes.*

Once enough values of the relation have been tabulated, the coordinate axes should be scaled so that the values obtained can be properly represented on the graph.

> **DEFINITION** A **scale** is a fixed standard length.

A good rule of thumb to obtain a scale factor is to form a ratio between the span of the tabulated domain values and the span of the tabulated range values. If the larger span is divided by the smaller, the resulting ratio will give the unit step variation that the variable with the larger span should have as compared to the unit step variation of the variable with the smaller span. The ratio should be adjusted so that as many data points as possible fall on division lines.

$$\text{Scale factor} = \frac{\text{Larger span}}{\text{Smaller span}}$$

Examples 2-2 and 2-3 illustrate the scaling process.

> **EXAMPLE 2-2** Scale the coordinate axes for the relation
>
> $$y = \rho(x) = 3x - 2$$

First, tabulate the values of x that best determine the behavior of the relation; then calculate the corresponding values of y. The points selected usually include the points where the graph crosses the axes and several nearby points. It is often convenient to write the ordered pairs in two columns, with the domain values in the left column and the range values in the right column, as follows.

x value	y value
-3	-11
-2	-8
-1	-5
0	-2
1	1
2	4
3	7

From the table, we see that the x values span 6 units, and the y values span 18 units. The formula for the scale factor yields

$$\text{Scale factor} = \frac{18}{6} = \frac{3}{1}$$

Thus, if every division on the D axis represents a step of 1 unit, then every division on the R axis represents a step of 3 units.

EXAMPLE 2-3   Scale the coordinate axes for the relation

$$y = \rho(x) = 25x^2$$

The tabulation is as follows.

x value	y value
-3	175
-2	100
-1	25
0	0
1	25
2	100
3	175

From the scale factor formula,

$$\text{Scale factor} = \frac{175}{6} = 29.166\ldots$$

In this case, the scale factor is not a whole number. The nearest convenient value would be 30, but if 30 is used, the data points would not fall on the division lines of the y axis. Here, the student can use a little judgment. Since the y values are divisible by 25, an adjustment to this scale factor would locate the y value data points on the division lines, resulting in a more accurate plot. It is not always possible to do this, but try to locate as many data points as possible on division lines.

Thus, each division on the D axis represents a step of 1 unit, and each division on the R axis represents a step of 25 units.

Step 4 *Plot the Values.*

Once the elements have been tabulated and the coordinate axes scaled, it is a simple matter to plot the points. Represent each ordered pair from the table by a point on the graph.

Step 5 *Carefully Connect the Points on the Graph.*

Once the points have been plotted, we can connect them with a smooth curve to form a picture of the relation. Although this step may seem to be very simple, it is actually the one that causes the most trouble. In connecting any two plotted points, we must assume that each intermediate point on the connecting path is included in the domain and range of the relation. The mistake most commonly made in connecting two points is the inclusion of values that are not in the domain or not in the range.

Examples of Graphing

As an example illustrating these five steps, consider the relation

$$yx - y - 16 = 0$$

Step 1 Assume that x is the independent variable; then express y in terms of x. Thus,

$$y(x - 1) - 16 = 0$$
$$y(x - 1) = 16$$
$$y = \rho(x) = \frac{16}{x - 1}$$

Step 2 Select various elements of the domain and from them compute the corresponding elements of the range. It is useful to investigate the D and R intercepts of the curve, if they exist. When $x = 0$, we have

$$y = \frac{16}{0 - 1} = -16$$

Hence, the first entry of the table is the ordered pair $(0, -16)$. Since this point has an x value of 0, the curve must intercept the R axis at the value $y = -16$.

It is not possible to obtain a value of x corresponding to $y = 0$. This can be seen by solving for x in terms of y, which yields the expression

$$x = \frac{16}{y} + 1$$

Since division by 0 is never possible, no value of x can force y to be equal to 0. Hence, there is no D axis intercept, and $0 \notin \mathcal{R}$.

Returning to the original expression,

$$y = \frac{16}{x - 1}$$

we can now investigate other values of x. For convenience, select integer values near 0, for example, -3, -2, -1, 1, 2, and 3. For each of these values except $x = +1$, a value of y is obtained, and the tabulation is shown below.

x	y
-3	-4
-2	$-16/3$
-1	-8
0	-16
$+1$	?
$+2$	$+16$
$+3$	$+8$

Note that when $x = 1$,

$$y = \frac{16}{1 - 1}$$

$$y = \frac{16}{0} = ?$$

Since division by 0 is never possible, $x = +1$ is *not* in the domain of the relation, i.e., $1 \notin \mathcal{D}$.

Step 3 Scale the axes for the graph. Note that the values of x varied from $x = -3$ to $x = +3$, and the values of y varied from -16 to $+16$. Thus, the scale factor is computed as

$$\text{Scale factor} = \frac{32}{6} = 5.\overline{3}$$

Since the range values in the tabulation are mainly multiples of 4, a convenient scale factor that is close to 5 would be 4. Thus, the scale lengths are 1 unit on the D axis and 4 units on the R axis.

Step 4 Once the reference lines have been scaled, we can plot the tabulated points. For example, the point $(0, -16)$ lies 16 units below the origin on the R axis. We continue this process until all available points have been plotted, as shown in Figure 2-7.

Step 5 The final step is to draw the graph of the relation, utilizing the plotted points. Again, it cannot be overstressed that great care must be

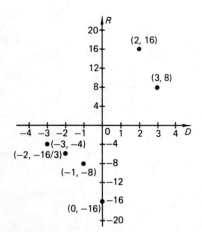

FIGURE 2-7

taken, in connecting these points, to avoid drawing the graph through values that are not in the domain or range of the relation.

As an illustration of this common mistake, suppose we successively connect the points on the graph in Figure 2-7, as shown in Figure 2-8. Then the graph so obtained is in *gross error*. The part of the curve connecting the points $(0, -16)$ and $(2, +16)$ is completely wrong for two reasons. It has gone through a point where $x = 1$, which is not in the domain, and it has gone through a point where $y = 0$, which is not in the range. The most the graph can do is approach the values $x = 1$ and $y = 0$. Substitution shows that as x gets closer and closer to $+1$ from the left, the value of y becomes larger and larger in the negative direction, and as x gets closer and closer to $+1$ from the right, the value of y becomes larger in the positive direction. Thus, the points in the plane for which $x = +1$ can be thought of as an invisible barrier that the graph of this relation can approach but cannot cross. Such a barrier is called an *asymptote*.

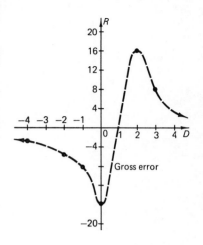

FIGURE 2-8

> ✳ **DEFINITION**   An **asymptote** of a graph is a line (or curve) such that the distance between the line and the graph gets smaller and smaller as the magnitude of either x or y increases without bound.

An asymptote is usually a straight line. For the relation $yx - y - 16 = 0$, the same situation occurs again for $y = 0$. As y gets closer to 0 from above, the value of x becomes larger in the positive direction, and as y gets closer to 0 from below, x becomes larger in the negative direction. Since $y = 0$ on the domain axis, the D axis is another asymptote of the graph.

Utilizing this information, we can represent the asymptotes as dotted lines, so that the barriers are shown, and then redraw the graph. This is done in Figure 2–9. To clarify the graph further, the points for x values

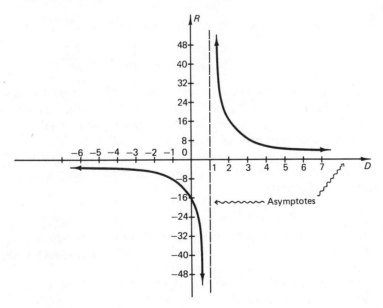

FIGURE 2-9

of $\frac{1}{2}$ and $\frac{3}{2}$ have been included. The inclusion of these points, which are $(\frac{1}{2}, -32)$ and $(\frac{3}{2}, 32)$, clearly shows that the line drawn between $(0, -16)$ and $(2, 16)$ in Figure 2-8 was in error. (Note that the scale on the vertical axis in Figure 2-9 has been changed to permit inclusion of more of the graph.)

It may seem to the student that the graph of a relation may never cross an asymptote, but this is not true. An asymptote represents a value approached by the relation in some region of the domain or range. It is quite possible for the graph to cross an extension of the asymptote in some other region of the domain or range. Examples of this will be given in Section 9-3, which deals with rational functions.

EXAMPLE 2-4 Graph the relation ρ given by

$$y^2 = \rho(x) = x$$

where x is the domain variable and y the range variable.

The table of ordered pairs is given below. Note that since x and y must be real, x cannot be negative. If x were negative, then y^2 would be negative, which would make y imaginary.

x	y
0	0
1	1 or -1
4	2 or -2
9	3 or -3
16	4 or -4
25	5 or -5

Next, we determine the scale factor for the graph.

$$\text{Scale factor} = \frac{\text{Larger span}}{\text{Smaller span}} = \frac{25}{10} = \frac{5}{2} = \frac{2.5}{1}$$

This means that each unit distance on the D axis must be 2.5 times the unit distance on the R axis. Note that except for $(0, 0)$, the ordered pairs have two range values for each domain value. Figure 2-10 shows these ordered pairs connected by a smooth curve.

The only restriction on the domain or range values was that $x \geqslant 0$. This restriction means that no ordered pair could appear in the left half of the DR plane.

We reiterate the steps in graphing:

1. Write the relationship in terms of a single variable, if possible
2. Obtain a sufficient set of ordered pairs, utilizing the intercepts and observing proper domain and range values
3. Determine a scale for the rectangular coordinate system
4. Plot the set of ordered pairs

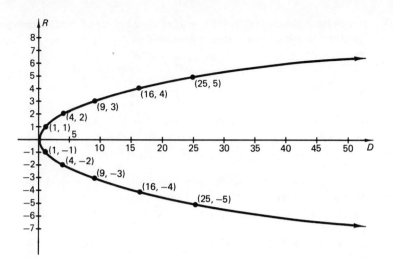

FIGURE 2-10

5. Connect these points with a smooth curve for proper domain values, observing any asymptotes

EXERCISES 2-1

Set A

1. Graph the following relations in the Cartesian system
   (a) $\rho = \{(0, 3), (0, 4), (1, 7), (-4, 9), (-3, -2)\}$
   (b) $\rho = \{(-6, -1), (-6, 3), (-6, 7), (-6, 10)\}$
   (c) $\rho = \{(1, 1), (2, 2), (3, 3), (4, 4), (4, 5), (4, 6)\}$

2. Table 2-3 was experimentally obtained from an electronic amplifier. Write the mathematical relation between the input and each of the outputs.

TABLE 2-3

Input X	Output 1 Y	Output 2 Z	Output 3 W
−5	50	−5	−20
−4	40	−4	−16
−3	30	−3	−12
−2	20	−2	−8
−1	10	−1	−4
0	0	0	0
1	−10	1	4
2	−20	2	8
3	−30	3	12
4	−40	4	16
5	−50	5	20
6	−60	6	24

3. Graph the following relations, $y = \rho(x)$, on a system of rectangular axes. Use the methods illustrated in this section.
   (a) $y = 3x - 4$ (b) $y = x^2$
   (c) $y = x^3$ (d) $y = x^2 - 6x + 5$
   (e) $y = x^3 - 8x$ (f) $y = \dfrac{4}{(x-2)^2}$
   (g) $yx^2 + 4y - x^2 - 2 = 0$ (h) $xy^2 - 3xy - 6 = 0$
   (i) $xy - 3x = 9$ (j) $y^2 - 4x - 4 = 0$

Set B

4. In the following problems, assume that x and y must be real numbers. In each case, find the domain and range.
   (a) $y = 4 - x$ (b) $y = \sqrt{16 - x^2}$
   (c) $y = \sqrt{x - 4}$ (d) $y = \sqrt{x^2 - 16}$
   (e) $y = 3x + 4$ (f) $y = x^2$
   (g) $y = 3x - \dfrac{1}{x}$ (h) $y = \sqrt{\dfrac{4}{x-1}}$

5. It is possible to make up a new system of graphing by slanting the R axis at an angle of 45° with the D axis, as in Figure 2-11. In this system, lines representing constant values in $\mathcal{D}$ are still parallel to the R axis, and lines representing constant values in $\mathcal{R}$ are still parallel to the D axis. Regraph the functions in Exercise 3 in this new system. How do the graphs change with respect to those obtained in Exercise 3?

● 6. Using an electronic calculator, graph the function
$$y = 1.10x^2 + 3.92x + 4.70$$
for $1.5 \leqslant x \leqslant 2.5$, x in increments of 0.1 (i.e., the values of x increase by 0.1).

● 7. Using an electronic calculator, graph the function
$$y = 0.72x^4 - 3.76x^3 + 1.10x^2 + 2.76x - 9.32$$
for $-3 \leqslant x \leqslant 3$, in increments of 0.5.

8. Graph the following relations in the Cartesian system:
   (a) $\rho = \{(x, y) \mid y^2 = x^3\}$
   (b) $\rho = \{(x, y) \mid y^2 = x^2 - x\}$

2-2 FUNCTIONS—CONCEPTS AND NOTATION

The Concept of a Function

In the preceding section, we discussed the concept of a relation as a set of ordered pairs. However, this concept does not reflect the fact that, in some relations, one variable is completely dependent upon the other variable. In order to refer to a relation having this characteristic, we use the term *function*.

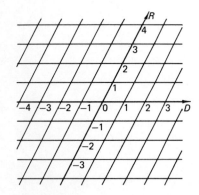

FIGURE 2-11

DEFINITION A **function** is a relation such that to each value in the domain there corresponds one and only one value in the range.

Thus, a function is a special kind of relation, one that allows only one result in the range for any value selected from the domain. The model of the gear train considered in the previous section provides an example of a function, because there is only one output speed corresponding to each input speed.

We can also define a function in terms of ordered pairs.

DEFINITION A **function** is a relation such that no two distinct ordered pairs have the same first element.

For example, the relation represented by the set of ordered pairs $\{(1, 2), (2, 4), (3, 7)\}$ is a function, because no two distinct ordered pairs have the same first element. Note that a function may have two or more distinct ordered pairs with the same *second* element. The relation $\{(1,2), (2, 4), (3, 4)\}$ is also a function. Even though two distinct ordered pairs have the same *second* element, no two ordered pairs have the same *first* element. However, the relation $\{(1, 2), (1, 4), (3, 7)\}$ is *not* a function, because there are two distinct ordered pairs with the same first element. Corresponding to the value 1 in the domain, there are two different values in the range, namely, 2 and 4.

Figure 2-12 illustrates the concept of a function. The elements of set A are designated x, and the elements of set B are designated y. The arrows illustrate a function from A to B, which establishes a set of ordered pairs (x, y) such that for each $x \in \mathcal{D} \subseteq A$, there exists *exactly* one value $y \in \mathcal{R} \subseteq B$, called the *image* of x. Symbolically, we write

▶ $f = \{(x, y) \mid x \in \mathcal{D}, y \in \mathcal{R}, x$ and y satisfy the rule for f, and for any (x_1, y_1) and $(x_2, y_2) \in f$, $y_1 \neq y_2$ implies $x_1 \neq x_2\}$

It is conventional to assume that $\mathcal{D} = A$ instead of $\mathcal{D} \subseteq A$. Henceforth, $\mathcal{D} = A$, unless otherwise stated.

Figures 2-13(a) and 2-13(b) show representations of relations that are also functions. In each case, for each value selected in the domain, there is one and only one corresponding image value in the range. However, the relations shown in Figure 2-14(a) and 2-14(b) are *not* functions, because in each case there are at least two values in the range that correspond to the same value in the domain.

Since $\mathcal{R} \subseteq B$, function f is a rule that maps each $x \in A$ to exactly one image value $y \in B$. Symbolically, this is denoted

▶ $f: A \rightarrow B$

where A is the domain of f and B is the set containing the image of A (the range of f). As applied to an individual point x, the function f is written

▶ $f: x \rightarrow f(x)$

where $x \in A$ and $f(x) \in B$. The value $f(x)$ is the image of x under function f, and the notation

▶ $y = f(x)$

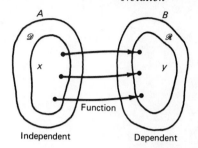

FIGURE 2-12

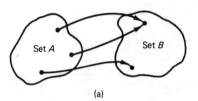

(a)

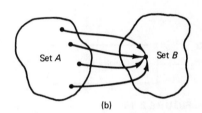

(b)

FIGURE 2-13

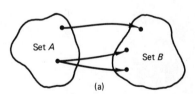

(a)

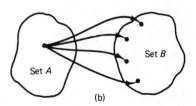

(b)

FIGURE 2-14

describes the process whereby f maps $x \in A$ to $y \in B$. For example,

$$y = 3x$$

means that each number $x \in \mathscr{D}$ is mapped to the number $3x$. As was the case with relations, x is called the independent variable and y the dependent variable.

We will loosely refer to the rule

$$y = f(x)$$

as the function f itself. For example, the rule $y = 4x - 7$ stands for the function that maps each real number x to the number $4x - 7$; the rule $y = x^2 + 2x - 3$ stands for the function that maps each real number x to the number $x^2 + 2x - 3$; and the rule $y = x^3/5$ stands for the function that maps each real number x to the number $x^3/5$.

Models of Functions

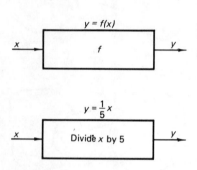

FIGURE 2-15

As with relations, the concept of a function can easily be represented by a black box model that relates input and output values. The diagram in Figure 2-15 is a black box model of the gear train discussed in Section 2-1. The input to the box is represented by the variable x, and the output of the box is represented by y. The box performs an operation on x; this operation is symbolized by f. In this case, the function divides the input value by 5; hence, the output is

$$y = f(x) = \tfrac{1}{5}x$$

In general, a function may be any operation or combination of operations, algebraic or otherwise. Regardless of the type of operation, the function operates on the input, or independent value, and the result of this operation is the output, or dependent value.

EXAMPLE 2-5 Let $F(x)$ be the function defined by the rule $y = x^2 + 3x + 1$. Find $F(3)$, $F(0)$, and $F(-4)$.

The expression $F(3)$ means the output corresponding to the input 3. We have

$$\begin{aligned} F(3) &= (3)^2 + 3(3) + 1 \\ &= 9 + 9 + 1 \\ &= 19 \end{aligned}$$

Similarly,

$$\begin{aligned} F(0) &= (0)^2 + 3(0) + 1 \\ &= 0 + 0 + 1 \\ &= 1 \end{aligned}$$

and

$$\begin{aligned} F(-4) &= (-4)^2 + 3(-4) + 1 \\ &= 16 - 12 + 1 \\ &= 5 \end{aligned}$$

As another example, suppose a function consists of the following operations: "Multiply the input by 5, add the result to the square of the input, and subtract 3 from the resulting sum." To stress the significance of the function, rather than any particular input or output values, we represent the input value by the symbol $\#$. The black box model for this function has the output expression

$$f(\#) = 5\# + \#^2 - 3$$

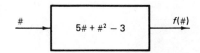

FIGURE 2-16

as shown in Figure 2-16. If 4 is an element of the domain, then

$$f(4) = 5(4) + 4^2 - 3 = 20 + 16 - 3 = 33$$

Similarly,

$$f(5) = 5(5) + 5^2 - 3 = 47$$
$$f(1) = 5(1) + 1^2 - 3 = 3$$

$$f(-2) = 5(-2) + (-2)^2 - 3 = -9$$

A more exotic example of the working of this function would be

$$f(\text{goldfish}) = 5(\text{goldfish}) + (\text{goldfish})^2 - 3$$

Naturally, this expression does not have a numerical value, because the number associated with "goldfish" is not known. However, the manner in which the function is to operate on the independent variable is still the same.

As the reader can see, input values to functions need not always be numbers. Very often, the elements of the domain are represented by letters. Consider the function $F(x) = x^2 + 3x + 1$ of Example 2-5, which is represented in Figure 2-17. However, let the input values be represented by $\$$, Q, and H. Since these are letter symbols representing unspecified numbers in the domain of f, the outputs of the function will also be expressed in terms of letter symbols, as follows.

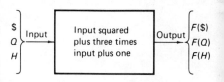

FIGURE 2-17

$$F(\$) = (\$)^2 + 3(\$) + 1$$
$$= \$^2 + 3\$ + 1$$

$$F(Q) = (Q)^2 + 3(Q) + 1$$
$$= Q^2 + 3Q + 1$$

$$F(H) = (H)^2 + 3(H) + 1$$
$$= H^2 + 3H + 1$$

Expressions such as $f(x^2 + 1)$ are permissible and meaningful. For example, if f is the function with the rule

$$f(x) = \sqrt{x}$$

then the expression $f(x^2 + 1)$ means

$$\sqrt{x^2 + 1}$$

Note that only real numbers $x \geqslant 0$ can be substituted into the expression $f(x) = \sqrt{x}$, because if $x < 0$, $\sqrt{x}$ is not a real number. On the other hand, any real number x can be substituted into the expression $f(x^2 + 1) = \sqrt{x^2 + 1}$. This is true because for any real number x, x^2 cannot be negative, and thus $x^2 + 1$ is always positive. Therefore, $\sqrt{x^2 + 1}$ is a real number for any real value of x. The expression within the parentheses of the function is commonly called the *argument* of the function. Thus, for the expression $f(x)$, x is the argument, and for $f(x^2 + 1)$, $x^2 + 1$ is the argument.

EXAMPLE 2-6   For

$$F(x) = x^2 + 3x + 1$$

express F for arguments $H + Q$, $t - 2$, and $x + \Delta$.

$$\begin{aligned}
F(H + Q) &= (H + Q)^2 + 3(H + Q) + 1 \\
&= H^2 + 2HQ + Q^2 + 3H + 3Q + 1
\end{aligned}$$

$$\begin{aligned}
F(t - 2) &= (t - 2)^2 + 3(t - 2) + 1 \\
&= t^2 - 4t + 4 + 3t - 6 + 1 \\
&= t^2 - t - 1
\end{aligned}$$

$$\begin{aligned}
F(x + \Delta) &= (x + \Delta)^2 + 3(x + \Delta) + 1 \\
&= x^2 + 2x\Delta + \Delta^2 + 3x + 3\Delta + 1
\end{aligned}$$

Note that in the previous example, the expressions were expanded algebraically. This should be done and the expression simplified whenever possible. Only when the numerical values of the symbols are specified will the numerical output of the function be known. In the case of the function F evaluated at $t - 2$, the result was $t^2 - t - 1$. When $t = 5$, the output represented by $F(t - 2)$ is $5^2 - (5) - 1 = 19$. This is the same result that was obtained in Example 2-5 when the function was evaluated at $x = 3$. This is true because when $t = 5$, $t - 2 = 5 - 2 = 3$, so the output must be the same.

Composite Functions

We return to the black box model of functions. There is no reason why one function must terminate at its output. It is possible to have a "chain" of functions, which in our model would be represented as one black box connected to another black box, and that black box connected to still another black box, and so on. For example, consider the operation of an automobile. Assume that input values are generated from the rotation in revolutions per minute of the engine. These revolutions per minute quantities are fed into a gear box called the transmission, which is the first black box. The output of the transmission is transformed, through the axle and wheels, into the forward motion of the automobile. The rotation of the wheels can be considered a second black box, whose output is the forward motion of the automobile.

Figure 2-18 illustrates this model. The symbol T represents the function

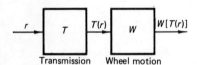

Transmission   Wheel motion

FIGURE 2-18

that describes the transmission, W the function that describes the wheel operation, and r the revolutions per minute, or speed, of the engine. Since r is the input of the transmission, the output of the transmission is $T(r)$. This output is the input to the wheel motion. Hence,

Wheel input = transmission output = T(Engine speed) = $T(r)$

and

Wheel output = W(Wheel input)

So

Wheel output = $W[T(r)]$

The wheel output is a function of transmission output, which in turn is a function of engine speed. Equivalently, each value of engine speed determines a value of the transmission output, which in turn determines a value of the wheel output. Thus, wheel output is a function of r, and the combination of the two black boxes can be considered a single function. Functions of this type are called *composite functions*.

> **DEFINITION** Let $f: A_f \rightarrow B_f$ and $g: A_g \rightarrow B_g$ define functions f and g. The **composite function** of g on f, denoted $g \circ f: A \rightarrow B$ in set form, is given by the rule
>
> ▶ $(g \circ f)(x) = g[f(x)]$
>
> i.e., the argument of g is $f(x)$. If A is the domain of $g \circ f$ and B is a set containing the range of $g \circ f$, then the conditions for $g \circ f$ to be a valid composite function are
>
> (1) $B_f \subseteq A_g$ (main condition)
> (2) $A \subseteq A_f$ and $B \subseteq B_g$ (subsidiary conditions)

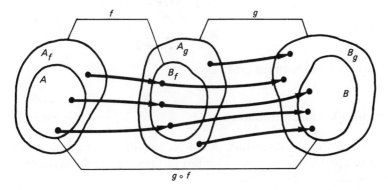

FIGURE 2-19

Figure 2-19 illustrates the composite function $g \circ f$, along with the stated set relationships. The conditions on the sets will be illustrated later in this section. The following examples illustrate the *algebra* of some composite functions:

EXAMPLE 2-7 Let $g(x) = x^2 + 2$ and $f(x) = 3x$. Find an algebraic expression for

$$g[f(x)]$$

The notation $g[f(x)]$ means that the function g operates on the argument $f(x)$. Since $g(x) = x^2 + 2$,

$$g[f(x)] = [f(x)]^2 + 2$$

and since $f(x) = 3x$,

$$g[f(x)] = [3x]^2 + 2$$
$$= 9x^2 + 2$$

which is the required expression. Thus, if $x = -3$, then $g[f(-3)] = 9(-3)^2 + 2 = 83$.

EXAMPLE 2-8 Let $h(x) = x - 1$ and $g(x) = 1/(x^2 + 1)$. Find an algebraic expression for

$$g[h(x)]$$

The function g operating on the argument $h(x)$ means

$$g[h(x)] = \frac{1}{[h(x)]^2 + 1}$$

Substituting $x - 1$ for $h(x)$, we obtain

$$g[h(x)] = \frac{1}{(x - 1)^2 + 1}$$
$$= \frac{1}{(x^2 - 2x + 1) + 1}$$
$$= \frac{1}{x^2 - 2x + 2}$$

which is the required expression.

Forming Valid Composites

We return to the discussion of the set conditions for which $g \circ f$ is a valid composite function. As described in Figure 2-19 and the definition, the conditions on the various sets are

$$B_f \subseteq A_g \quad \text{(main condition)}$$
$$A \subseteq A_f \quad \text{and} \quad B \subseteq B_g \quad \text{(subsidiary conditions)}$$

The following example illustrates the use of the set conditions in the construction of a valid composite function.

EXAMPLE 2-9   Given the functions

2-2 Functions— **61**
Concepts and
Notation

$$y = F(t) = \sqrt{t - 1}; \qquad A_F = \{t \mid t \geqslant 1\}, \quad B_F = \{y \mid y \geqslant 0\}$$

and

$$z = G(x) = x^2 - 8; \qquad A_G = \{x \mid x \in \mathbb{R}\}, \quad B_G = \{z \mid z \geqslant -8\}$$

Determine whether the composite functions $G \circ F$ and $F \circ G$ are valid, and if not, what domain and range adjustments must be made for the composite to be properly defined.

(a) $G \circ F$: First, we must check whether the main set condition is satisfied. For the composite $G \circ F$, this condition is $B_F \subseteq A_G$. Since $B_F = \{y \mid y \geqslant 0\}$ and $A_G = \{x \mid x \in \mathbb{R}\}$, the condition is satisfied:

$$\{y \mid y \geqslant 0\} \subseteq \{x \mid x \in \mathbb{R}\}$$

To find A, the domain of $G \circ F$, we note that

$$z = (G \circ F)(t) = G[F(t)] = (\sqrt{t - 1})^2 - 8 = t - 9$$

where the t values *must* come from A_F. Therefore,

$$z = t - 9 \quad \text{and} \quad A = A_F = \{t \mid t \geqslant 1\}$$

Since $z = t - 9 \geqslant -8$ when $t \geqslant 1$, this implies that $B = B_G = \{z \mid z \geqslant -8\}$. Clearly, the two subsidiary conditions are satisfied, since

$$A \subseteq A_F \quad \text{and} \quad B \subseteq B_G$$

Therefore, $G \circ F$ is a valid composite function requiring no restrictions.

(b) $F \circ G$: Figure 2-20 shows the operation of the composite $F \circ G$ and the conditions for $F \circ G$ to be valid, which are

$$B_G \subseteq A_F \qquad \text{(main condition)}$$
$$A \subseteq A_G \quad \text{and} \quad B \subseteq B_F \qquad \text{(subsidiary conditions)}$$

Since $B_G = \{z \mid z \geqslant -8\}$ and $A_F = \{t \mid t \geqslant 1\}$, we immediately see that

$$B_G \nsubseteq A_F$$

Therefore, restrictions must be placed on A_G or B_G in order to form a valid composite function. The most obvious solution is to find what adjustment on the domain of G would make the range of G become A_F. If we define a new range for G as

$$\hat{B}_G = A_F$$

then

$$\hat{B}_G = \{z \mid z \geqslant 1\}$$

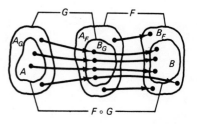

FIGURE 2-20

Since $z = x^2 - 8$, the restriction $z \geqslant 1$ on the range of G implies the restriction

$$x^2 \geqslant 9$$

on the domain of G. So we define a new domain, $\hat{A}_G$, for G:

$$\hat{A}_G = \{x \mid x^2 \geqslant 9\}; \quad \hat{A}_G \subseteq A_G$$

Now, with these restrictions,

$$y = (F \circ G)(x) = \sqrt{(x^2 - 8) - 1} = \sqrt{x^2 - 9}, \quad \text{where} \quad x \in \hat{A}_G$$

Therefore, $A = \hat{A}_G = \{x \mid x^2 \geqslant 9\}$, which implies that $B = \{y \mid y \geqslant 0\}$. Now, the student can see that the set conditions are satisfied.

$$\hat{B}_G \subseteq A_F, \quad A \subseteq \hat{A}_G, \quad \text{and} \quad B \subseteq B_F$$

where

$$\hat{A}_G \subseteq A_G \quad \text{and} \quad \hat{B}_G \subseteq B_G.$$

The composite $F \circ G$ is now properly defined.

In the previous example, when forming the composite $F \circ G$, the way to select $\hat{A}_G$ such that $\hat{B}_G \subseteq A_F$ was to let $\hat{B}_G = A_F$. In general, the selection of $\hat{A}_G$ (the restricted domain) is obtained by letting $\hat{B}_G = B_G \cap A_F$. It is not necessary to have $B_G \subseteq A_F$ or $A_F \subseteq B_G$ to form the restricted range. In fact, A_F and B_G may even be disjoint, in which case $\hat{B}_G = \varnothing$ and it is not possible to form a valid composite $F \circ G$.

EXAMPLE 2-10 Let $y = G(t) = t^2$, $A_G = \{t \mid t \in \mathbb{R}\}$, $B_G = \{y \mid y \geqslant 0\}$; and $z = F(x) = \sqrt{16 - x^2}$, $A_F = \{x \mid -4 \leqslant x \leqslant 4\}$, $B_F = \{z \mid 0 \leqslant z \leqslant 4\}$. The valid composite $F \circ G$ requires $B_G \subseteq A_F$. Clearly, this is not so. Therefore, A_G must be restricted to $\hat{A}_G$ such that $\hat{B}_G = B_G \cap A_F$. Thus, $\hat{B}_G = \{y \mid 0 \leqslant y \leqslant 4\}$ and $\hat{A}_G = \{t \mid -2 \leqslant t \leqslant 2\}$.

It is left to the reader to show that under these restrictions, the conditions $A \subseteq A_G$ and $B \subseteq B_F$ are satisfied.

Algebra of Functions

There are other useful operations on functions that must be defined for future use. These are the sum, difference, product, and quotient of two functions.

DEFINITION Let $f : A_f \to B_f$ and $g : A_g \to B_g$ define functions f and g with their respective domains and ranges. Then

The **sum** of f and g, $f + g$, is given by the rule

▶ $(f + g)(x) = f(x) + g(x)$ for $x \in A_f \cap A_g$

The following functions can also be defined:

The **difference**, $f - g$, is given by the rule

$$\blacktriangleright (f - g)(x) = f(x) - g(x) \quad \text{for} \quad x \in A_f \cap A_g$$

The **product**, $f \cdot g$, is given by the rule

$$\blacktriangleright (f \cdot g)(x) = f(x) \cdot g(x) \quad \text{for} \quad x \in A_f \cap A_g$$

The **quotient**, f/g, is given by the rule

$$\blacktriangleright (f/g)(x) = f(x)/g(x) \quad \text{for} \quad x \in A_f \cap A_g \quad \text{such that} \quad g(x) \neq 0$$

The following examples illustrate these operations:

EXAMPLE 2-11   Let $f(x) = \sqrt{x - 1}$ and $g(x) = x - 2$. Then

$$A_f = \{x \mid x \geqslant 1\}, \qquad B_f = \{y \mid y \geqslant 0\}$$
$$A_g = \{x \mid x \in \mathbb{R}\}, \qquad B_g = \{y \mid y \in \mathbb{R}\}$$

The sum of f and g is

$$(f + g)(x) = f(x) + g(x) = \sqrt{x - 1} + x - 2$$

where

$$x \in A_f \cap A_g = \{x \mid x \geqslant 1\}$$

The difference is

$$(f - g)(x) = f(x) - g(x) = \sqrt{x - 1} - (x - 2)$$
$$= \sqrt{x - 1} - x + 2$$

where

$$x \in A_f \cap A_g = \{x \mid x \geqslant 1\}$$

The product is

$$(f \cdot g)(x) = f(x) \cdot g(x) = (\sqrt{x - 1})(x - 2)$$

where

$$x \in A_f \cap A_g = \{x \mid x \geqslant 1\}$$

The quotient is

$$\left(\frac{f}{g}\right)(x) = \frac{f(x)}{g(x)} = \frac{\sqrt{x - 1}}{x - 2}$$

where $x \in A_f \cap A_g$ but $g(x) \neq 0$, that is,

$$x \in A_f \cap A_g - \{2\} = \{x \mid x \geqslant 1, x \neq 2\}$$

DEFINITION   Let $f: A_f \to B_f$ define a function f, and let $c \in \mathbb{R}$. Then the function cf is given by the rule

$$cf(x) = c \cdot f(x) \quad \text{for} \quad x \in A_f$$

EXAMPLE 2-12 Let $f(x) = x^2 - 1$. Then $A_f = \{x \mid x \in \mathbb{R}\}$ and $B_f = \{y \mid y \geqslant -1\}$. For $c = 3$, $cf(x) = 3(x^2 - 1) = 3x^2 - 3$. The domain of cf is $\{x \mid x \in \mathbb{R}\}$, and the range of cf is $\{y \mid y \geqslant -3\}$.

More on Functional Models

The symbols shown in Figure 2-21 can be used to set up black box models of more complicated functions than those illustrated so far. For example, consider the expression

$$y = F(x) = 6x^3 - 4x^2 + 6x$$

where x is the input and y is the output. Three operations involving x are required to obtain y. These are the cubing of x, the squaring of x, and multiplications of x, x^2, and x^3 by real numbers. The black box model for this system is given in Figure 2-22. Note that the adder–subtractor is used to combine the terms $6x^3$, $4x^2$, and $6x$, with their proper signs to get y.

FIGURE 2-21

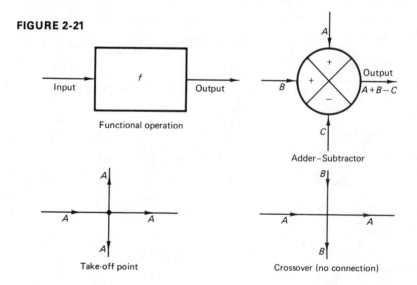

FIGURE 2-22

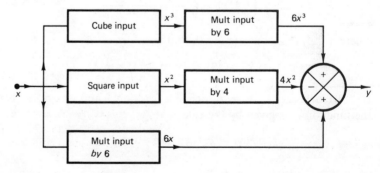

Set A

1. Which of the following sets of ordered pairs satisfy the definition of a function?
    (a) {(0, 1), (1, 2), (2, 3), (3, 4)}
    (b) {(0, 3), (0, 6), (1, 4), (2, 5)}
    (c) {(1, 2), (2, 3), (3, 3), (4, 5)}
    (d) {(−2, 1), (−1, 0), (0, 1), (0, 2), (1, 2)}

2. In Table 2-4 are listed sets X, Y, Z, and W. If ordered pairs are taken from the columns of the table as indicated below, determine which sets of ordered pairs are functions.
    (a) {(Y, Z)}   (b) {(Z, W)}
    (c) {(W, X)}   (d) {(Y, X)}
    (e) {(W, Z)}

TABLE 2-4

X	Y	Z	W
−5	50	−5	−20
−4	40	−4	−16
−3	30	−3	−12
−2	20	−2	−8
−1	10	−1	−4
0	0	0	0
1	−10	−1	4
2	−20	−2	8
3	−30	−3	12
4	−40	−4	16
5	−50	−5	20
6	−60	−6	24

3. Given that $f(x) = 2x^2 - 1$ and $g(x) = 5x + 2$, find the following:
    (a) $f(0)$ (b) $g(4)$ (c) $g(0)$
    (d) $f(3)$ (e) $f(\#)$ (f) $g(\$)$
    (g) $f(-2)$ (h) $g(-7)$ (i) $f(x^2 + 1)$
    (j) $f(3 - 2\Delta)$ (k) $g[f(x)]$ (l) $f[g(x)]$
    (m) $f[g(2)]$ (n) $g[f(5)]$ (o) $(f + g)(3)$
    (p) $(f - g)(2)$ (q) $(f + 2g)(0)$ (r) $(2f - 3g)(-2)$
    (s) $(f \cdot g)(3)$ (t) $(g \cdot f)(-1)$ (u) $(f/g)(6)$
    (v) $(g/f)(0)$ (w) $(f + g)(x)$ (x) $(f - g)(x)$
    (y) $(f/g)(x)$ (z) $(g/f)(x)$
    Find the domains of the functions in parts (k), (l), (w), (x), (y), and (z).

4. Given the composite function $w = W[V(x)]$ where $W(x) = x^2$ and $V(x) = 3x$, find w for all integers x such that $-5 \leqslant x \leqslant 5$.

5. Suppose $f(x) = 2x - 1$ and $g(x) = (x + 1)/2$. Find algebraic expressions for $f[g(x)]$ and $g[f(x)]$. Find the values of $f[g(x)]$ and $g[f(x)]$ for all integers x such that $-3 \leqslant x \leqslant 3$. What can be said about these two composite functions?

Set B

6. Suppose that numbers are being drawn from a bag containing positive integers. Every time an even integer is drawn, an ordered pair is formed by linking it with a 0, for example, (2, 0), (6, 0). Every time an odd integer is drawn, an ordered pair is formed by linking it with 1, for example, (3, 1), (5, 1). Does this process result in a function if all the integers in the bag are different? If repetitions are allowed?

● 7. For the system of functions shown in Figure 2-23, evaluate y and z if

$$y = f(x) = x^3 - 7x + 9$$
$$z = g(y) = 2y^2 - 10y + 27$$

for $0 \leqslant x \leqslant 2$, x in increments of 0.2.

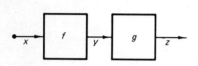

FIGURE 2-23

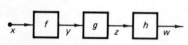

FIGURE 2-24

● 8. For the system of functions shown in Figure 2-24, evaluate y, z, and w if

$$y = f(x) = x^3 + 2x^2 - 9$$
$$z = g(y) = 2y^2 - 10y + 27$$
$$w = h(z) = 3z + 8$$

for $-1 \leqslant x \leqslant 1$, x in increments of 0.1.

9. Using the partial diagram shown in Figure 2-25, symbolize $y = x^3 - 4x^2 + 6x$ as the sum and difference of three functions. The symbol x is to be considered the input for each operation and the symbol y the total output. Fill in the given diagram and show the proper signal flow.

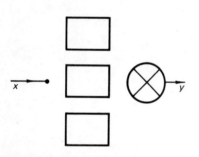

10. For each pair of functions below, find algebraic expressions for $f \circ g$ and $g \circ f$. Then determine which composites are valid. For those that are not, formulate the proper restrictions to make the composite valid.
(a) $y = f(t) = t/\sqrt{t^2 - 1}$, $z = g(x) = x + 3$
(b) $y = f(t) = \sqrt{1 - t}$, $z = g(x) = x^2 - x$
(c) $y = f(t) = t^2/(t^2 - 1)$, $z = g(x) = \sqrt{x + 1}$

FIGURE 2-25

11. In the field of automatic control systems, the control is achieved by feeding back a portion of the output to the input of the functional operation in such a way that it is subtracted from the input signal. Let $f(x)$ be the functional operation, β the portion of the output fed back to the adder-subtractor, I the input, and O the output. Set up the model of this feedback system by filling in the appropriate symbols given in Figure 2-26 and by showing proper signal flow.

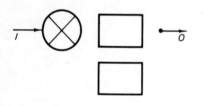

FIGURE 2-26

12. A certain corporation consists of four vice-presidents, one president, and a board of directors. The decision-making process consists of information I, given to the four vice-presidents, who pass on decisions to the president. The president passes on decisions to the board and also feeds back some decisions as information to each of the vice-presidents, thus adding to their total information. The board makes the final decision, D, and also feeds back part of this as information to the president. Draw a black box description of this corporate decision-making process, with proper flow for direction of information and decisions.

13. A chemical company wishes to set up a functional model of a process it uses to manufacture product X from raw materials R. Four operations (1, 2, 3, and 4) are intertwined to produce the product. The following is a description of what occurs.
     (a) Raw materials are fed into operations 1 and 3.
     (b) Half of the output of operation 1 is fed to operation 2 and half to operation 4.
     (c) Four-fifths of the output of operation 2 is fed to operation 3 and one-tenth is fed back and added to the input of operation 1, and the remaining one-tenth of the output of operation 2 is fed to the input of operation 4.
     (d) Five-sixths of the operation 3 output is fed to the input of operation 4, and one-sixth is fed back and added to the input of operation 2.
     (e) The total output of operation 4 is X.
     Draw the functional model of this process.

2-3 INVERSE RELATIONS AND FUNCTIONS

Inverse Relations

So far, in our study of relations, it has been understood that the elements of the domain were chosen independently and the corresponding elements of the range depended on those choices. But the question sometimes arises, If a range element of a relation is known, how does one find the corresponding domain element? To answer this question, the relation must be reversed, that is, the elements of the range must be considered the independent choices and the elements of the domain the dependent results. This reversal of domain and range roles leads to the concept of an *inverse relation.*

> **DEFINITION**   Let relation $\rho = \{(x, y) \mid y = \rho(x), x \in \mathscr{D}, y \in \mathscr{R}\}$. Then the **inverse relation** of ρ, denoted ρ^{-1}, is defined as
>
> ▶ $\rho^{-1} = \{(y, x) \mid (x, y) \in \rho\}$

The inverse relation ρ^{-1} has domain $\bar{\mathscr{D}} = \mathscr{R}$ and $\bar{\mathscr{R}} = \mathscr{D}$. That is, the domain of ρ^{-1} is the range of ρ, and the range of ρ^{-1} is the domain of ρ.

EXAMPLE 2-13   Let

$$\rho = \{(5, 6), (2, 3), (7, 9), (6, 5)\}$$

Then $\mathscr{D} = \{5, 2, 7, 6\}$ and $\mathscr{R} = \{6, 3, 9, 5\}$, and

$$\rho^{-1} = \{(6, 5), (3, 2), (9, 7), (5, 6)\}$$

The inverse relation has domain $\bar{\mathscr{D}} = \{6, 3, 9, 5\}$ and range $\bar{\mathscr{R}} = \{5, 2, 7, 6\}$. Again, note that $\bar{\mathscr{D}} = \mathscr{R}$ and $\bar{\mathscr{R}} = \mathscr{D}$.

In many instances, we seek the inverse of an equation that describes a relation. For example, the equation $y = x/2$ describes the relation $\rho = \{(x, y) \mid y = x/2\}$. Here, the domain elements are symbolized by the letter x and the corresponding range values by y. If we consider the range element 6, we can calculate the corresponding domain element, which is 12, because when $x = 12$, $y = \frac{1}{2}(12) = 6$. However, to do this for all possible elements of the range of the relation would be both tedious and unnecessary. Since it is known that $y = x/2$, we can easily find the value of x by rewriting this expression as $x = 2y$. This shows that each element of the domain (x) is twice the corresponding element of the range (y). If we consider the independent choices to be the range elements rather than the domain elements, then the equation $x = 2y$ describes the inverse relation,

$$\rho^{-1} = \{(y, x) \mid x = 2y\}$$

Inverses of Functions

If the relation is a function (that is, if to each element of the domain there corresponds one and only one element of the range), then we can speak of input values and output values of the function. In the case of the function

$$y = F(x) = \frac{x}{2}$$

the input values (x), or independent choices, of F are twice the output values (y), or dependent results. For these particular roles of x and y, the equations

$$2y = x \quad \text{and} \quad y = \frac{x}{2}$$

represent the same function F. To form the inverse relation of F, denoted F^{-1}, the roles of x and y must be interchanged; that is, the y values of F are the domain values, or independent choices, of F^{-1}, and the x values of F are the range values, or dependent results, of F^{-1}. Thus,

$$F^{-1} = \{(y, x) \mid x = 2y\}$$

Since it is customary to call the domain variable x and the range variable y, the inverse relation is written

$$F^{-1} = \{(x, y) \mid y = 2x\}$$

Thus, if

$$F(x) = \frac{x}{2}, \quad x \in \mathcal{D}_F$$

then

$$F^{-1}(x) = 2x, \quad x \in \mathcal{R}_F$$

Figure 2-27 illustrates the operation of the function $F(x)$ and its inverse relation $F^{-1}(x)$.

If F is any function and F^{-1} is the inverse relation of F, we may ask: When is F^{-1} a function and, if it is not, under what restrictions will it become a function? It happens that the inverse relation of a function is not necessarily a function. For example, the function $y = F(x) = x^2$ has an inverse relation that is not a function. To see this, consider some representative elements of the domain, say, -2, 0, and 2; then the set of ordered pairs

$$\{(-2, 4), (0, 0), (2, 4)\}$$

is a subset of F. The set of ordered pairs $\{(4, -2), (0, 0), (4, 2)\}$ is thus a subset of F^{-1}. Clearly, this set is not a function, because two distinct ordered pairs have the same first component; therefore, F^{-1} is not a function either.

The graph of $F(x) = x^2$ is shown in Figure 2-28. The graph of a function can be used to show that an inverse function does not exist. Any horizontal line represents a constant range value, and if some horizontal line cuts the graph in more than one place, then the *inverse* relation must contain at least two ordered pairs with the same first component, and thus, the inverse relation is *not* a function. Any horizontal line above the D axis cuts the graph of $F(x) = x^2$ in two places, so we see again that the inverse of $F(x) = x^2$ is not a function.

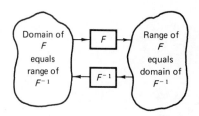

FIGURE 2-27

One-to-One and Onto Functions

When the inverse of a function F is not a function, it is often possible to restrict the domain and range of F in such a way that F^{-1} becomes a function. In order to discuss this procedure, it is necessary to develop some additional concepts. The first is that of a *one-to-one function*.

> **DEFINITION** Let $f: A \to B$ define a function f. Then f is a **one-to-one function** if to each element of the range, there corresponds one and only one element of A. That is, for $x_1, x_2 \in A$, $f(x_1) = f(x_2)$ implies that $x_1 = x_2$, i.e., $x_1 \neq x_2$ implies that $f(x_1) \neq f(x_2)$.

Recall that the definition of a function requires that each domain element have one and only one range element associated with it, but a function may have two different domain elements associated with the same range element. For example, we have just seen that

$$y = F(x) = x^2$$

is a function. However, it is not one to one, since some range elements, (for example, 9) are associated with more than one domain element (namely, 3 and -3), as was shown in Figure 2-28.

The next concept needed is that of an *onto* function.

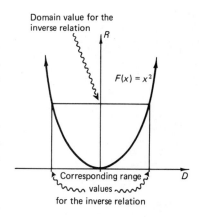

FIGURE 2-28

DEFINITION Let $f: A \to B$ define a function f with domain A. If *every* element of B is the image under f of at least one element of A, then f is said to map A **onto** B and is denoted $f: A \twoheadrightarrow B$.

A function always maps its domain onto its range. Thus, a function $f: A \to B$ is onto when $B = \mathscr{R}$.

EXAMPLE 2-14 The function

$$y = f(x) = x^3$$

maps the domain

$$A = \{x \mid x \in \mathbb{R}\}$$

onto the set

$$B = \{y \mid y \in \mathbb{R}\}$$

because for any $y \in \mathbb{R}$, there is an $x \in \mathbb{R}$ (namely, $x = \sqrt[3]{y}$) such that $y = x^3$. Thus, every element in B is the image of at least one element in A, and B is the range of f.

EXAMPLE 2-15 The function

$$y = f(x) = x^2$$

with domain

$$A = \{x \mid x \in \mathbb{R}\}$$

does not map domain A onto the set

$$B = \{y \mid y \in \mathbb{R}\}$$

because f maps real numbers only to nonnegative real numbers; thus, the negative real numbers are not images of any elements in domain A. However, this function does map A onto the set

$$\hat{B} = \{y \mid y \geqslant 0\}$$

The student can verify that the definition of an onto function is satisfied for this image set, $\hat{B}$.

Inverse Functions

If the function f is both one to one and onto, then for every element of the domain, there is a unique element of the range, and for every element of the range, there is a unique element of the domain. Therefore, the inverse relation, f^{-1}, is also a function and is one to one and onto. Symbolically, we write

$$f: A \twoheadrightarrow B \quad \text{and} \quad f^{-1}: B \twoheadrightarrow A$$

and call f^{-1} the *inverse function* of f.

DEFINITION Let $f: A \to B$ define a function f. Then the relation f^{-1} is the **inverse function** of f if f is one to one and onto. In this case, f^{-1} is given by

▶ $f^{-1} = \{(y, x) \mid (x, y) \in f\}$

One additional consequence results when f is one to one and onto. If the composite of f^{-1} on f is formed, we get

$$f^{-1} \circ f: A \twoheadrightarrow A$$

In point form, this becomes

▶ $f^{-1}[f(x)] = x$ for every $x \in A$

Similarly, if the composite of f on f^{-1} is formed, we get

$$f \circ f^{-1}: B \twoheadrightarrow B$$

In point form, this becomes

▶ $f[f^{-1}(y)] = y$ for every $y \in B$

Since any letter can be used to represent the variable, we can also write

$$f[f^{-1}(x)] = x \quad \text{for all } x \in B$$

This leads to the following alternative definition of the inverse function, f^{-1}, of the function f.

DEFINITION Let f and g be two functions such that $(g \circ f)(t) = t$ for every t in the domain of f and $(f \circ g)(t) = t$ for every t in the domain of g. Then g and f are **inverse functions** of each other; this is symbolized

$$g = f^{-1} \quad \text{or} \quad f = g^{-1}$$

The main and subsidiary conditions for a valid composite function are automatically met when a composite is formed between a function f and its inverse function, f^{-1}, because the domain of one is the range of the other. The following examples show how the alternative definition can be used to obtain the inverse of functions described by algebraic equations.

EXAMPLE 2-16 Given the function

$$f(x) = 3x - 7, \quad x \in \mathbb{R}$$

find the inverse function, if it exists.

Using the alternative definition, we require that the composite $f^{-1} \circ f$ satisfy the condition

$$f^{-1}[f(x)] = x, \quad x \in \mathscr{D}_f$$

If we let $f(x) = z$, then

$$z = 3x - 7$$

Solving for x, we get

$$x = \tfrac{1}{3}(z + 7)$$

Substituting first z for $f(x)$, then $\tfrac{1}{3}(z + 7)$ for x in the equation $f^{-1}[f(x)] = x$ yields

$$f^{-1}(z) = \tfrac{1}{3}(z + 7), \quad z \in \mathscr{D}_{f^{-1}}$$

As a check, form the composite $f \circ f^{-1}$. We should get

$$f[f^{-1}(z)] = z$$

By the definition of a composite function,

$$f[f^{-1}(z)] = 3[f^{-1}(z)] - 7$$

Substituting $\tfrac{1}{3}(z + 7)$ for $f^{-1}(z)$, we get

$$\begin{aligned} f[f^{-1}(z)] &= 3[\tfrac{1}{3}(z + 7)] - 7 \\ &= (z + 7) - 7 \\ &= z \end{aligned}$$

This confirms that

$$f(x) = 3x - 7, \quad x \in \mathbb{R}$$

has an inverse function given by

$$f^{-1}(z) = \tfrac{1}{3}(z + 7), \quad z \in \mathbb{R}$$

EXAMPLE 2-17   Given $f(x) = \sqrt{x}$, $x \geqslant 0$, find $f^{-1}(z)$, if it exists as a function.

We use the method developed in the last example. The function f^{-1} must satisfy the condition

$$f^{-1}[f(x)] = x$$

so we let $f(x) = z$. Then

$$\sqrt{x} = z$$

which is equivalent to

$$x = z^2$$

Since $\sqrt{x} \geqslant 0$, we have $z \geqslant 0$. Substituting first z for $f(x)$, then z^2 for x in the equation $f^{-1}[f(x)] = x$ yields

$$f^{-1}(z) = z^2, \quad z \geqslant 0$$

It is left to the reader to verify that this is the inverse function by finding the remaining composite, $f \circ f^{-1}$.

EXAMPLE 2-18   Given

2-3 *Inverse Relations*   **73**
and Functions

$$f(x) = \frac{1}{x^2 + 1}, \quad x \in \mathbb{R}$$

find $f^{-1}(x)$ if it exists as a function.
The required inverse must satisfy

$$f^{-1}[f(x)] = x$$

Let $z = f(x)$; then

$$z = \frac{1}{x^2 + 1}, \quad 0 < z \leqslant 1$$

(The student should verify that the range of f is $\{z \mid 0 < z \leqslant 1\}$.)
Solving for x, we obtain

$$x = \pm\sqrt{\frac{1-z}{z}}$$

Upon substitution into the equation $f^{-1}[f(x)] = x$, we have

$$f^{-1}(z) = \pm\sqrt{\frac{1-z}{z}}$$

The double-valued solution for x indicates that the original function, f, is not one to one; therefore, the inverse relation is *not* a function. This is obvious from the graph of the function.

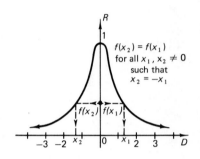

FIGURE 2-29

The graph of $y = f(x) = 1/(x^2 + 1)$ immediately shows that except for $x = 0$, each value in the range of f is the image of two domain values. (See Figure 2-29.) We can overcome this problem by redefining the domain of f. If we select the portion of the function for which $x \geqslant 0$, then the solution for x no longer requires the plus or minus sign, and hence

$$x = \sqrt{\frac{1-z}{z}}, \quad 0 < z \leqslant 1$$

Now, the substitution yields

$$f^{-1}(z) = \sqrt{\frac{1-z}{z}}, \quad 0 < z \leqslant 1$$

as the inverse function of

$$f(x) = \frac{1}{x^2 + 1}, \quad x \geqslant 0$$

We again leave it to the reader to show that this result is valid by using these results to find the remaining composite, $f \circ f^{-1}$. This operation of redefining the domain of f is called *selecting the principal branch of f*. (Note: To be sure that the proper principal branch has been selected, check that both composites, $f^{-1} \circ f$ and $f \circ f^{-1}$, conform to the alternative definition of the inverse function. For the example just presented,

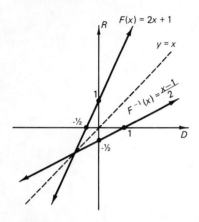

FIGURE 2-30

if we had used the restriction $x \leqslant 0$, the alternative definition would not be satisfied.)

Graphical Properties of Inverse Functions

Another interesting characteristic of inverse functions can be seen when the alternative definition of an inverse function is used in conjunction with graphing. We begin by defining the *identity function*.

DEFINITION A function I is an **identity function** if $I(x) = x$ for every x in the domain of I.

By definition, the composite $(F^{-1} \circ F)(x) = x$ for all $x \in \mathscr{D}_F$. If we let $y = (F^{-1} \circ F)(x)$, then this composite is the identity function, I. It can be shown that the graphs of $F(x)$ and $F^{-1}(x)$ must be symmetrical about the line

$$y = x$$

which is the graph of the identity function. This property can best be illustrated by graphing a function and its inverse function on one coordinate system and noting the geometric properties they possess. For $F(x) = 2x + 1$, $x \in \mathbb{R}$, the inverse function is $F^{-1}(z) = (z-1)/2$, $z \in \mathbb{R}$. To graph both functions on the same coordinate axes, the same letters must be used to represent the range and domain variables in each of the functions; thus, Figure 2-30 shows the graph of $F^{-1}(x) = (x-1)/2$. Clearly, each graph is the reflection of the other about the line $y = x$. Inverse functions always possess this reflection property.

EXAMPLE 2-19 Find the inverse function of $F(x) = x^3 - 8$, and show that the graph of $F^{-1}(x)$ is the reflection of the graph of $F(x)$ about the graph of the identity function.

Since $F(x) = x^3 - 8$, then $F^{-1}(x) = \sqrt[3]{x + 8}$. These two functions are graphed in Figure 2-31. Note their symmetry about the line $y = x$, which is the graph of the identity function.

Inverse and Strictly Monotonic Functions

Another concept that will be useful in discussing the inverse relations of functions is that of a *strictly monotonic function*.

DEFINITION A function $F : A \to B$ is said to be **strictly monotonic** if either

$$F(x_2) > F(x_1)$$

whenever $x_2 > x_1$ (for $x_1, x_2 \in A$), or

$$F(x_2) < F(x_1)$$

whenever $x_2 > x_1$ ($x_1, x_2 \in A$).

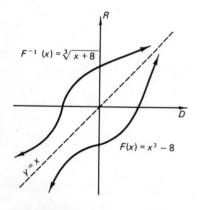

FIGURE 2-31

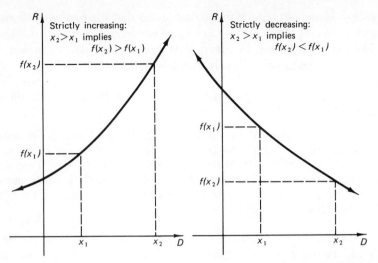

FIGURE 2-32

In the first case, the function F is said to be **strictly increasing**; in the second case, F is said to be **strictly decreasing.**

Figure 2-32 illustrates a strictly increasing function and a strictly decreasing function. As further examples, Figure 2-33 shows the graphs of the functions

$$F(x) = x^3, \quad x \in \mathbb{R}$$

which is strictly increasing, and

$$G(x) = -2x + 1, \quad x \in \mathbb{R}$$

which is strictly decreasing. On the other hand, the functions graphed in

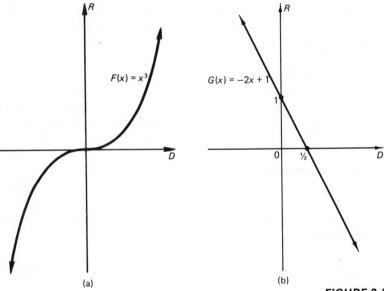

FIGURE 2-33

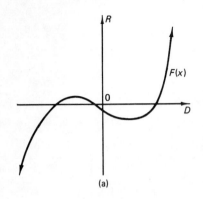

(a)

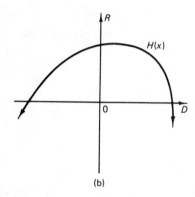

(b)

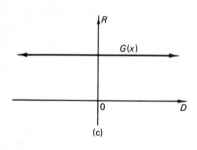

(c)

FIGURE 2-34

Figure 2-34 are not strictly monotonic. Note that the function shown in Figure 2-34(c) is nonincreasing as well as nondecreasing.

The examples shown in Figure 2-33 suggest that strictly monotonic functions are one to one. This is true, as we show next.

THEOREM 2-1 If the function $f: A \rightarrow B$ is strictly monotonic, then it is one to one.

PROOF Assume that f is strictly monotonic. It must be shown that whenever $x_1 \neq x_2$, then $f(x_1) \neq f(x_2)$. So assume that $x_1 \neq x_2$; since one of the numbers x_1 and x_2 must be greater than the other, suppose $x_2 > x_1$. Then since f is strictly monotonic, either $f(x_2) > f(x_1)$ or $f(x_2) < f(x_1)$, which implies that $f(x_2) \neq f(x_1)$. Thus, for any $x_1, x_2 \in A$, if $x_1 \neq x_2$, then $f(x_1) \neq f(x_2)$. Therefore, f is a one-to-one function. ∎

Furthermore, we have seen that with appropriate restrictions, any function can be made an onto function. Therefore, any strictly monotonic onto function has an inverse function.

THEOREM 2-2 Let $f: A \twoheadrightarrow B$ define an onto function. If f is strictly monotonic, then f^{-1} is the inverse function of f.

PROOF Suppose f^{-1} is not a function. Then there exists at least one point $\bar{y} \in B$ that is the image of at least two distinct points $x_1, x_2 \in A$; that is, $\bar{y} = f(x_1) = f(x_2)$ for $x_1 \neq x_2$. But then f is not a one-to-one function. By Theorem 2-1, this contradicts the assumption that f is strictly monotonic. Therefore, f^{-1} is the inverse function of f. ∎

Note that the converse of this theorem is not true; that is, the existence of an inverse function does *not* imply that the original function is strictly monotonic. Can you show some counterexamples? In summary, if a function is onto, then a convenient way of determining that it has an inverse function would be to show also that it is strictly monotonic. A graph of the function will demonstrate this quite readily.

EXAMPLE 2-20 Show that the function $F(x) = x^3 - 8$, $x \in \mathbb{R}$, has an inverse function given by $F^{-1}(z) = \sqrt[3]{z + 8}$, $z \in \mathbb{R}$.

Figure 2-35 shows the graph of F. The graph indicates that for two arbitrarily selected points from the domain, x_1 and x_2, where

$$x_2 > x_1$$

the corresponding range values, $F(x_1)$ and $F(x_2)$, will be such that

$$F(x_2) > F(x_1)$$

Therefore, F is a strictly increasing function. Since $F: \mathbb{R} \twoheadrightarrow \mathbb{R}$, by Theorem 2-2, the inverse function F^{-1}, exists.

To show that $F^{-1}(z) = \sqrt[3]{z + 8}$, $z \in \mathbb{R}$, is the inverse function, simply form the composite $F^{-1} \circ F$ and show that it is the identity function.

Set A

1. Find the inverses of the functions represented by the following equations:
    Where a square root is involved, choose the principal root.
    (a) $y = x + 3$
    (b) $2y = 3x - 4$
    (c) $y = x^2 - 2x + 3$
        (*Hint:* Use completion of the square.)

    (d) $y = \dfrac{x}{x + 2}$, $x \neq -2$

    (e) $y = \dfrac{x - 1}{x + 1}$, $x \neq -1$

    (f) $y = \dfrac{x + 6}{x}$, $x \neq 0$

2. Form the composite function $f[f^{-1}(t)]$ for each function in Exercise 1
    and show that the identity function results in each case.

3. Consider the relations represented by the following equations:

    (1) $y = \dfrac{5x}{2}$, $x \in \mathbb{R}$

    (2) $y^2 = 2x - 4$, $x \geqslant 2$
    (3) $x = 6t^2$, $t \in \mathbb{R}$

    (4) $y = \dfrac{x}{1 + x^2}$, $x \in \mathbb{R}$

    (5) $y = mx + b$, $m \neq 0, x \in \mathbb{R}$
    (6) $y = x^3 + 6$, $x \in \mathbb{R}$

    (a) By graphing, determine whether each relation is a function.
    (b) For those relations that are functions, find the inverse relation.
    (c) Determine whether the inverse relation is also a function. (Use the
         property of monotonicity.)
    (d) If the inverse relation is a function, determine the domain and
         range values for which the composites
         $$f[f^{-1}(t)] \quad \text{and} \quad f^{-1}[f(t)]$$
         are valid.
    (e) For the inverse relations that are not functions, determine what
         restrictions must be placed on the domain of the original function
         for an inverse function to exist. Solve for the algebraic form of
         this limited inverse function.

● 4. Find the inverse of the following function. Then, using x values of
    0.7, 1.6, 4.3, and 7.2 as inputs to f, verify numerically that the inverse
    found is correct.
    $$y = f(x) = 3x^2 - 7$$

● 5. Repeat the instructions for Exercise 4, using the x values -2.1,
    -0.3, 1.1, and 6.2 as inputs to the following function. (*Hint:* Use
    completion of the square.)
    $$y = f(x) = x^2 + 5x - 6$$

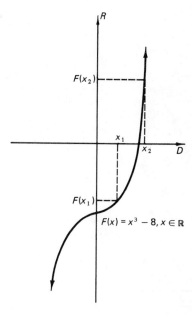

FIGURE 2-35

Set B

6. Using the notation and ideas already developed, show that

$$\psi(\psi^{-1}\{\phi[\phi^{-1}(x)]\}) = x$$

where ψ and ϕ are one to one and onto functions and $x \in A_{\phi^{-1}}$.

7. For the function represented by the equation $xy = k$, where k is a fixed real number greater than 0, show that $\phi = \phi^{-1}$, for $x \neq 0$ and $y \neq 0$.

8. Consider the relations $x + y = k$ and $x^2 + y^2 = k^2$, where k is a fixed real number. Show that $\phi = \phi^{-1}$ in both cases.

9. What property of the equations given in Exercises 7 and 8 gives rise to the result that the function is equal to its inverse?

10. Given

$$f(x) = \frac{ax + b}{cx + d}, \qquad x \neq -\frac{d}{c}, \qquad a, b, c, d \in \mathbb{R}, c \text{ and } d \text{ both} \neq 0$$

find the inverse function, f^{-1}, if it exists.

Set C

For Exercises 11 and 12, the reader may have to review complex number operations (see Section 8-1). The best way to proceed is to map the critical points of the circle in the z plane into the w plane.

11. In the field of complex variable theory, a technique called *conformal mapping* is often used in the solution of complicated problems. This method uses a linear transformation to map a region in one plane into a region in another plane. Suppose there are two complex planes, the z plane (where $z = x + iy$) and the w plane (where $w = u + iv$). In the z plane, the equation $x^2 + y^2 = r^2$ describes a circle of radius r centered at the origin. (See Figure 2-36.)

    (a) Show by substitution that the transformation

    $$w = \phi(z) = \frac{z - r}{z + r}, \qquad x, y, r \in \mathbb{R}$$

    maps the circle given in the z plane into the iv axis (the axis where $u = 0$) of the w plane.

    (b) For the transformation ϕ given in part (a), determine whether the interior of the circle in the z plane is mapped into the region to the right or to the left of the iv axis.

    (c) Find ϕ^{-1}.

12. (a) Show that the transformation

    $$w = \phi(z) = \frac{ri - z}{ri + z}, \qquad x, y, r \in \mathbb{R}$$

    also maps the circle $x^2 + y^2 = r^2$ of the z plane into the iv axis of the w plane (this condition again means $u = 0$). Is the interior of the circle mapped into the region to the left or to the right of the iv axis? (See Figure 2-36.)

    (b) Find ϕ^{-1}.

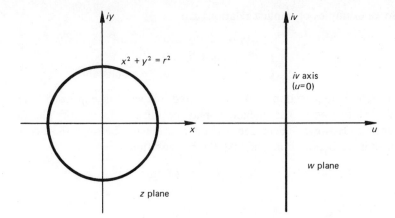

FIGURE 2-36

2-4 EXPLICIT AND IMPLICIT RELATIONS

Explicit Relations

We have discussed equations that represent one variable in terms of another variable. For example, in the equation $y = \frac{1}{2}x$, the range variable, y, is equal to an expression that contains *only* the variable x. In this case, it is said that y is explicitly expressed in terms of x. Relations represented in this way are called *explicit relations*.

> **DEFINITION**   An **explicit relation**, symbolized $y = \rho(x)$, is an expression whose range variable, y, is expressed solely in terms of its domain variable, x.

Some examples of explicit relations are

$$y = Q(t) = t^2 - 1, \qquad\qquad t \in \mathbb{R}$$
$$\lambda^2 = H(Q) = 7 + 2Q + Q^4, \qquad Q \in \mathbb{R}$$
$$E = E(t) = \operatorname{Sin} \omega t, \qquad\qquad \omega \in \mathbb{R}, \quad \omega \text{ a constant}, \quad t \in \mathbb{R}$$

Note that in each case, one variable is expressed solely in terms of the other variable.

Implicit Relations

If an equation does not express one variable in terms of the other variable, then we say that the variables are implicitly represented, and the expression is called an *implicit relation*.

> **DEFINITION**   An **implicit relation**, symbolized $F(x, y) = 0$, is an expression whose range variable, y, is not expressed solely in terms of its domain variable, x.

Some examples of implicit relations are

$$x^2y^2 - 2x = 4$$
$$4s^3 - 7t^2s^2 - 2st + s = 0$$
$$\zeta^2\eta^2 - \alpha\zeta\eta - 3 = 0, \quad \alpha \text{ a constant}$$

In each of these examples, we do not find one variable expressed in terms of the other variable; in fact, it may be difficult to identify the range variable. However, there does exist a relationship between the two variables in each equation. The first can be rewritten as

$$x^2y^2 - 2x - 4 = 0$$

or

$$F(x, y) = x^2y^2 - 2x - 4 = 0$$

The second can be rewritten as

$$G(t, s) = 4s^3 - 7t^2s^2 - 2st + s = 0$$

and the third as

$$\psi(\zeta, \eta) = \zeta^2\eta^2 - \alpha\zeta\eta - 3 = 0$$

Thus, F, G, and ψ represent relations of two variables, equal to 0. This is a common way to symbolize implicit relations. By convention, the first variable in the parentheses is considered the independent variable, or domain variable, and the second variable in the parentheses is the dependent variable, or range variable.

Although an explicit relation can always be written in implicit form, it is not always possible to write an implicit relation in explicit form. For example, we can write the equation $y = x^2$ in explicit form as $y = f(x) = x^2$. In implicit form, we can write

$$y - x^2 = 0 \quad \text{or} \quad F(x, y) = y - x^2 = 0$$

As another example, consider the equation $x^2y + 2y - 4 = 0$. We can easily write it in implicit form as

$$F(x, y) = x^2y + 2y - 4 = 0$$

But we can also write it as an explicit relation. If we factor y, then the equation becomes

$$y(x^2 + 2) - 4 = 0$$

or

$$y(x^2 + 2) = 4$$

or

$$y = \frac{4}{x^2 + 2}$$

Thus, y is expressed solely in terms of x, and we can use the explicit form

$$y = f(x) = \frac{4}{x^2 + 2}$$

However, not every implicit relation can be written in explicit form. For example, the relation

$$6x^3y^2 - 4x + 3xy^7 - 6 = 0$$

cannot be written explicitly. The student should verify this by attempting to write it in the form

$$y = \rho(x) \quad \text{or} \quad x = h(y)$$

Graphing Implicit Relations

Graphing an implicit relation is sometimes difficult. The following example outlines a common technique, which is used further in Section 4-2.

EXAMPLE 2-21 Graph the implicit relation

$$F(x, y) = xy + 6y - x^2 + 4 = 0$$

for $-5 \leqslant x \leqslant 5$, with x in increments of 1.

By simply substituting x values into the equation, we can find the corresponding y values. Table 2-5 shows the ordered pairs obtained, and Figure 2-37 shows the graph of this relation.

TABLE 2-5

x	y
-5	21
-4	6
-3	$\frac{5}{3}$
-2	0
-1	$-\frac{3}{5}$
0	$-\frac{2}{3}$
1	$-\frac{3}{7}$
2	0
3	$\frac{5}{9}$
4	$\frac{6}{5}$
5	$\frac{21}{11}$

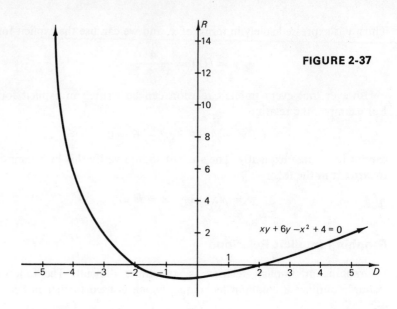

FIGURE 2-37

$xy + 6y - x^2 + 4 = 0$

Why is there no solution for $x = -6$? (*Hint:* Write the equation in explicit form, as $y = \rho(x)$.) The reader should also graph this relation for values $x \leqslant -7$.

EXERCISES 2-4

Set A

1. Classify each of the following equations as explicit or implicit. Rewrite the implicit equations, where possible, in explicit form.

   (a) $y = x^2 - 3x + 7$ (b) $xy + x = 6$

   (c) $x^2y^2 + 4xy + 4 = 16$ (d) $x^3y + x^2y - 4y = 27$

   (e) $x^2y + xy^2 - 3 = 0$ (f) $y = \dfrac{xy^2}{x^2 + 4}$

   (g) $y = \dfrac{x^2 + 2x - 3}{x^3 + 4x^2 - 8x + 7}$

2. (a) Write the relation represented by the model in Figure 2-38.
   (b) Is the relation represented by this model implicit or explicit?

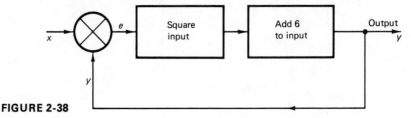

FIGURE 2-38

Set B

3. Sometimes an algebraic substitution of variables will turn an implicit equation into an explicit one. Show that the substitution $x = \hat{x} - 2$ and $y = \hat{y} - 2$ turns

$$x^2y + 7xy + 12y + 2x^2 + 14x + 10 = 0$$

into an explicit equation in terms of $\hat{x}$ and $\hat{y}$. Such a transformation is called a *translation* or *shift of reference axes*.

4. A manufacturer's profit, P, and product volume, V, are given by the equation

$$8PV^2 - P^2 + PV - 240 = 0$$

Find a positive value of V when $P = 10$.

● 5. Find two ordered pairs that satisfy the following equation. (*Hint:* Substitute an integer value for t and solve for v in the resulting equation.)

$$t^2v^2 - 2tv + 1 = 0, \quad t \neq 0, \quad v \neq 0$$

● 6. Find at least two ordered pairs that satisfy each of the following implicit relations, where $x, y \in \mathbb{R}$:
   (a) $2xy^2 - xy + 4 = 0$
   (b) $x^3y^2 + 4x^2 + 6 = 0$
   (c) $y^2 + 2xy - x + 5 = 0$

7. A scientist studying a colony of rats has determined that the population growth, P, is related to time, t, by the equation

$$Pt^2 + P - 4t = 0, \quad t \geq 0$$

where t is the time in years and P is the growth per year in hundreds of individuals. This equation is valid for $t \leq 5$. Construct a table for values of P, from $t = 0$ to $t = 5$, in half-year steps. Calculate the maximum value of the ratio $\Delta P/\Delta t$, where ΔP is the change in P over one half-year interval and Δt is, naturally, $\frac{1}{2}$ year. This ratio is a measure of the average growth rate over any half-year interval. What is the significance of a negative ratio?

Set C

8. Consider the following implicit equations:

$$x^2 + 3xy - 6y^2 = 8$$
$$x^2 - y^2 = 4$$

Show that the substitution $x = wy$ reduces them to explicit equations. In general, any quadratic implicit equation may be reduced to an explicit equation by this method.

9. In Section 2-2, we discussed the concept of evaluating a function when various symbolic inputs were used. If $y = f(x)$, then let $y + \Delta y = f(x + \Delta x)$. This means that a change in x of amount Δx results in a change in y of amount Δy. Then the ratio

$$\frac{f(x + \Delta x) - f(x)}{\Delta x} = \frac{(y + \Delta y) - y}{\Delta x} = \frac{\Delta y}{\Delta x}, \quad \Delta x \neq 0$$

is the basis of the derivative, a central concept in the calculus. Perform this operation for the following explicit functions, and find $\Delta y/\Delta x$.

   (a) $y = x^2$ (b) $y = \dfrac{x}{x + 3}$

10. In the case of an implicit relation, the ratio used as the basis of the derivative must be different, mainly because the variables may not be separated into the form $y = f(x)$. If the relation is in the form $F(x, y) = 0$,

then a change in x of amount Δx still causes a change in y of amount Δy, so the implicit relation becomes $F(x + \Delta x, y + \Delta y) = 0$. The ratio

$$\frac{F(x + \Delta x, y + \Delta y) - F(x, y)}{\Delta x} = 0, \quad \Delta x \neq 0$$

(which is 0 because the numerator of the ratio is 0) will yield an expression containing $\Delta y/\Delta x$ that can be solved algebraically for $\Delta y/\Delta x$. (This ratio may still be an implicit relation.) Perform the operation on the following implicit relations, and solve for $\Delta y/\Delta x$.

(a) $x^2y - xy^2 + 16 = 0$ (b) $xy + y^2 - 4 = 0$

2-5 EVEN AND ODD SYMMETRY

There are many different ways of classifying relations, and each method has certain uses in the analysis of problems. We have already encountered the classification of relations as implicit or explicit. Some other ways of classifying relations are as linear or nonlinear, algebraic or transcendental, real or complex, periodic or nonperiodic, and odd or even, but these by no means exhaust the classification types. Some of the types just mentioned will be discussed later.

The classification of relations as odd or even is based on the symmetry exhibited by certain relations when graphed. This symmetry is helpful in analysis, because once it is recognized, only half the relation need be analyzed to obtain the solution to an entire problem.

Even Symmetry

Consider the function

$$y = f(x) = \frac{1}{x^2 + 1}$$

As before, x is the independent variable and y the dependent variable. The usual method of graphing a function is to assign values to the independent variable, calculate the dependent variable, and plot each pair of related values as a point in the DR plane. When enough points have been plotted, they are carefully joined by a "smooth" curve to form the graph of the function. Using integer values for x, we obtain points for this function as shown in Table 2-6. When these points are plotted and connected with a smooth curve, we obtain the graph shown in Figure 2-39.

The graph shows a certain symmetry: The curve for positive values of x is the mirror image of the curve for negative values of x, and the R axis is the axis of reflection, or *axis of symmetry*. The data in Table 2-6 clearly show the reason for this. The value of y for a given positive value of x is the same as the y value for $-x$. The equation for this function shows why the data have this characteristic: The variable x appears only

TABLE 2-6

$$y = \frac{1}{x^2 + 1}$$

x	y	x	y	x	y
-7	$\frac{1}{50}$	-2	$\frac{1}{5}$	3	$\frac{1}{10}$
-6	$\frac{1}{37}$	-1	$\frac{1}{2}$	4	$\frac{1}{17}$
-5	$\frac{1}{26}$	0	1	5	$\frac{1}{26}$
-4	$\frac{1}{17}$	1	$\frac{1}{2}$	6	$\frac{1}{37}$
-3	$\frac{1}{10}$	2	$\frac{1}{5}$	7	$\frac{1}{50}$

in the denominator of the right side, in the expression $x^2 + 1$. Since x^2 has identical values for any given positive number x and for $-x$, the same is true of $x^2 + 1$ and of $1/(x^2 + 1)$. In other words, $f(-1) = f(1)$, $f(-2) = f(2)$, $f(-3) = f(3)$, and so on. In general for the relation ρ, we can say that $\rho(-x) = \rho(x)$. Relations with this property are said to have *even symmetry*.

DEFINITION An explicit relation $y = \rho(x)$ possesses **even symmetry** if the condition

$$\blacktriangleright \quad \rho(-x) = \rho(x)$$

is true for all x in the domain of ρ.

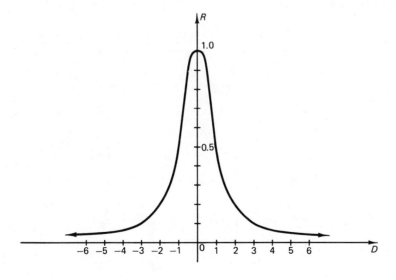

FIGURE 2-39

An implicit relation $F(x, y) = 0$ possesses **even symmetry** if the condition

$$F(-x, y) = F(x, y)$$

is true for all x in the domain of F and y in the range of F.

A relation possessing even symmetry is called an *even relation* or, if the relation is a function, an *even function*.

EXAMPLE 2-22 Show that $y = (x^2 - 4)/(x^2 + 2)$ is an even function.

Let $y = f(x)$. Then $f(x) = (x^2 - 4)/(x^2 + 2)$ for all positive x, and

$$f(-x) = \frac{(-x)^2 - 4}{(-x)^2 + 2} = \frac{x^2 - 4}{x^2 + 2}$$

Since $f(-x) = f(x)$, the function is even.

EXAMPLE 2-23 Show that the implicit relation $F(x, y) = x^2y^3 - 4x^4y^2 - 6 = 0$ is even.

We have $F(-x, y) = (-x)^2y^3 - 4(-x)^4y^2 - 6 = x^2y^3 - 4x^4y^2 - 6 = F(x, y)$. Since $F(-x, y) = F(x, y)$, F is an even relation.

Odd Symmetry

Now suppose that instead of $y = 1/(x^2 + 1)$, we consider

$$y = f(x) = \frac{x}{x^2 + 1}$$

How will the values of y be affected? Using the same values for x as in Table 2-6, we obtain the ordered pairs listed in Table 2-7. The resulting graph is shown in Figure 2-40.

TABLE 2-7

x	y	x	y	x	y
-7	$-\dfrac{7}{50}$	-2	$-\dfrac{2}{5}$	3	$\dfrac{3}{10}$
-6	$-\dfrac{6}{37}$	-1	$-\dfrac{1}{2}$	4	$\dfrac{4}{17}$
-5	$-\dfrac{5}{26}$	0	0	5	$\dfrac{5}{26}$
-4	$-\dfrac{4}{17}$	1	$\dfrac{1}{2}$	6	$\dfrac{6}{37}$
-3	$-\dfrac{3}{10}$	2	$\dfrac{2}{5}$	7	$\dfrac{7}{50}$

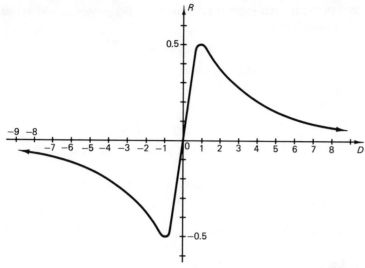

FIGURE 2-40

If we compare the curves in Figures 2-39 and 2-40, clearly, there no longer exists a mirror symmetry with respect to the R axis, and yet a symmetry seems to exist. There are a few other differences between the curves, and the reasons for them will be discussed later: The curve in Figure 2-39 is always above the D axis and never reaches the value $y = 0$; both curves have bounded y values and both approach $y = 0$, *but not in the same way*. There are other differences, which are more subtle and require knowledge of the calculus to understand. It is this "inverted rotational" symmetry that concerns us. (Note that the word "inverted" does not refer to the inverse of a function.) If the part of the curve for positive x is rotated about the D axis, and again about the R axis, then the portion of the curve for negative x results. In Table 2-7, this is indicated by the fact that

$$f(-1) = -f(1), \quad f(-2) = -f(2)$$

Analysis shows that the denominator, as before, has the same value for a given x and for $-x$. So it is the numerator that determines the sign of y. Depending on whether x is positive or negative, the numerator will change only in sign, positive for x positive and negative for x negative; hence, the ratio

$$y = \frac{x}{x^2 + 1}$$

changes only in sign when the sign of x is changed.
  Hence, in general,

$$f(-x) = -f(x)$$

Relations with this property are said to have *odd symmetry* and to be *symmetric with respect to the origin*.

DEFINITION An explicit relation $y = \rho(x)$ possesses **odd symmetry** if the condition

$$\blacktriangleright \quad \rho(-x) = -\rho(x)$$

is true for all x in the domain of ρ.

An implicit relation $F(x, y) = 0$ possesses **odd symmetry** if the condition

$$\blacktriangleright \quad F(-x, -y) = -F(x, y)$$

is true for all x in the domain of F and y in the range of F.

A relation possessing odd symmetry is called an *odd relation* or, if the relation is a function, an *odd function*.

EXAMPLE 2-24 Show that $y = (x^2 - 4)/(x^3 - x)$ is an odd function.

Let $y = f(x)$. Then $f(x) = (x^2 - 4)/(x^3 - x)$, and

$$f(-x) = \frac{(-x)^2 - 4}{(-x)^3 - (-x)} = \frac{x^2 - 4}{-x^3 + x} = \frac{x^2 - 4}{-(x^3 - x)}$$

$$= -\frac{x^2 - 4}{x^3 - x} = -[f(x)] = -f(x)$$

Since $f(-x) = -f(x)$, the function is odd.

EXAMPLE 2-25 Show that $x^2y - xy^2 + 6x = 0$ is an odd implicit relation.

Let $F(x, y) = x^2y - xy^2 + 6x$. Then

$$F(-x, -y) = (-x)^2(-y) - (-x)(-y)^2 + 6(-x)$$
$$= -x^2y + xy^2 - 6x$$
$$= -(x^2y - xy^2 + 6x) = -[F(x, y)] = -F(x, y)$$

Since $F(-x, -y) = -F(x, y)$, $F(x, y)$ is an odd implicit relation.

EXERCISES 2-5

Set A

1. Figure 2-41 shows the graphs of various functions. Classify them as odd, even, or neither.

2. Test the following functions to determine whether they are odd, even, or neither.

   (a) $y = 6x^4 + 2x^2$ (b) $y = x + 2$
   (c) $y = x^3 - 8x$ (d) $y = x^2 + 4x - 3$
   (e) $y = x^5 - 7x^3 + 4x$ (f) $y = x^2 + 6$

Set B

3. Often, relations possess symmetry that is neither odd nor even. A shift in

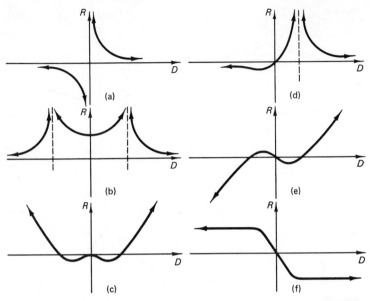

FIGURE 2-41

coordinate axes will sometimes convert this symmetry to odd or even symmetry. For the graphs in Figure 2-42, indicate which functions are odd and which are even. For those that are neither, indicate what shift of the D or R axis (or both) will make them even or odd functions.

4. Test the following relations to determine whether they are odd or even. Indicate any values of x for which the tests are not valid.

(a) $y = \dfrac{x}{x^2 + 4}$ (b) $y = \dfrac{x^2 - 3}{x^3 + x}$

(c) $y = \dfrac{2x + 4}{x^2 - 3x - 4}$ (d) $x^4y^2 - x^2 + x^2y = 0$

(e) $3x^3y + 7x - 6y = 0$ (f) $y = \dfrac{x^2}{x^2 - 7x - 18}$

 5. Find several ordered pairs belonging to the relations given below. Then graph the results and estimate the axes of symmetry and the type of symmetry, if any. Give the domain and range of each relation.
(a) $F(x, y) = yx^2 + 9y - x^2 = 0$
(b) $F(x, y) = x^2y - 6xy + 17y - 3x^2 + 17x - 48 = 0$

(c) $y^2 + 6y + 9 = \dfrac{36}{x^2 - 4x + 5}$

Set C

6. In organic chemistry, molecular structures often exhibit symmetry or periodic symmetry. Use the definitions of odd and even relations to classify the molecules in Figure 2-43. Give reasons for your classifications, and draw the reference axes used.

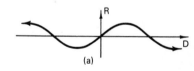
(a)

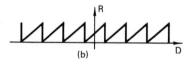
(b)

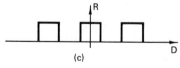
(c)

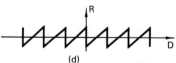
(d)

FIGURE 2-42

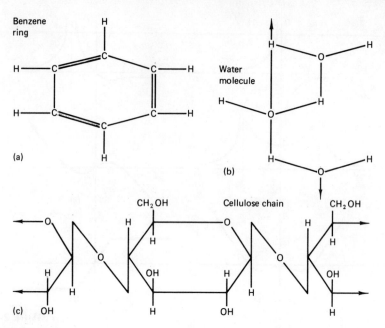

Benzene ring

(a)

Water molecule

(b)

CH$_2$OH

Cellulose chain

CH$_2$OH

(c) OH

FIGURE 2-43

7. Research the topic of Bessel functions of the first kind. Determine whether these functions demonstrate any symmetry properties and, if so, discuss them.

REVIEW EXERCISES FOR CHAPTER 2

1. Let $f(x) = x^3 - x$, $g(x) = x + 1$, with $x \in \mathbb{R}$ for both f and g. Find the following:
   (a) $f(2)$ (b) $g(2)$
   (c) $g[f(x)]$ (d) $f[g(x)]$
   (e) $g[f(3)]$ (f) $f[g(5)]$

2. Find the domain and range of the following relations. Assume that x and y are real numbers.
   (a) $y = \sqrt{x - 9} + 1$ (b) $y = \sqrt{9 - x} - 3$
   (c) $y = \dfrac{3}{x + 1}$ (d) $y = \sqrt{25 - x^2}$

3. Using a rectangular coordinate system, graph the following relations.
   (a) $y = \sqrt{x - 9}$, $x \geq 9$
   (b) $y = \sqrt{25 - x^2}$, $-5 \leq x \leq 5$
   (c) $y = x^3 - x^2$, $-4 \leq x \leq 4$
   (d) $y = \dfrac{x^2}{x^2 + 1}$, $x \in \mathbb{R}$

4. Find the inverse relations to the following expressions. Establish the domain of the relation so that the inverse is a function.

(a) $f(x) = \dfrac{4 - x}{2}$, $x \in \mathbb{R}$

(b) $f(x) = \dfrac{x^2}{x^2 - 4x + 4}$, $x \neq 2$ (*Hint:* Factor denominator.)

(c) $f(x) = \sqrt{x - 4}$, $x \geq 4$

(d) $f(x) = x^2 - 6x + 8$, $x \in \mathbb{R}$

5. Where possible, write the following implicit relations in explicit form:
   (a) $x^2y^2 - 4xy + 4 = 0$ (b) $x^2y + 3y - x - 1 = 0$
   (c) $4xy + 3xy^2 - 6 = 0$

6. Determine whether the following relations possess odd or even symmetry.
   (a) $x^2y^2 - 4xy + 4 = 0$ (b) $xy^2 - yx^2 = 16$
   (c) $xy - 4 = 0$ (d) $y = (x - 2)^2$

7. For the following pairs of functions, determine what restrictions, if any, are required to make the composites $F \circ G$ and $G \circ F$ valid. Find the composites.

   (a) $y = F(t) = \dfrac{t^2}{(t - 2)^2}$, $z = G(x) = \sqrt{x + 4}$

   (b) $y = F(t) = \sqrt{25 - t^2}$, $z = G(x) = \dfrac{3}{x + 1}$

8. A scientist working on a control theory problem finds that the functions

   $$f(t) = \sqrt{25 - t^2}, \qquad g(x) = \dfrac{1}{\sqrt{(x + 3)^2 - 16}}$$

   are partial solutions to a problem. It is also necessary to form the composites $f \circ g$ and $g \circ f$. What problems, if any, does this involve?

Linear Functions

3-1 THE LINEAR FUNCTION

The simplest type of relation having $\mathbb{R}$ as both domain and range is the *linear function*, whose graph is a straight line. Figure 3-1 shows the graph, L, of a typical linear function. In order to use this function, we must develop a mathematical equation to describe the correspondence between the domain and range variables. We base this development on the fact that the graph of a linear function is a straight line.

Figure 3-2 shows a portion of this straight line and three distinct points, P, Q, and R, on the line. Construct lines PST and QV parallel to the D axis and lines QS and RVT parallel to the R axis. Then the triangles PQS, PRT, and QRV are similar right triangles. From plane geometry, we know that similar triangles have proportional corresponding sides, so

$$\frac{RT}{PT} = \frac{RV}{QV} = \frac{QS}{PS}$$

Let us call the common value of these ratios m. If the coordinates of point Q are (x_1, y_1) and those of R are (x_2, y_2), then point V has coordinates (x_2, y_1). Since

$$\frac{RV}{QV} = m$$

we can write, in terms of the coordinates of Q, R, and V,

$$\frac{y_2 - y_1}{x_2 - x_1} = m$$

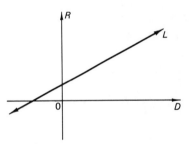

FIGURE 3-1

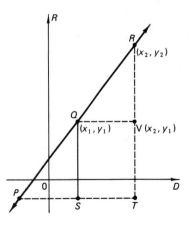

FIGURE 3-2

Since the points P, Q, and R were arbitrarily chosen (that is, they could be any three distinct points on L), we would obtain the same value for m regardless of which points on L we used. Thus, the ratio m is a unique real number associated with line L. This constant ratio, which is a fundamental characteristic of the straight line L, is called its *slope*.

> **DEFINITION**   Let L be a straight line, and let (x_1, y_1) and (x_2, y_2) be any two distinct points on L, where $x_1 \neq x_2$. Then the **slope** of L is
>
> $$\blacktriangleright \quad m = \frac{y_2 - y_1}{x_2 - x_1}$$

EXAMPLE 3-1   Let L be a straight line containing the points $(2, 4)$ and $(-1, -2)$. Then the slope of L is

$$m = \frac{4 - (-2)}{2 - (-1)} = \frac{6}{3} = 2$$

The reader should verify that if the order of the two points was reversed, the same value of m would result.

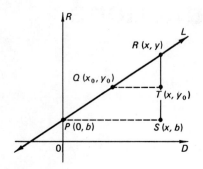

FIGURE 3-3

Now consider any nonvertical straight line, L, whose corresponding linear function, $\mathscr{L}$, is given by the rule $y = \mathscr{L}(x)$. As shown in Figure 3-3, we let $P = (0, b)$ be the point where L crosses the R axis, $Q = (x_0, y_0)$ be any fixed point on L, and $R = (x, y)$ be any other point on L. Then for right triangle PSR, we can write

$$\frac{SR}{PS} = m$$

where m is the slope of L. Using the coordinates of the given points, we can rewrite this equation as

$$\frac{y - b}{x - 0} = m$$

Solving for y yields

$$\blacktriangleright \quad y = mx + b$$

Since $y = \mathscr{L}(x)$, the linear function is given by

$$\mathscr{L}(x) = mx + b$$

where $m \in \mathbb{R}$ is the slope of line L and b is called the R *axis intercept* of L.

The domain of $\mathscr{L}$ can easily be shown to be the set of all real numbers. In functional notation,

$$\mathscr{L} : \mathbb{R} \to \mathbb{R}$$

That is, a linear function $\mathscr{L}$ maps each real number to an image that is also an element of the set of real numbers. Furthermore, if $m \neq 0$, then $\mathscr{L}$ is an onto mapping and can be written

$$\mathscr{L} : \mathbb{R} \twoheadrightarrow \mathbb{R}$$

The equation $y = mx + b$ is called the *slope–intercept form* of the equation of the straight line with an R axis intercept of b and a slope of m. An alternative form of the equation of a straight line (that is, of a linear function) can be derived using a different triangle, QTR, from Figure 3-3. Using triangle QTR, we can write

$$\frac{TR}{QT} = m$$

Substituting the coordinate values, we obtain the equation

$$\frac{y - y_0}{x - x_0} = m$$

With some algebraic manipulation, this can be put into the form

▶ $y - y_0 = m(x - x_0)$

where m is the slope of L and (x_0, y_0) are the coordinates of any fixed point on L. This is the *point–slope form* of the equation of a straight line.

The point–slope form and the slope–intercept form for the equation of a straight line are equivalent. Expanding the point–slope form and solving for y gives

$$y = mx + (y_0 - mx_0)$$

Since y_0, m, and x_0 are known constants, the term $(y_0 - mx_0)$ is a constant. Since both equations represent the same line, L, a term-by-term comparison of both equations yields

$$y_0 - mx_0 = b$$

the R axis intercept.

In all the ratios used to define the slope, the numerators represent the change in the range value, and the denominators represent the corresponding change in the domain value. Hence, the slope can also be thought of as

$$m = \frac{\text{Change in range value}}{\text{Change in domain value}}$$

which is symbolized as

$$m = \frac{\Delta y}{\Delta x}$$

where $\Delta x \neq 0$.

The following examples illustrate the different ways a line can be represented by equations and graphs.

EXAMPLE 3-2 The graph of the equation

$$y = 3x$$

is a line with R axis intercept 0 (that is, passing through the origin) and with a slope of 3. This means that for each unit change in the domain value, there is a corresponding change of 3 units in the range value:

$$\frac{\Delta y}{\Delta x} = 3$$

This line is graphed in Figure 3-4.

EXAMPLE 3-3 Consider the function

$$r = -2s$$

Here, the range elements are represented by r and the domain elements by s. The equation can also be written as $r = (-2)s$. Hence, the slope is -2, which means that the ratio between the change in the range value and the corresponding change in the domain value is -2. That is, to each unit change in the domain value there corresponds a change of -2 units in the range value. Geometrically, when s changes 1 unit to the right, r changes 2 units downward, rather than 2 units upward as would be the case if the slope were $+2$. To state this another way, when s changes 1 unit to the left, r changes 2 units upward. This can be seen clearly from Figure 3-5.

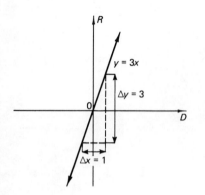

FIGURE 3-4

Now suppose the slope is written as a ratio of two constant values, say, α and β; that is,

$$m = \frac{\alpha}{\beta}, \quad \beta \neq 0$$

Substituting this in the slope–intercept form of the equation of a straight line yields

$$y = \frac{\alpha}{\beta} x + b$$

Multiplying by β gives

$$\beta y = \alpha x + \beta b$$

Rearranging terms (and keeping in mind that x and y are variables and α, β, and b are constants), we obtain

$$(\alpha)x + (-\beta)y + (\beta b) = 0$$

If we let $A = \alpha$, $B = -\beta$, and $C = \beta b$, this becomes

$$\blacktriangleright \quad Ax + By + C = 0$$

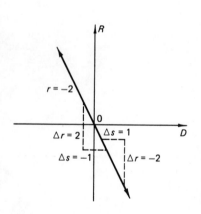

FIGURE 3-5

where A and B are *not both* 0. This is commonly called the *general form* of the equation of a straight line.

In summary, a straight line will usually have an equation in one of the following forms:

$$Ax + By + C = 0$$

$$y = mx + b$$

or

$$y - y_0 = m(x - x_0)$$

EXAMPLE 3-4 Find the slope and R axis intercept of the graph of the equation

$$6x + 4y - 5 = 0$$

The equation is in the general form and should be converted to the slope–intercept form, as follows:

$$4y = -6x + 5$$
$$y = -\tfrac{3}{2}x + \tfrac{5}{4}$$

The slope is $-\tfrac{3}{2}$ and the R axis intercept is $\tfrac{5}{4}$. The graph is shown in Figure 3-6.

EXAMPLE 3-5 Find the equation of the line having a slope of 2 and passing through the point (4, 5).
Since the slope and a point are given, the point–slope form of the line should be used.

$$y - y_0 = m(x - x_0)$$

or

$$y - 5 = 2(x - 4)$$

This equation may be written in explicit form as

$$y - 5 = 2x - 8$$

or

$$y = 2x - 3$$

Figure 3-7 shows the graph of this equation.
Since a straight line can be drawn with a straight edge and two points uniquely determine a straight line, we can quickly graph a linear function by merely identifying two points on its graph. We can think of these two points as "anchor points" that determine the line's position. When working with the general equation

$$Ax + By + C = 0$$

a quick way to find two points is to find the R axis and D axis intercepts (the points where $x = 0$ and where $y = 0$), provided that the line is neither horizontal nor vertical and does not pass through the origin.

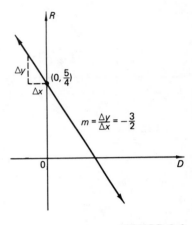

FIGURE 3-6

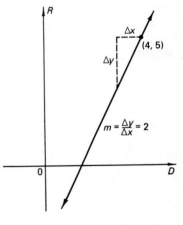

FIGURE 3-7

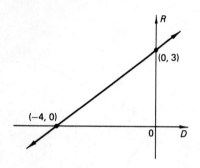

FIGURE 3-8

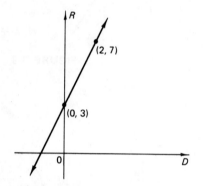

FIGURE 3-9

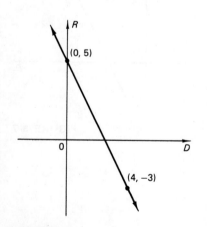

FIGURE 3-10

EXAMPLE 3-6 Sketch the graph of the function

$$3x - 4y + 12 = 0$$

To find the R axis intercept, set $x = 0$:

$$-4y + 12 = 0, \quad \text{or} \quad y = 3$$

To find the D axis intercept, set $y = 0$:

$$3x + 12 = 0, \quad \text{or} \quad x = -4$$

Hence, the intercepts are $(0, 3)$ and $(-4, 0)$. The graph of the line is shown in Figure 3-8.

When the equation is in slope–intercept form, use the R axis intercept as one of the anchor points and obtain the second point by substituting any convenient value of x to obtain y; then draw the line through the two points.

EXAMPLE 3-7 Graph the equation

$$y = 2x + 3$$

Since 3 is the R axis intercept, one point on the line is $(0, 3)$. Substitution of any convenient value for x, say, $x = 2$, yields the corresponding y value, $y = 7$, which gives us a second point. The graph is shown in Figure 3-9.

When the equation is in point–slope form, use the given point as the anchor and obtain the R axis intercept by rewriting the equation in slope–intercept form.

EXAMPLE 3-8 Graph the equation

$$y + 3 = -2(x - 4)$$

In this case, the anchor point is $(4, -3)$. We rewrite the equation to obtain

$$y + 3 = -2x + 8$$

or

$$y = -2x + 5$$

Hence, the R axis intercept is 5. Using these two facts, we draw the graph as shown in Figure 3-10.

The Distance Equation

We now derive the formula for finding the distance between any two points in the DR plane. This result will be used in the rest of this section and in portions of Chapter 4.

Figure 3-11 shows two points, P_1 and P_2, in the DR plane. We wish to develop a formula that gives the distance, d, between these points in terms of their coordinates. Form the right triangle shown; then, by the Pythagorean Theorem,

$$d^2 = (x_2 - x_1)^2 + (y_2 - y_1)^2$$

or

▶ $d = \sqrt{(x_2 - x_1)^2 + (y_2 - y_1)^2}$

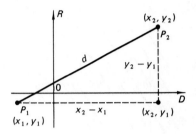

FIGURE 3-11

We choose the positive square root, because distance is nonnegative. Note that in this equation, the starting reference point is P_2; and once the reference point is chosen, its components and those of P_1 should be ordered as shown in the equation. Since $(x_2 - x_1)^2 = (x_1 - x_2)^2$ and $(y_2 - y_1)^2 = (y_1 - y_2)^2$, P_1 could just as easily be chosen as the first point, in which case the equation would become

$$d = \sqrt{(x_1 - x_2)^2 + (y_1 - y_2)^2}$$

EXAMPLE 3-9 Find the distance between the points $(-2, 3)$ and $(6, -4)$. By the distance formula,

$$d = \sqrt{[6 - (-2)]^2 + (-4 - 3)^2} = \sqrt{8^2 + (-7)^2}$$
$$= \sqrt{64 + 49} = \sqrt{113}$$

Note that if the line joining P_1 and P_2 is vertical, then the distance becomes $d = \sqrt{(y_2 - y_1)^2} = |y_2 - y_1|$. Similarly, if the line is horizontal, then $d = |x_2 - x_1|$.

Parallel and Perpendicular Lines

Certain mathematical problems involve finding lines parallel to a given line or perpendicular to a given line. The following theorems establish the conditions that must be satisfied.

THEOREM 3-1 (Parallel Lines) Let L_1 and L_2 be two nonvertical, noncollinear straight lines with respective slopes m_1 and m_2. Then L_1 is parallel to L_2 if and only if

▶ $m_1 = m_2$

PROOF See page 101. ▮

THEOREM 3-2 (Perpendicular Lines) Let L_1 and L_2 be two nonvertical, nonhorizontal straight lines with respective slopes m_1 and m_2. Then L_1 is perpendicular to L_2 if and only if

▶ $m_1 = -\dfrac{1}{m_2}, \quad m_1, m_2 \neq 0$

PROOF   See page 102. ∎

Note that lines whose equations are $y = b$ and $x = a$, where a and b are constants, $a, b \in \mathbb{R}$, are perpendicular to each other.

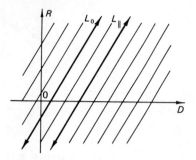

FIGURE 3-12

EXAMPLE 3-10   The line L_0 with equation $y = \frac{2}{3}x - 1$ has slope $m_0 = \frac{2}{3}$. Any line parallel to L_0 will also have slope $\frac{2}{3}$. Figure 3-12 shows line L_0 and the family of lines parallel to L_0. Any line perpendicular to L_0 will have slope $-1/(\frac{2}{3}) = -\frac{3}{2}$. Figure 3-13 shows the given line L_0 and the family of lines perpendicular to L_0.

As can be seen from Figures 3-12 and 3-13, there are an infinite number of lines parallel to L_0 and an infinite number of lines perpendicular to L_0. In order to determine a specific line from one of these families, it is necessary to use another property of the line, such as one of its intercepts or, more generally, a point on it.

EXAMPLE 3-11   Find the equation of the line that is parallel to the line $y = \frac{2}{3}x - 1$ and passes through the point $(9, 1)$.

Since the given line has slope $\frac{2}{3}$, the equation of any line parallel to it is

$$y = \tfrac{2}{3}x + b$$

The equation of the line through the point $(9, 1)$ must be satisfied for $x = 1$ and $y = 9$; therefore,

$$1 = \tfrac{2}{3}(9) + b$$
$$1 = 6 + b$$
$$b = -5$$

Hence, the required equation is

$$y = \tfrac{2}{3}x - 5$$

This line is shown in Figure 3-12 as $L_{\parallel}$.

EXAMPLE 3-12   Find the equation of the line that is perpendicular to the line $y = \frac{2}{3}x - 1$ and passes through the origin.

Since the given line has slope $\frac{2}{3}$, any line perpendicular to it has slope $-\frac{3}{2}$ and is described by the equation

$$y = -\tfrac{3}{2}x + b$$

For the specific point $(0, 0)$, the value of b is 0, and the required equation is

$$y = -\tfrac{3}{2}x$$

This line is shown in Figure 3-13 as $L_{\perp}$.

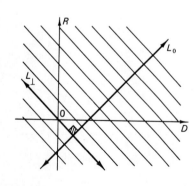

FIGURE 3-13

EXAMPLE 3-13   Find the equation of the line that passes through the points $(3, 7)$ and $(5, -2)$. Then find the equation of the line perpendicular to this line and passing through the point (3, 7).

To find the equation of the first line, we need the slope and at least one point. To calculate the slope, we let $P = (3, 7)$ and $Q = (5, -2)$. In going *from P to Q* (see Figure 3-14), the change in the domain value is $5 - 3 = 2$, and the change in the range value is $-2 - (7) = -9$. Therefore,

$$m_1 = -\frac{9}{2}$$

Using the point–slope form with point P as (x_0, y_0), we obtain

$$y - 7 = -\frac{9}{2}(x - 3)$$

In slope–intercept form, this becomes

$$y = -\frac{9}{2}x + \frac{41}{2}$$

The line perpendicular to this one will have slope

$$m_2 = \frac{-1}{m_1} = -\frac{1}{-\frac{9}{2}} = \frac{2}{9}$$

Again using the point–slope form, where $(x_0, y_0) = (3, 7)$ and $m = \frac{2}{9}$, we can write the equation of the perpendicular line as

$$y - 7 = \frac{2}{9}(x - 3)$$

In slope–intercept form, this becomes

$$y = \frac{2}{9}x + \frac{19}{3}$$

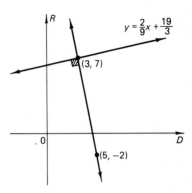

FIGURE 3-14

Earlier, we mentioned that any nonvertical straight line with $m \neq 0$ was an onto mapping. From the graphs, it is evident that any linear function $\mathcal{L}$ is also strictly monotonic. From Theorem 2-2 in Section 2-3, any strictly monotonic function that is an onto mapping possesses an inverse function. Therefore, any nonvertical straight line with $m \neq 0$ has an inverse function. To find an algebraic expression for this inverse, the student should take the slope–intercept form

$$y = \mathcal{L}(x) = mx + b, \quad m \neq 0, x \in \mathbb{R}$$

and prove that the inverse function, $\mathcal{L}^{-1}$, is given by

$$\mathcal{L}^{-1}(z) = \frac{z - b}{m}, \quad m \neq 0, z \in \mathbb{R}$$

Figure 3-15 shows the symmetry of $\mathcal{L}$ and $\mathcal{L}^{-1}$ about the graph of the identity function, $y = x$.

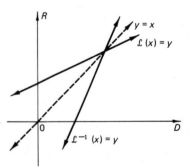

FIGURE 3-15

Proof of Theorem 3-1 (optional)

Figure 3-16 shows two straight lines, L_1 and L_2, in the DR plane. We show that if L_1 and L_2 are parallel, then their slopes are equal. Draw distinct lines L_3 and L_4 parallel to the R axis; then certainly, L_3 and L_4 are parallel to each other. Since L_1 and L_2 are assumed to be parallel, the figure $ABCD$ is a parallelogram.

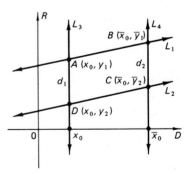

FIGURE 3-16

From geometry, we know that opposite sides of a parallelogram are equal, so $d_1 = d_2$. Since points A and D have the same x coordinate,

$$d_1 = y_1 - y_2$$

Similarly,

$$d_2 = \bar{y}_1 - \bar{y}_2$$

Let the equations of L_1 and L_2 be given by

$$y = m_1 x + b_1 \quad \text{and} \quad y = m_2 x + b_2$$

respectively. Then

$$y_1 = m_1 x_0 + b_1, \qquad y_2 = m_2 x_0 + b_2$$

and

$$\bar{y}_1 = m_1 \bar{x}_0 + b_1, \qquad \bar{y}_2 = m_2 \bar{x}_0 + b_2$$

Substituting these expressions in the distance equations above, we obtain

$$d_1 = y_1 - y_2 = (m_1 - m_2)x_0 + (b_1 - b_2)$$

and

$$d_2 = \bar{y}_1 - \bar{y}_2 = (m_1 - m_2)\bar{x}_0 + (b_1 - b_2)$$

Equating d_1 and d_2 yields

$$(m_1 - m_2)x_0 + (b_1 - b_2) = (m_1 - m_2)\bar{x}_0 + (b_1 - b_2)$$

which reduces to

$$(m_1 - m_2)x_0 = (m_1 - m_2)\bar{x}_0$$

Rewrite this as

$$(m_1 - m_2)(\bar{x}_0 - x_0) = 0$$

Now, since L_3 and L_4 are distinct lines parallel to the R axis, $\bar{x}_0 - x_0 \neq 0$. Thus, the only condition that makes the equation true is

$$m_1 - m_2 = 0$$

which yields

$$m_1 = m_2$$

Therefore, if two straight lines are parallel, they have equal slopes. The proof just presented establishes what is termed a *necessary condition* for two lines to be parallel. To establish that this condition is sufficient, the student should redo the proof, starting with the assumption that the slopes are equal and then showing that the lines must be parallel. ∎

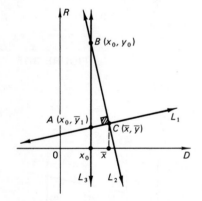

FIGURE 3-17

Proof of Theorem 3-2 (optional)

Figure 3-17 shows two lines, L_1 and L_2, which intersect at point C. To find the condition for which L_1 and L_2 are perpendicular, proceed as follows. Draw line L_3 parallel to the R axis. Then if L_1 and L_2 are perpendicular, triangle ABC is a right triangle, and the Pythagorean Theorem applies to it:

$$(AB)^2 = (AC)^2 + (BC)^2$$

Let the equations of L_1 and L_2 be

$$y = m_1 x + b_1 \quad \text{and} \quad y = m_2 x + b_2$$

respectively, and let points A, B, and C have coordinates $(x_0, \bar{y}_1)$, (x_0, y_0), and $(\bar{x}, \bar{y})$, respectively. (Points A and B have the same x coordinate because they are on the same vertical line.) From this,

$$\bar{y}_1 = m_1 x_0 + b_1 \quad \text{and} \quad y_0 = m_2 x_0 + b_2$$

Furthermore, the point $C = (\bar{x}, \bar{y})$ satisfies both the equations

$$\bar{y} = m_1 \bar{x} + b_1 \quad \text{and} \quad \bar{y} = m_2 \bar{x} + b_2$$

These can be equated as follows:

$$m_1 \bar{x} + b_1 = m_2 \bar{x} + b_2$$

Solving for $\bar{x}$ yields

$$\bar{x} = \frac{-(b_2 - b_1)}{m_2 - m_1}$$

This relationship will be used later.

Now, the lengths of the sides of the triangle may be written in terms of the coordinate values:

$$
\begin{aligned}
BC &= \sqrt{(\bar{x} - x_0)^2 + (\bar{y} - y_0)^2} \\
&= \sqrt{(\bar{x} - x_0)^2 + [m_2 \bar{x} + b_2 - (m_2 x_0 + b_2)]^2} \\
&= \sqrt{(\bar{x} - x_0)^2 + [m_2(\bar{x} - x_0)]^2} \\
* \quad BC &= \sqrt{(1 + m_2^2)(\bar{x} - x_0)^2} \\
AC &= \sqrt{(\bar{x} - x_0)^2 + (\bar{y} - \bar{y}_1)^2} \\
&= \sqrt{(\bar{x} - x_0)^2 + [m_1 \bar{x} + b_1 - (m_1 x_0 + b_1)]^2} \\
&= \sqrt{(\bar{x} - x_0)^2 + [m_1(\bar{x} - x_0)]^2} \\
* \quad AC &= \sqrt{(1 + m_1^2)(\bar{x} - x_0)^2} \\
AB &= y_0 - \bar{y}_1 = m_2 x_0 + b_2 - (m_1 x_0 + b_1) \\
* \quad AB &= (m_2 - m_1)x_0 + (b_2 - b_1)
\end{aligned}
$$

From the relationship developed earlier for $\bar{x}$, we have

$$(b_2 - b_1) = -(m_2 - m_1)\bar{x}$$

So AB can be written as

$$
\begin{aligned}
AB &= (m_2 - m_1)x_0 - (m_2 - m_1)\bar{x} \\
&= (m_2 - m_1)(x_0 - \bar{x})
\end{aligned}
$$

An alternative form is

$$AB = -(m_2 - m_1)(\bar{x} - x_0)$$

This is the form we will use.

Substitution of the distance values given by the starred equations into the

Pythagorean relationship

$$(AB)^2 = (BC)^2 + (AC)^2$$

yields

$$(m_2 - m_1)^2(\bar{x} - x_0)^2 = (1 + m_2^2)(\bar{x} - x_0)^2 + (1 + m_1^2)(\bar{x} - x_0)^2$$

Dividing by $(\bar{x} - x_0)^2$ (which is not equal to 0) yields

$$(m_2 - m_1)^2 = (1 + m_1^2) + (1 + m_2^2)$$
$$= 2 + m_1^2 + m_2^2$$

Expanding the left side, we have

$$m_2^2 + m_1^2 - 2m_2m_1 = 2 + m_1^2 + m_2^2$$

This reduces to

$$-2m_1m_2 = 2$$

Dividing both sides by -2 yields

$$m_1m_2 = -1$$

or

$$m_2 = \frac{-1}{m_1}, \qquad m_1 \text{ and } m_2 \neq 0$$

In other words, if two straight lines are perpendicular, then their slopes have a product of -1; alternatively, their slopes are *negative reciprocals*. As before, this proof has established the necessary condition for two lines to be perpendicular. By redoing the proof from the assumption that the slopes are negative reciprocals and then showing that the lines are mutually perpendicular, the student should establish the sufficient condition for two lines to be perpendicular. ∎

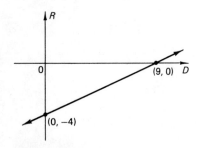

FIGURE 3-18

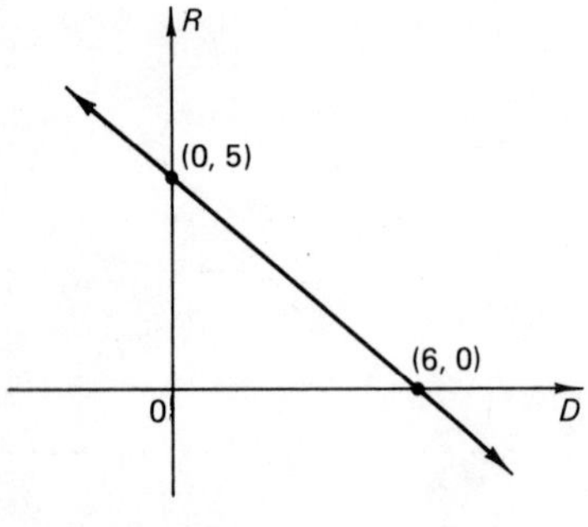

EXERCISES 3-1

Set A

1. Show algebraically that the given slope–intercept and point–slope equations are equivalent (i.e., that they represent the same straight line).
   (a) $y = 2x - 1$ and $y - 7 = 2(x - 4)$
   (b) $y = \frac{3}{4}x + 2$ and $y - 5 = \frac{3}{4}(x - 4)$

2. Determine the slopes of the lines in Figures 3-18 and 3-19.

3. Graph the function $\mathcal{L}(t) = mt$, $t \in \mathbb{R}$, for the following values of m:
   (a) $m = 2$ (b) $m = \frac{3}{2}$
   (c) $m = -\frac{2}{3}$ (d) $m = -\frac{3}{2}$
   (e) $m = 4$ (f) $m = -3$

4. Find the slope and R axis intercept of each of the following linear functions:
   (a) $2x + y - 4 = 0$ (b) $6x - 3y + 12 = 0$
   (c) $6x + 4y + 3 = 0$ (d) $8x - 7y + 2 = 0$

FIGURE 3-19

5. Graph the equations given in Exercise 4.

6. Consider the equation $3x - 4y = 5$ and the point $P = (6, 8)$.
   (a) Find the equation of the line parallel to the given line and passing through point P.
   (b) Find the equation of the line perpendicular to the given line and passing through point P.

7. Graph the following linear functions:
   (a) $y = -\frac{2}{5}x + 7$ (b) $y = \frac{2}{3}x + 4$
   (c) $(y - 2) = \frac{4}{3}x + 2$ (d) $(y + 1) = -\frac{3}{2}(x - 2)$
   (e) $y + 1 = \frac{4}{3}x + 2$ (f) $y = -\frac{1}{4}x + \frac{5}{2}$

8. Let $P = (4, 7)$ and $Q = (7, 12)$.
   (a) Find the equation of the line parallel to the line joining P and Q and passing through the point $(5, -1)$.
   (b) Find the equation of the line perpendicular to the line joining P and Q and passing through the point $(-4, -2)$.

9. Determine whether the three points $(4, 7)$, $(2, 5)$, and $(3, 2)$ are collinear.

Set B

10. Find the coordinates of the midpoint of the line joining points $P = (4, 7)$ and $Q = (-2, -1)$ by the use of similar triangles.

11. Repeat Exercise 10 for $P = (1, 3)$ and $Q = (6, 16)$.

12. From the results of Exercises 10 and 11, show that in general, if $P = (x_1, y_1)$ and $Q = (x_2, y_2)$, then the coordinates of the midpoint of the line joining P and Q are given by

$$x_m = \tfrac{1}{2}(x_2 + x_1), \qquad y_m = \tfrac{1}{2}(y_2 + y_1)$$

● 13. Find the intercepts of the following functions and graph them using the points found:

   (a) $y - 6.84 = 3.4(7.2 - x)$ (b) $\dfrac{y + 7.8}{x + 2.9} = 2.73$

Set C

14. From the study of linear algebra, we find that if any three lines intersect at a common point, the equation of one line can be obtained by taking a linear combination of the equations of the remaining two lines. Figure 3-20 shows three distinct lines, L, L_1, and L_2, all intersecting at a common point, $(\bar{x}, \bar{y})$. The equation of line L is $y = mx + b$; that of L_1 is $y = m_1x + b_1$; and that of L_2 is $y = m_2x + b_2$. Show that if m, m_1, m_2, b, b_1, and b_2 are known constants, the equation for L can be obtained by taking a multiple of the equation for L_1 and adding it to a multiple of the equation for L_2.

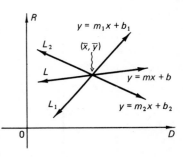

FIGURE 3-20

15. Exercise 14 is designed to show the concept of linear dependence. Research the topic of linear dependence and linear independence, and relate the results of Exercise 14 to the solution of a system of linear functions.

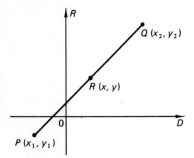

FIGURE 3-21

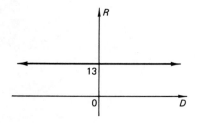

FIGURE 3-22

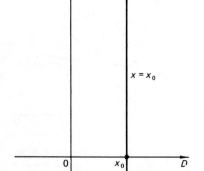

FIGURE 3-23

16. Figure 3-21 shows a straight line joining points $P = (x_1, y_1)$ and $Q = (x_2, y_2)$. Point $R = (x, y)$ divides the line PQ such that the ratio

$$\frac{PR}{PQ} = k, \qquad 0 < k < 1$$

Find a formula for x and y in terms of the coordinates of P and Q.

3-2 SPECIAL LINEAR FUNCTIONS AND TRANSLATION

Horizontal Lines

A *horizontal line* is a straight line whose slope is 0. This is a special case of the linear function,

$$\mathcal{L}(x) = mx + b$$

Let $\mathcal{K}$ be a linear function whose slope is 0. Then

$$\mathcal{K}(x) = 0(x) + b = b$$

Hence,

▶ $\mathcal{K} = \{(x, y) \mid y = b, x \in \mathbb{R}\}$

or

$$\mathcal{K} : \mathbb{R} \twoheadrightarrow B$$

where $B = \{y \mid y = b\}$. That is, $\mathcal{K}$ is a function that maps all real numbers onto a single number, b. For this reason, $\mathcal{K}$ is called a *constant function*.

EXAMPLE 3-14 $\mathcal{K}(t) = 13$ is a constant function, since it maps all $t \in \mathbb{R}$ onto the range value 13. This function is graphed in Figure 3-22.

Vertical Lines

Another special type of straight line is a line parallel to the R axis, known as a *vertical line*. For example, Figure 3-23 shows a vertical line that intercepts the D axis at x_0. Clearly, this is *not* the graph of a function, because the domain element has the set of all real numbers as its image. This graph requires a special definition.

DEFINITION Let $\nu: A \to \mathbb{R}$ be a relation whose domain, A, contains exactly one element, x_0, and whose range is $\mathbb{R}$; that is,

▶ $\nu = \{(x, y) \mid x = x_0, y \in \mathbb{R}\}$

Then the graph of ν is a **vertical line** and is described by the equation $x = x_0$.

Hence, every real number is in the range of ν and is the image of exactly one element of the domain.

EXAMPLE 3-15 The graph of the relation $v = \{(3, y) \mid y \in \mathbb{R}\}$ is a vertical line, because this relation maps the domain element 3 into all real numbers and every real number is an image of the domain element 3. If t represents the elements of the domain, then the equation of this line is $t = 3$.

Step Functions

A function that has particular importance in science and business is the *step function*. A step function takes on a fixed range value for certain parts of the domain and then jumps to another fixed value in another part of the domain. For example, a step function might map all domain elements less than 0 to a particular constant (say, C_1) and map all domain elements greater than or equal to 0 to another constant (say, C_2). Situations described by this type of function are commonly found in mechanical or electrical applications; for example, a switch or a valve may be closed for a period of time and then suddenly opened.

As a particular example of a step function, consider the *unit step function*, U, defined as the function whose range value is 0 for all negative values in the domain and 1 for all nonnegative values in the domain.

> **DEFINITION** Let $t \in \mathbb{R}$. The **unit step function**, denoted U, is defined by the rule
>
> $$\blacktriangleright \quad U(t) = \begin{cases} 0 & \text{for } t < 0 \\ 1 & \text{for } t \geqslant 0 \end{cases}$$

The graph of this function is shown in Figure 3-24. Note that this graph exhibits a nonzero change in range value at $t = 0$. Any function exhibiting such an abrupt change at a particular domain value is said to be *graphically discontinuous*.

> **DEFINITION** A function $y = f(t)$ possesses a **graphical discontinuity** at $t = b$ if its graph exhibits a nonzero change in range value at $t = b$. If this change in range value is finite, it is called a **finite discontinuity**; if the change is not finite, it is called an **infinite discontinuity**.

Functions not possessing points of graphical discontinuity are said to be *graphically continuous*. The unit step function is an example of a function with a finite discontinuity. Such functions seem to have two possible values at the points where these discontinuities occur. To remove this ambiguity, it is conventional to place a solid dot on one portion of the graph to indicate which value the function takes on at the point of finite discontinuity. Thus, in Figure 3-24, the solid dot at $y = 1$ for $t = 0$ indicates that the unit step function has the value 1 at $t = 0$.

The reader will notice that to the right of the point of discontinuity, the step function is continuous; the same is true to the left of this point. For this reason, the step function is also said to be *graphically piecewise continuous*.

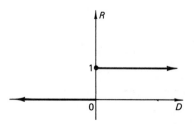

FIGURE 3-24

DEFINITION A function is **graphically piecewise continuous** if its graph has only a finite number of graphical discontinuities.

A graphically piecewise continuous function is graphically continuous everywhere except at its points of graphical discontinuity. Figure 3-25 shows a function that is piecewise continuous, with three points of graphical discontinuity.

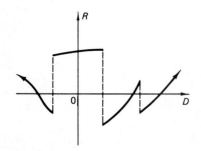

FIGURE 3-25

The Signum Function

Another special type of linear function is the sgn, or signum, function, which is defined as follows.

DEFINITION Let $t \in \mathbb{R}$. The **signum function** of t, denoted sgn, is defined by the rule

$$\blacktriangleright \text{ sgn}(t) = \begin{cases} -1 & \text{for } t < 0 \\ 0 & \text{for } t = 0 \\ +1 & \text{for } t > 0 \end{cases}$$

This function is similar to the unit step function and has a graphical discontinuity at $t = 0$. Figure 3-26 illustrates the signum function. Note that the range of the signum function contains exactly three elements, -1, 0, and 1. That is, the signum function maps all real numbers onto $B = \{-1, 0, 1\}$:

$$\text{sgn}: \mathbb{R} \twoheadrightarrow B$$

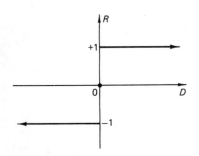

FIGURE 3-26

The Greatest Integer Function

Another type of step function is the *greatest integer function*.

DEFINITION Let $t \in \mathbb{R}$, and let $M \in \mathbb{J}$ be the integer such that $M \leqslant t < M + 1$. Then the **greatest integer function**, denoted $[\![\ ]\!]$, is defined by the rule

$$\blacktriangleright [\![t]\!] = M \quad \text{where } M \leqslant t < M + 1$$

For example, $[\![\frac{1}{2}]\!] = 0$, $[\![1.7]\!] = 1$, $[\![-\frac{2}{3}]\!] = -1$, $[\![-2.3]\!] = -3$. Hence,

$$[\![\ ]\!]: \mathbb{R} \twoheadrightarrow \mathbb{J}$$

That is, the greatest integer function maps all real numbers onto the set of integers according to the rule given in the definition. The graph of the greatest integer function is shown in Figure 3-27. Such functions are useful when only the integral part of a number is required, as when we read a digital clock or a taxi meter.

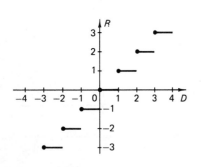

FIGURE 3-27

Translations

The step function can be used to develop the concept of translation. Suppose we wish to let all values that are less than 4 in the domain correspond to the range element 0 and all values that are greater than or equal to 4 correspond to the range element 1. This is the same as translating the graph of the unit step function 4 units to the right along the D axis.

DEFINITION A **translation** is an undistorted repositioning of a relation on the same set of axes.

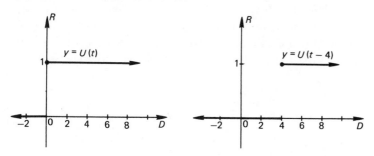

FIGURE 3-28

In Figure 3-28, the unit step function, $U(t)$, and its translated counterpart, $U(\hat{t})$, are shown on identical rectangular coordinate systems. Note that the range elements are the same in both cases (0 and 1), but the step occurs at a different domain value. Thus, the functions are structurally the same except for the translation.

In order to describe the translation algebraically, we must find how $\hat{t}$, the new argument, is related to the original domain variable, t. As long as the argument is negative, the value of the function U is 0, but when $\hat{t} \geqslant 0$, the value of U is 1. In terms of the variable t, the argument of U is negative for all $t < 4$. Hence, the position for the jump in the function is at

$$t = 4$$

which must be the point where $\hat{t} = 0$. Consider the algebraic expression

$$t - 4$$

If $t < 4$, say, $t = 3$, then $t - 4 = 3 - 4 = -1$, which is negative. If $t = 4$, then $t - 4 = 0$. If $t > 4$, say, $t = 6$, then $t - 4 = 6 - 4 = 2$, which is positive. Since this describes exactly how $\hat{t}$ behaves, let

$$\hat{t} = t - 4$$

The translated step function can now be represented in the following manner:

$$U(\hat{t}) = U(t - 4) = \begin{cases} 0 & \text{for } t < 4 \\ 1 & \text{for } t \geqslant 4 \end{cases}$$

DEFINITION Let ρ be an explicit relation, and let $h \in \mathbb{R}$. Then the **translation of ρ by h units along the D axis** is the relation $\hat{\rho}$ given by the rule

$$\hat{\rho}(x) = \rho(x - h) \quad \text{or} \quad y = \rho(x - h)$$

Note that if h is positive, then the change to the argument $x - h$ means a translation to the right. If h is negative, then the change to the argument $x - (-h) = x + h$ means a translation to the left. By this method, any relation can be translated along the D axis.

EXAMPLE 3-16   Sketch the functions $U(t - 3)$ and $U(t + 4)$.

Applying the D axis translation rule to $U(t)$, we see that $U(t - 3)$ is the unit step function translated 3 units to the right. Similarly, $U(t + 4)$ is the unit step function translated 4 units to the left. The graphs of $U(t - 3)$ and $U(t + 4)$ are shown in Figure 3-29.

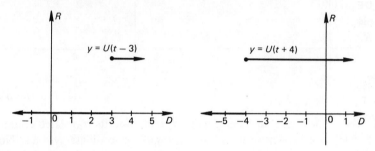

FIGURE 3-29

Now suppose the unit step function, $U(t)$, is translated 3 units *up* from the origin. To obtain this translated function, each range element of $U(t)$ must be increased by 3. Hence, this new step function, which we call $U_1(t)$, must be defined as

$$U_1(t) = \begin{cases} 0 + 3 = 3 & \text{for } t < 0 \\ 1 + 3 = 4 & \text{for } t \geqslant 0 \end{cases}$$

This may be written

$$U_1(t) = U(t) + 3$$

Subtracting 3 from both sides yields

$$U(t) = U_1(t) - 3$$

The graphs shown in Figure 3-30 give the original function, $U(t)$, and the translated function, $U_1(t)$.

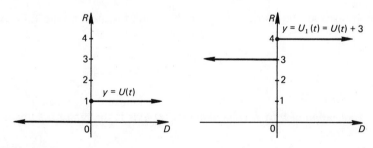

FIGURE 3-30

This translation along the R axis is generalized by the following definition.

DEFINITION Let ρ be an explicit relation, and let $k \in \mathbb{R}$. Then the **translation of ρ by k units along the R axis** is the relation $\hat{\rho}$ given by the rule

▶ $\rho(x) = \hat{\rho}(x) - k$ or $\rho(x) = y - k$

The definitions of D axis and R axis translations can be combined so that the graph of any relation ρ can be translated along both axes.

DEFINITION Let ρ be an explicit relation, and let $h, k \in \mathbb{R}$. Then the **planar translation of ρ by h units along the D axis and k units along the R axis** is the relation $\hat{\rho}$ given by the rule

▶ $\hat{\rho}(x) - k = \rho(x - h)$ or $y - k = \rho(x - h)$

It is possible to have a step function that makes a jump of size other than 1. This occurs when the unit step function, $U(t)$, is multiplied by a nonzero real number, A. The *step function*, $U_2(t)$, is given by

$$U_2(t) = AU(t) = \begin{cases} 0, & t < 0 \\ A, & t \geqslant 0 \end{cases}$$

The coefficient of $U(t)$, A, is often referred to as the *amplitude* of U_2. The following example illustrates planar translation of a step function.

EXAMPLE 3-17 Graph the functions

$$y = 6U(t - 3) + 4$$

and

$$y = -\tfrac{3}{2}U(t + 1) - 2$$

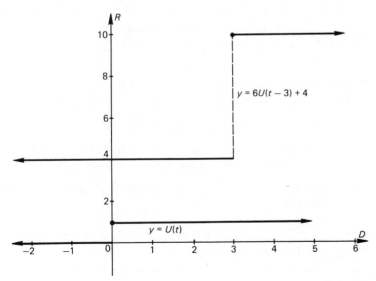

FIGURE 3-31

FIGURE 3-32

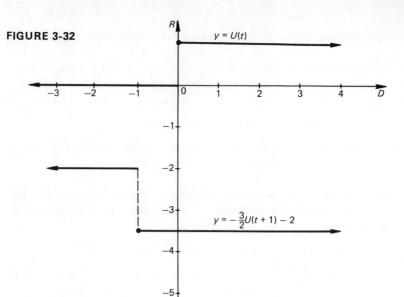

Rewrite the equations as

$$y - 4 = 6U(t - 3)$$

and

$$y - (-2) = -\tfrac{3}{2}U[t - (-1)]$$

The first function is the result of translating the unit step function 3 units to the right and 4 units upward, and then increasing its amplitude to +6. The graphs of $y = U(t)$ and $y = 6U(t - 3) + 4$ are shown in Figure 3-31.

The second function is the result of translating the unit step function 1 unit to the left and 2 units downward, and then changing its amplitude to $-\tfrac{3}{2}$ units (that is, the jump is negative). Figure 3-32 shows the graphs of $y = U(t)$ and $y = -\tfrac{3}{2}U(t + 1) - 2$.

EXAMPLE 3-18 Graph the function $y = -4\,\mathrm{sgn}(x + 2) + 3$.
After rearrangement of the terms, the function becomes

$$y - 3 = -4\,\mathrm{sgn}[x - (-2)]$$

which is the signum function translated 2 units to the left and 3 units upward, with amplitude of -4, as shown in Figure 3-33.

The following example illustrates the application of planar translation to more general relations.

EXAMPLE 3-19 Translate the relation $\rho(x) = x^2 + 1$ three units to the right and five units upward.
From the planar translation rule, we have $h = 3$ and $k = -5$, so the translated relation is given by

FIGURE 3-33

3-2 Special Linear **113**
*Functions
and Translation*

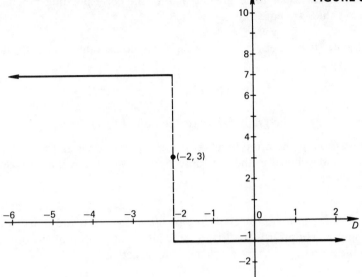

$$y - (-5) = p(x - 3) = (x - 3)^2 + 1$$
$$y + 5 = (x - 3)^2 + 1$$
$$y + 5 = x^2 - 6x + 10$$

which yields $y = x^2 - 6x + 5$. Thus, the translated relation is

$$\hat{p}(x) = x^2 - 6x + 5$$

as graphed in Figure 3-34.

EXAMPLE 3-20 Translate the relation

$$y = p(x) = \frac{16}{x - 1}$$

5 units to the right along the D axis. (Note that this is the relation graphed in Figure 2-9.) By the D axis translation rule, the translated relation, $\hat{p}(x)$, is

$$\hat{p}(x) = p(x - 5) = \frac{16}{(x - 5) - 1}$$

which reduces to

$$\hat{p}(x) = \frac{16}{x - 6}$$

The graph of $y = \hat{p}(x)$ is shown in Figure 3-35.

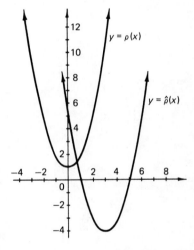

FIGURE 3-34

The Ramp Function

Another function of special interest is the *ramp function*. This ramp function takes on the value 0 for all negative values in the domain; for

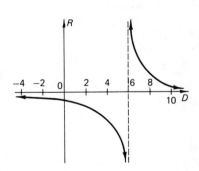

FIGURE 3-35

domain values equal to or greater than 0, the corresponding range and domain values are equal.

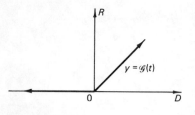

FIGURE 3-36

> **DEFINITION** Let $t \in \mathbb{R}$. The **ramp function**, denoted $\mathscr{G}$, is defined by the rule

$$\blacktriangleright \quad \mathscr{G}(t) = \begin{cases} 0 & \text{for } t < 0 \\ t & \text{for } t \geqslant 0 \end{cases}$$

Figure 3-36 gives the graphical representation of this function.

Translation of the ramp function is accomplished by using the rules of translation developed in the last subsection. As an illustration, we sketch the graph of

$$y - 2 = \mathscr{G}(t + 3)$$

Here, $k = 2$ and $h = -3$. The ramp function is translated 3 units to the left and 2 units upward. See Figure 3-37 for a comparison of the original ramp function, $\mathscr{G}$, and the translated ramp function.

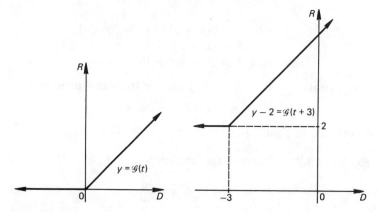

FIGURE 3-37

The ramp function differs from the step function in two ways: First, the ramp function has no graphical discontinuity. Second, the portions of the functions for nonnegative domain values have different characteristics; the step function is constant to the right of the R axis, whereas in that part of the DR plane, the ramp function is the linear function with slope 1 and R axis intercept 0. Just as it is possible to have step functions whose jumps are of size other than 1 (as defined for the basic step function), it is also possible to have ramp functions with slope different from 1. This is illustrated in the following examples.

> **EXAMPLE 3-21** Graph the ramp function $y = \frac{2}{3}\mathscr{G}(t)$ with the slope properly scaled.
> Since

$$m = \frac{\Delta y}{\Delta t} = \frac{2}{3}$$

this implies that for a change of 3 units in t, there is a change of 2 units in y. Note that for any point with $t \geqslant 0$, the slope is the same. At $t = 6$, for instance, the slope could be computed as $\Delta y / \Delta t = 1/(1.5)$. This obviously equals $\frac{2}{3}$, as shown in Figure 3-38.

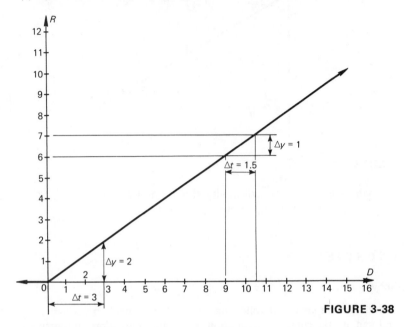

FIGURE 3-38

EXAMPLE 3-22 Graph the ramp function $y = -\frac{3}{5}\mathscr{G}(x)$ with the slope properly scaled.

Since

$$m = \frac{\Delta y}{\Delta x} = -\frac{3}{5}$$

then for a change of 5 units in x, there will be a change of -3 units in y. In this case, the ramp will slope downward, as shown in Figure 3-39.

The equation of the ramp function, with corner point (h, k) and slope m, has the standard form

$$y - k = m\mathscr{G}(t - h)$$

That is,

$$y - k = \begin{cases} mt & \text{for } t \geqslant h \\ 0 & \text{for } t < h \end{cases}$$

EXAMPLE 3-23 Graph the function $y = 3.4 + 2\mathscr{G}(t + \sqrt{2})$.

In standard form, this is written

$$y - 3.4 = 2\mathscr{G}[t - (-\sqrt{2})]$$
$$= \begin{cases} 2t & \text{for } t \geqslant -\sqrt{2} \\ 0 & \text{for } t < -\sqrt{2} \end{cases}$$

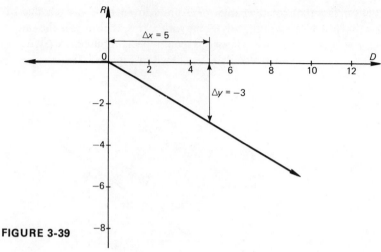

FIGURE 3-39

which is a ramp function with slope 2 and corner point $(-\sqrt{2}, 3.4)$.
The graph of this function is given in Figure 3-40.

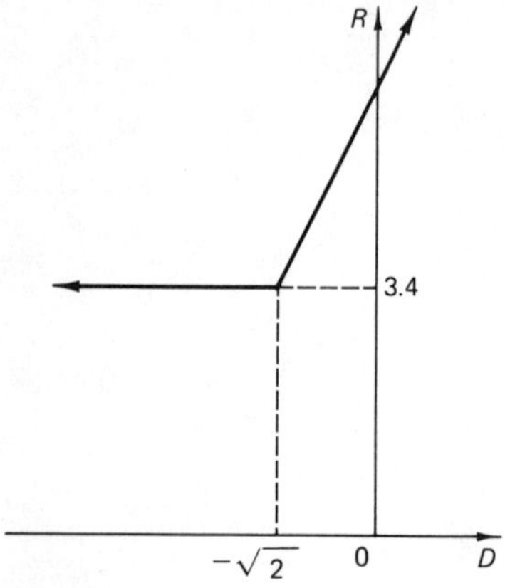

FIGURE 3-40

EXERCISES 3-2

Set A

Sketch the graphs of the following special linear functions, where $\mathcal{K}$, U, $\mathcal{G}$,
and sgn are the constant, step, ramp, and signum functions, respectively.

1. $\mathcal{K}(w) = 3$
2. $y = 3\mathcal{G}(t)$
3. $y = 4U(t - 4)$
4. $y = -2U(t + 1)$
5. $y + 3 = 4U(t - 3)$
6. $y - 7 = -3\mathcal{G}(t + 4)$
7. $y = \mathcal{G}(t - 2)$
8. $y - 3 = \mathcal{G}(t - 1)$
9. $y = \frac{2}{5}\mathcal{G}(t - 5)$
10. $y = \text{sgn}(x + 1)$
11. $y = 4 \text{ sgn}(t - 4)$
12. $y - 3 = -2 \text{ sgn}(t + 1)$

Set B

For Exercises 13 through 18, use the translation rules to write new algebraic
expressions for the given relations when translated as indicated. Then
graph, on the same set of axes, the relations as given below and the translated
relations.

13. $y = x^2$, translated 3 units to the right.
14. $y = x^2 + 3x + 2$, translated 2 units to the left and 1 unit downward.
15. $y = x^3 - x$, translated 1 unit to the left and 1 unit downward.
16. $y = x^3 - x$, translated 1 unit upward.
17. $y = x^3 - 3x$, translated 2 units to the left and 1 unit downward.
18. $y = x^4 - 8x^2$, translated 3 units to the right and 2 units upward.

19. Show that the definition of slope, $m = (y_2 - y_1)/(x_2 - x_1)$, cannot be used in the description of a vertical line.

Set C

20. Use addition of step functions whose steps occur at different times and whose step sizes may differ from 1 to reconstruct the graphs of the functions given in Figures 3-41, 3-42, and 3-43.

21. A plastics manufacturer has determined that curing ovens must operate at a temperature, T, that is a function of time, t, as described by the equation

$$T = 50\mathcal{G}(t) + 10U(t - 3) + 30\mathcal{G}(t - 5),$$
for T in °C and t in hours, $T \geqslant 0, t \geqslant 0$

How much time is required for an oven to reach a temperature of 420°C?

Hint: Graph T.

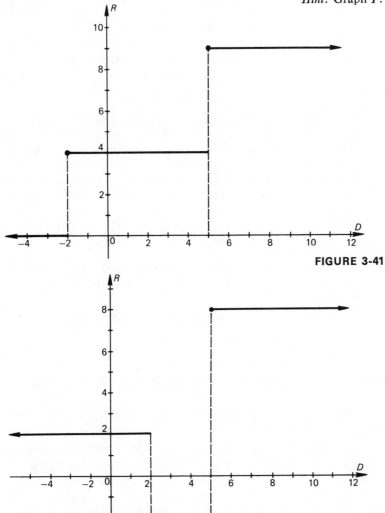

FIGURE 3-41

FIGURE 3-42

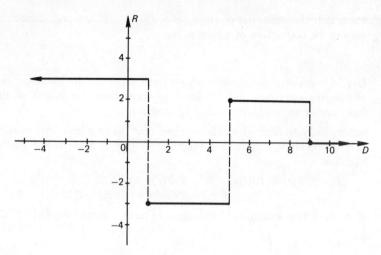

FIGURE 3-43

22. Let $F(x) = x - 4$. Show graphically that the product $F(x) \cdot U(x - 4)$ is equivalent to the ramp function

$$\mathcal{G}(x - 4)$$

23. A mattress manufacturing company has worked out the cost and income functions for its Model A mattress. The functions involved are sums and differences of step and ramp functions. If x represents the number of thousands of mattresses and y represents money in units of \$10,000, find the approximate values of x and y for which the company breaks even. Do this by graphing the cost and income functions on the same set of axes and finding where the graphs intersect.

> Cost function: $y = 10U(x) + 4\mathcal{G}(x) - 2\mathcal{G}(x - 3) - \mathcal{G}(x - 5)$
> Income function: $y = \frac{1}{2}\mathcal{G}(x) + \frac{3}{2}\mathcal{G}(x - 3) + 2\mathcal{G}(x - 5)$

24. Using the step function and the greatest integer function, construct the function that represents the operation of a taxi meter, given the following parameters:

> 65¢ for the first $\frac{1}{5}$ mile and 10¢ for each additional $\frac{1}{5}$ mile

(*Hint:* Use the results obtained in Exercise 22.)

3-3 INEQUALITIES AND ABSOLUTE VALUE

Although we use many processes that produce numerical values, it is very rare for the results of such processes to be truly exact. To name a few cases, all measurements, results of medical tests, sales projections, and insurance predictions are not exact but fall into ranges of values. These situations lead to the extremely important concept of inequality.

The meaning of the inequality symbol, $<$, was discussed in Chapter 1. Briefly, the "arrow" always points from the larger to the smaller quantity, and this symbol can be combined with the equality symbol as necessary.

Operations on Inequalities

The rules for operations on inequality statements are almost the same as those for equality statements. The differences occur in multiplying or dividing an inequality by a negative number.

INEQUALITY RULES   Let A, B, and C be real numbers. Then if $A > B$,

(1) $A + C > B + C$
(2) $A - C > B - C$
(3) $AC > BC$ if $C > 0$
    $AC < BC$ if $C < 0$
(4) $A/C > B/C$ if $C > 0$
    $A/C < B/C$ if $C < 0$

Note that when an inequality is divided or multiplied by a negative number, the inequality symbol reverses its direction. The most common mistake made in using inequalities is to forget that this reversal takes place. The following examples illustrate the applications of the rules.

EXAMPLE 3-24   Multiply both sides of the inequality $7 < 9$ by -2. We have

$$(-2){\cdot}7 \quad ? \quad (-2){\cdot}9$$

or

$$-14 \quad ? \quad -18$$

Since -14 is greater than -18, we have

$$-14 > -18$$

When multiplying by a negative quantity, reverse the direction of the inequality. (See Figure 3-44.)

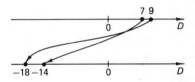

FIGURE 3-44

EXAMPLE 3-25   Find the set of values of x for which the following inequality is true:

$$3x - 8 < 4$$

Add 8 to both sides; the inequality becomes

$$3x < 12$$

Next, divide both sides by the positive number 3. This yields $x < 4$. The solution set, S, is

$$S = \{x \mid x < 4\}$$

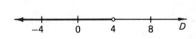

FIGURE 3-45

This solution can be graphed on the real number line as shown in Figure 3-45. The darkened portion of the line represents all numbers less than 4. The open circle at the number 4 indicates that this number is *excluded* from the region of solution. (Points, such as this one, that are on the border between the points satisfying an inequality and the points not satisfying it are called *critical points*.) The arrow denotes indefinite extension of the solution region in the direction indicated.

EXAMPLE 3-26 Find and graph the set of values of x for which the following inequality holds:

$$5x + 9 \geqslant -16$$

Add -9 to both sides; the inequality becomes

$$5x \geqslant -25$$

Dividing both sides by 5 yields the solution set,

$$S = \{x \mid x \geqslant -5\}$$

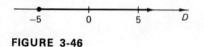

FIGURE 3-46

The graph of the solution is shown in Figure 3-46. The solid circle at -5 indicates that the critical point, -5, is *included* in the solution region.

In Examples 3-25 and 3-26, the solution sets were continuous sections, or *intervals*, on the real number line. The solutions of inequalities often take the form of such intervals, which may be either finite or infinite in length. Up to now, we have used set notation to describe intervals. The following definition provides a more convenient way to represent them.

DEFINITION Let $a, b \in \mathbb{R}$. Then

$$[a, b] = \{x \mid a \leqslant x \leqslant b\}$$
$$[a, b) = \{x \mid a \leqslant x < b\}$$
$$(a, b] = \{x \mid a < x \leqslant b\}$$
$$(a, b) = \{x \mid a < x < b\}$$
$$[a, \infty) = \{x \mid a \leqslant x\}$$
$$(a, \infty) = \{x \mid a < x\}$$
$$(-\infty, b] = \{x \mid x \leqslant b\}$$
$$(-\infty, b) = \{x \mid x < b\}$$
$$(-\infty, \infty) = \{x \mid x \in \mathbb{R}\}$$

Thus, a bracket means that the endpoint is included in the interval, whereas a parenthesis means that the endpoint is not included. The interval $[a, b]$ is called a *closed interval*, (a, b) is called an *open interval*, and $[a, b)$ and $(a, b]$ are called *half-open* or *half-closed intervals*. These are classified as *bounded intervals*, since they are proper subsets of $\mathbb{R}$. Any interval involving ∞ or $-\infty$ is an *unbounded interval*. However, intervals such as $[a, \infty]$ and $[-\infty, b)$ have no meaning, since $\infty \notin \mathbb{R}$.

For purposes of graphing intervals on the real number line, parentheses are equivalent to the open circle and brackets to the solid circle. These symbols will be used interchangeably in the examples that follow. Note that the bounded open interval (a, b) should not be confused with the ordered pair (a, b); the context should make clear which meaning the notation has.

EXAMPLE 3-27 Find and graph the set of values of x for which the following inequality is true:

$$7 - 3x < 4$$

Add -7 to both sides; the inequality becomes

$$-3x < -3$$

Now divide both sides by -3. However, remember that in the case of division by a negative number, the direction of the inequality reverses. The solution set

$$S = \{x \mid x > 1\} = (1, \infty)$$

is graphed in Figure 3-47.

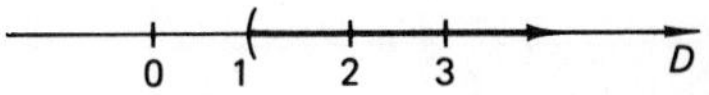

FIGURE 3-47

Compound Statements

Compound mathematical statements are formed when simple statements are joined by a connective. The connectives we will use are *and* and *or*. Using the notation and methods of set theory, we can find and describe the solutions of compound statements.

When simple statements are connected by *and*, the solution of the compound statement must simultaneously satisfy each of the simple statements. This is equivalent to set intersection, since any solution of the compound statement must belong to the solution set of each of the simple statements.

EXAMPLE 3-28 Find and graph the solution of the compound statement

$$3x + 7 \leqslant 19 \quad \textit{and} \quad 2x - 1 > -3$$

First, solve and graph each statement.

$$\begin{aligned} 3x + 7 &\leqslant 19 \\ 3x &\leqslant 12 \\ x &\leqslant 4 \end{aligned}$$

So the first solution set is

$$\begin{aligned} S_1 &= \{x \mid x \leqslant 4\} \\ &= (-\infty, 4] \end{aligned}$$

Next,

$$\begin{aligned} 2x - 1 &> -3 \\ 2x &> -2 \\ x &> -1 \end{aligned}$$

So the second solution set is

$$\begin{aligned} S_2 &= \{x \mid x > -1\} \\ &= (-1, \infty) \end{aligned}$$

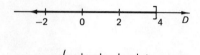

FIGURE 3-48

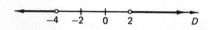

FIGURE 3-49

These solutions are graphed in Figure 3-48. Since the connective *and* requires the intersection of sets S_1 and S_2, the solution set for the compound statement is

$$S = S_1 \cap S_2 = \{x \mid x \leqslant 4\} \cap \{x \mid x > -1\} = (-\infty, 4] \cap (-1, \infty)$$

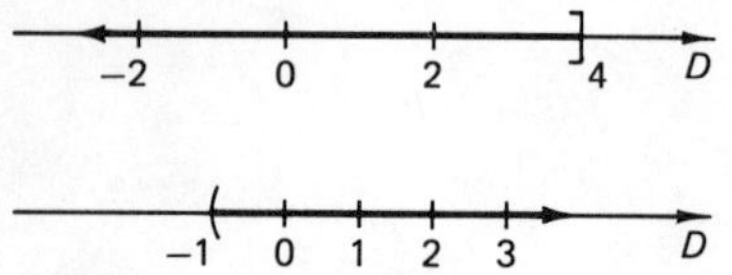

Therefore,

$$S = \{x \mid -1 < x \leqslant 4\} = (-1, 4]$$

The set S is graphed in Figure 3-49.

When simple statements are connected by *or*, the solution of the compound statement must satisfy at least one of the simple statements. This is equivalent to set union, since any solution of the compound statement must be an element of the solution set of at least one of the simple statements. Thus, the solution set of the compound statement is simply the union of the solution sets of the simple statements.

EXAMPLE 3-29 Find and graph the solution of the compound statement

$$x + 7 < 3 \quad \textit{or} \quad 2x - 1 > 3$$

First, solve and graph each statement.

$$x + 7 < 3$$
$$x < -4$$

So the first solution set is

$$S_1 = \{x \mid x < -4\}$$
$$= (-\infty, -4)$$

Next,

$$2x - 1 > 3$$
$$2x > 4$$
$$x > 2$$

So the second solution set is

$$S_2 = \{x \mid x > 2\}$$
$$= (2, \infty)$$

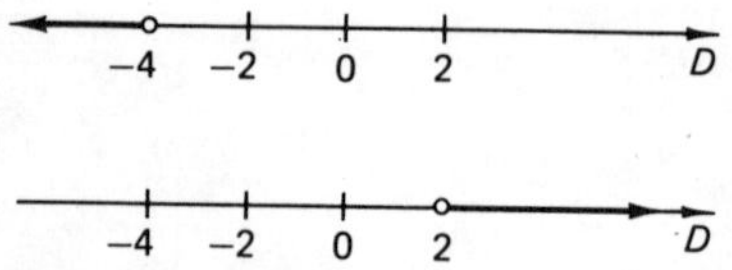

The sets S_1 and S_2 are graphed in Figure 3-50. The solution set is

$$S = S_1 \cup S_2 = \{x \mid x < -4\} \cup \{x \mid x > 2\}$$
$$= \{x \mid x < -4 \text{ or } x > 2\}$$

In interval notation, we can write

$$S = (-\infty, -4) \cup (2, \infty) = \mathbb{R} - [-4, 2]$$

Note that there is no simpler way to write the union of these disjoint intervals. The set S is graphed in Figure 3-51.

FIGURE 3-50

FIGURE 3-51

EXAMPLE 3-30 Find and graph the solution of the inequality

$$\frac{x-3}{x+2} \geqslant 0$$

To obtain the solution, we must use several properties of the real numbers. The steps involved in the solution are as follows.

(a) Since we have a division, there is a restriction on the values x can assume, namely,

$$x + 2 \neq 0$$

Therefore,

$$x \neq -2$$

(b) Next, consider the case

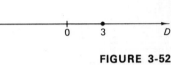

FIGURE 3-52

$$\frac{x-3}{x+2} = 0$$

A fraction can be zero only if its numerator is 0. Therefore,

$$x - 3 = 0$$

or

$$x = 3$$

This is shown graphically in Figure 3-52.

(c) Now we solve the case

$$\frac{x-3}{x+2} > 0$$

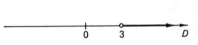

FIGURE 3-53

This is true only if both numerator and denominator have the same sign, that is, if they are both positive *or* both negative. If both are positive, we have

$$x - 3 > 0 \quad and \quad x + 2 > 0$$

The graphical solution for this compound inequality is given in Figure 3-53.

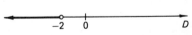

FIGURE 3-54

If both numerator and denominator are negative, we have

$$x - 3 < 0 \quad and \quad x + 2 < 0$$

The graphical solution for this compound inequality is given in Figure 3-54. To obtain the complete solution, we must take the union of the graphical solutions found in (b) and (c), making sure to take into account the restriction mentioned in (a). The final result is graphed in Figure 3-55. The solution set S is written $S = (-\infty, -2) \cup [3, \infty)$ or $S = \mathbb{R} - [-2, 3)$.

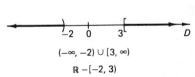

$(-\infty, -2) \cup [3, \infty)$

$\mathbb{R} - [-2, 3)$

FIGURE 3-55

Two-Dimensional Inequalities

The concept of inequality can be extended to more than one dimension. Recall that by the Trichotomy Law, any real number a satisfies exactly one of the following: $a < 0$, $a = 0$, or $a > 0$. Therefore, given any real numbers b and c, exactly one of the following must hold:

$$b - c < 0, \quad \text{that is, } b < c$$
$$b - c = 0, \quad \text{that is, } b = c$$
$$b - c > 0, \quad \text{that is, } b > c$$

What is important here is that the second case separates the "greater than" case from the "less than" case. Geometrically, the numbers that are less than c are to the left of c on the real number line, and those that are greater than c are to the right. To see how this idea is extended to the two-dimensional plane, consider the function

$$y = 2x + 1$$

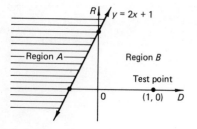

FIGURE 3-56

which is graphed in Figure 3-56. This line, which represents those ordered pairs (x, y) that satisfy the given equation, divides the DR plane into two regions, region A and region B. What significance do these regions have? The line $y = 2x + 1$ is the boundary that divides the DR plane into the regions

$$\{(x, y) \mid y > 2x + 1\} \quad \text{and} \quad \{(x, y) \mid y < 2x + 1\}$$

We can tell which region represents which inequality by recognizing that each of these inequalities is satisfied either by *every* point in region A or by *every* point in region B. So we simply pick any convenient point not on the boundary line and test it to see which of the inequalities it satisfies; this determines which inequality describes the region occupied by that point. The remaining region is described by the other inequality.

For this illustration, let us arbitrarily select the point $(1, 0)$ (which is not on the boundary line, $y = 2x + 1$) for testing. Substituting, we get

$$(0) \ ? \ 2(1) + 1$$
$$0 < 3$$

So region B is described by the inequality

$$y < 2x + 1$$

and region A by the inequality

$$y > 2x + 1$$

The reader should confirm these results by testing other points in each region.

EXAMPLE 3-31 Graph the region described by the compound inequality

$$y > 2x + 1 \quad \text{and} \quad y \leqslant -x + 2$$

As in the one-dimensional case, we begin by solving each inequality. Then we find the intersection of the two solutions, since the statement requires both inequalities to be simultaneously satisfied.

(a) First, graph the function $y = 2x + 1$. Then select a point for testing. We have chosen $(1, 1)$. Substituting, we get

$$(1) < 2(1) + 1$$

This point does not satisfy the inequality $y > 2x + 1$. Therefore, the solution is the region that *does not* contain $(1, 1)$, as shown in Figure 3-57. The line $y = 2x + 1$ is dashed to indicate that it is not part of the solution.

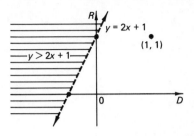

FIGURE 3-57

(b) As in (a), first graph the line

$$y = -x + 2$$

Now select a test point. We have arbitrarily chosen $(3, 0)$. Testing, we get

$$(3) > -(0) + 2$$

Since $(3, 0)$ does not satisfy the given inequality, the solution we seek is the region that *does not* contain $(3, 0)$. The solution is shown in Figure 3-58. The line $y = -x + 2$ is solid to indicate that it *is* part of the solution.

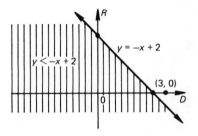

FIGURE 3-58

To find the intersection of the two solutions just obtained, simply see what region is common to them. Figure 3-59 shows both solutions plotted on the same axes; the intersection is the cross-hatched region.

If the problem had been to graph

$$y > 2x + 1 \quad or \quad y \leqslant -x + 2$$

the final solution would have been the *union* of both solutions, that is, the entire region distinguished by the presence of hatching. This is shown as the shaded region in Figure 3-60.

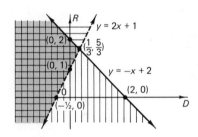

FIGURE 3-59

The Absolute Value Function

A man who doesn't trust doctors decides to keep a daily record of his blood pressure for a period of one week. He will seek medical help only if the average of the difference between his daily blood pressure and the normal value of 120, over this weekly period, exceeds 20. The results of his weekly record are given in the following table:

Day	M	Tu	W	Th	F	S	S
Pressure	180	90	200	60	80	170	60
Difference	+60	−30	+80	−60	−40	+50	−60

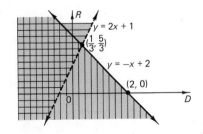

FIGURE 3-60

He computes the average of the differences by adding them and dividing by 7. The computation yields an average total difference of 0, so the man cheerfully reports to his doctor that he is normal. Upon seeing the record, the doctor says that the patient's pressure is extremely abnormal. What did the patient do wrong?

In order to compute the average of the differences correctly, the man should have considered the *sizes* of the differences regardless of their signs. The correct computation gives

$$\frac{60 + 30 + 80 + 60 + 40 + 50 + 60}{7} \cong 54.28$$

a number different enough from 0 to justify the doctor's concern. The mathematical relation that considers the value of a number irrespective of its sign is called the *absolute value function*, defined as follows.

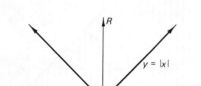

DEFINITION   Let $t \in \mathbb{R}$. Then the **absolute value function**, denoted $|\;|$, is defined by the rule

$$\blacktriangleright \quad |t| = \begin{cases} t & \text{for } t \geqslant 0 \\ -t & \text{for } t < 0 \end{cases}$$

Hence, the absolute value function maps the set of all real numbers onto the set of nonnegative real numbers. Symbolically,

$$|\;| : \mathbb{R} \twoheadrightarrow A$$

FIGURE 3-61

where $A = \{y \mid y \geqslant 0\}$. Figure 3-61 shows the graph of the absolute value function.

From Figure 3-61, it can be seen that the absolute value function is neither strictly monotonic nor one to one. Therefore, even though the absolute value function is an onto mapping for the given set A, it does not have an inverse function as defined, because it is not one to one. However, it is possible to construct an inverse function by restricting the domain.

The translation rules can be used to graph planar translations of the absolute value function.

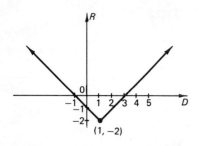

EXAMPLE 3-32   Graph the absolute value function given by

$$y + 2 = |x - 1|$$

This is the equation of a translated absolute value function, with $h = 1$ and $k = -2$. The graph is given in Figure 3-62.

FIGURE 3-62

Statements Using Absolute Value

Certain types of absolute value functions arise in the study of mathematical problems. One involves solving equations or inequalities that involve absolute values; this requires determining the domain of the absolute value function that maps onto a particular restricted range. Such problems are classified into three types. If a is a fixed real number, $a \geqslant 0$, then we can consider the problems of finding the following sets:

$$\{\zeta \in \mathbb{R} \mid |\zeta| < a\}$$
$$\{\zeta \in \mathbb{R} \mid |\zeta| = a\}$$
$$\{\zeta \in \mathbb{R} \mid |\zeta| > a\}$$

These sets are the restrictions on the domain of the absolute value function that result from restricting its range to $\{x \in \mathbb{R} \mid x < a\}$, $\{x \in \mathbb{R} \mid x = a\}$, and $\{x \in \mathbb{R} \mid x > a\}$, respectively. Clearly, the three problems cover all possible relationships of $|\zeta|$ to a. The second case is the borderline between the first and third cases, so its solution will separate the solutions of the other two.

FIGURE 3-63

First, we solve the equation

$$|\zeta| = a$$

From the definition of the absolute value function, if ζ is positive, then

$$\zeta = a$$

and if ζ is negative, then

$$-\zeta = a$$

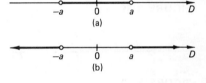

FIGURE 3-64

The combination of these two cases yields the solution

$$\zeta = -a \quad \text{and} \quad \zeta = a$$

The graph of this solution is shown in Figure 3-63.

Since the solutions of $|\zeta| < a$ and of $|\zeta| > a$ are separated by the solution just found, their graphs will be separated by the graph shown in Figure 3-63. The regions of the D axis determined by this graph are shown in Figure 3-64. Because the graph in Figure 3-64(a) is a continuous segment, either every point in this region satisfies $|\zeta| < a$ or every point in this region satisfies $|\zeta| > a$. A test of any point in this region, such as $a/2$ or $-a/4$, clearly shows that the region is the solution of $|\zeta| < a$. The second graph, therefore, is the solution of $|\zeta| > a$. These results, which are summarized in Figure 3-65, will be used as the basis for the solution of linear absolute value problems.

EXAMPLE 3-33 Find the graphical solution of the inequality

$$|2x - 3| \leqslant 5$$

Let $\zeta = 2x - 3$; then the problem becomes

$$|\zeta| \leqslant 5$$

FIGURE 3-65

In terms of ζ, the solution is the union of the solutions of $|\zeta| < 5$ and $|\zeta| = 5$. This union is graphed in Figure 3-66. However, we want the solution in terms of x, not of ζ. Since the equation that relates ζ and x is linear, the graph of the solution in terms of x will look identical to that in Figure 3-66 except that the critical values in terms of x will be

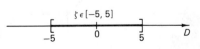

FIGURE 3-66

128 *Linear Functions*

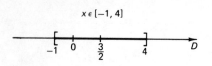

$x \in [-1, 4]$

FIGURE 3-67

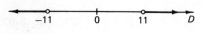

FIGURE 3-68

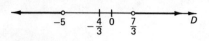

FIGURE 3-69

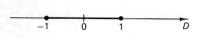

FIGURE 3-70

FIGURE 3-71

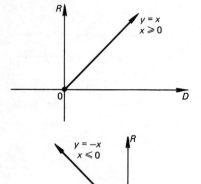

FIGURE 3-72

different. We can calculate these values by substituting the critical values of ζ into the equation $\zeta = 2x - 3$. For $\zeta = 5$, we get

$$5 = 2x - 3$$
$$8 = 2x$$
$$4 = x$$

For $\zeta = -5$,

$$-5 = 2x - 3$$
$$-2 = 2x$$
$$-1 = x$$

So the solution in terms of x is $[-1, 4]$, as shown in Figure 3-67.

EXAMPLE 3-34 Find the graphical solution of

$$|3x + 4| > 11$$

Let $\zeta = 3x + 4$; then the problem becomes $|\zeta| > 11$. The graphical solution in terms of ζ is shown in Figure 3-68. The graph in terms of x will look the same, but with different critical values. Using the equation that relates ζ and x, we get, for $\zeta = 11$,

$$11 = 3x + 4$$
$$7 = 3x$$
$$\tfrac{7}{3} = x$$

For $\zeta = -11$,

$$-11 = 3x + 4$$
$$-15 = 3x$$
$$-5 = x$$

So the solution in terms of x is $(-\infty, 5) \cup (\tfrac{7}{3}, \infty)$, as shown in Figure 3-69.

EXAMPLE 3-35 Find the graphical solution of

$$|\tfrac{1}{2}x + 3| \leqslant 1$$

Let $\zeta = \tfrac{1}{2}x + 3$; then the problem becomes

$$|\zeta| \leqslant 1$$

whose graphical solution in terms of ζ is shown in Figure 3-70. The graphical solution in terms of x will look the same. To find the critical values of x, we use the equation that relates ζ and x. For $\zeta = 1$,

$$1 = \tfrac{1}{2}x + 3$$
$$-2 = \tfrac{1}{2}x$$
$$-4 = x$$

For $\zeta = -1$,

$$-1 = \tfrac{1}{2}x + 3$$
$$-4 = \tfrac{1}{2}x$$
$$-8 = x$$

So the solution in terms of x is $[-8, -4]$, as shown in Figure 3-71.

As we did for inequalities, we can extend absolute value concepts to two-dimensional systems. Some simple examples will illustrate the technique.

EXAMPLE 3-36 Find the regions of the DR plane that represent

$$y > |x| \quad \text{and} \quad y < |x|$$

We obtain the solution by using the definition of the absolute value function.

$$y = \begin{cases} x & \text{for } x > 0 \\ -x & \text{for } x < 0 \\ 0 & \text{for } x = 0 \end{cases}$$

Figure 3-72(a) shows the graph of $y = |x|$ for the first condition listed ($x > 0$), and Figure 3-72(b) shows the graph for the second condition listed ($x < 0$). The combined graph is shown in Figure 3-73. Since the two parts of the graph meet at the point $(0, 0)$, which is called the *vertex* of the graph, the third condition is also satisfied. By using a test point, the reader should show that the region above the graph of $y = |x|$ represents the solution to

$$y > |x|$$

and that the region below is the solution to

$$y < |x|$$

EXAMPLE 3-37 Graph the region of the DR plane that is the solution to

$$y > |x + 4|$$

By the definition of the absolute value function,

$$y = \begin{cases} x + 4 & \text{for } x + 4 > 0 \\ -(x + 4) & \text{for } x + 4 < 0 \\ 0 & \text{for } x + 4 = 0 \end{cases}$$

The graphs for the first two conditions are shown in Figures 3-74(a) and (b). The two parts of the graph meet at $x = -4$, so the third condition is satisfied. The combined graph is shown in Figure 3-75.

To obtain the solution to the inequality problem, we use the test point $(5, 0)$. This shows that the region *above* the graph of $y = |x + 4|$ is the region we seek. The final solution is the shaded region shown in Figure 3-76. The dotted borderline indicates that the graph of $y = |x + 4|$ is *not* part of the solution.

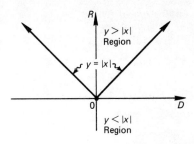

FIGURE 3-73

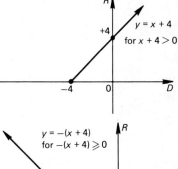

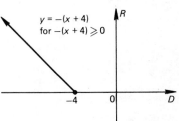

FIGURE 3-74

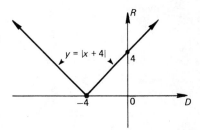

FIGURE 3-75

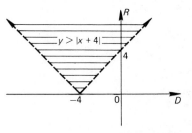

FIGURE 3-76

EXERCISES 3-3

Set A

Find and graph the solutions of the inequalities in Exercises 1 through 12.

1. $7 - 4x \leqslant 3$
2. $\frac{3}{4}x - 1 > 2$
3. $x + \frac{3}{2} \geqslant 2$
4. $-6 - 4x < 8$
5. $\frac{2}{3}x - \frac{1}{2} < \frac{3}{4}$
6. $-\frac{1}{3}x + \frac{7}{8} \leqslant \frac{3}{4}$
7. $|3x + 2| > 1$
8. $|2x - 4| \leqslant 3$
9. $|6 - x| < 3$
10. $|\frac{3}{4}x + 4| \geqslant 9$
11. $|1 - 3x| \geqslant 6$
12. $|5x + 7| > 12$

For Exercises 13 through 20, graph the region that satisfies the inequalities.

13. $y > 3x - 4$
14. $y \leqslant -2x + 3$
15. $y \geqslant 2x + 3$
16. $y < x + 4$
17. $y > |x + 6|$
18. $y \leqslant |2x - 1|$
19. $y \geqslant |-x + 4|$
20. $y < |3x + 4|$

Set B

Find and graph the solutions of the compound sentences in Exercises 21 through 30.

21. $3x + 7 < 5 \text{ and } x - 4 > -6$
22. $\frac{1}{4}x - 6 > 2 \text{ or } 3 - 2x > -1$
23. $2x < 7 - x \text{ or } 3x - 8 > 13$
24. $|x - 4| \geqslant 8 \text{ or } |x - 4| < 2$
25. $|2x - 3| \geqslant 4 \text{ and } |x + 4| \leqslant 8$
26. $|3x + 2| < 6 \text{ and } |x - 4| \leqslant 9$
27. $\frac{2x - 1}{3x - 4} < 0$
28. $\frac{x - 2}{x} \geqslant 0$
29. $\frac{x}{x + 5} \leqslant 0$
30. $\frac{3x}{x - 6} > 0$

31. Graph the following functions:
    (a) $y = |x - 3|$ (b) $y = 4 + |x + 2|$
    (c) $y = 3|x|$ (d) $y = 2|x + 4|$
    (e) $y = 3 - 2|x - 1|$ (f) $y = -4|x + 3| - 2$

32. For the following absolute value functions, state what domain restrictions are necessary for the inverse relation to be a function. Find the inverse function.
    (a) $y = |x|$ (b) $y = |x + 1|$
    (c) $y = 2|x + 3|$ (d) $y = 2 + 3|x - 1|$

Set C

● In Exercises 33 through 37, by substituting values for the variable, determine for which regions each statement is true. (Give answers to the nearest tenth.)

33. $x^2 + 3x - 9 > 12$

34. $|x^3 - 2x^2 + 7x - 4| > 2$

35. $|x^4 - 2x^3 - x^2 + x + 1| \leq 12$

36. $\dfrac{x(x-1)}{x+3} \leq 0$

37. $\dfrac{x-1}{x^2-4} > 0$

3-4 SOLUTION OF LINEAR SYSTEMS

Many problems involve more than one variable, and it may be necessary to use a system of equations, rather than just one equation, to describe these problems. An example of a system of equations is

$$2x + y = 5$$
$$x - 3y = 6$$

and a solution of such a system is an ordered pair, (x, y), that satisfies both equations at the same time. This is the two-variable counterpart to the compound statements discussed in Section 3-3. Since the solution must satisfy both statements at the same time, the solution set of the system will be given by the intersection of the set of all ordered pairs satisfying the first equation with the set of all ordered pairs satisfying the second equation.

It has already been shown that the graph of an equation of the form $Ax + By + C = 0$ is a straight line, which represents all ordered pairs (x, y) that satisfy the equation. If an ordered pair satisfies two linear equations, it must lie on the graphs of both equations. The fact that these graphs are straight lines implies that if they are distinct, then their intersection can be at most a single point. The only other possibilities are no solution (if the lines are parallel) or an infinite number of solutions (if the lines coincide). These three cases are shown in Figure 3-77(a), (b), and (c).

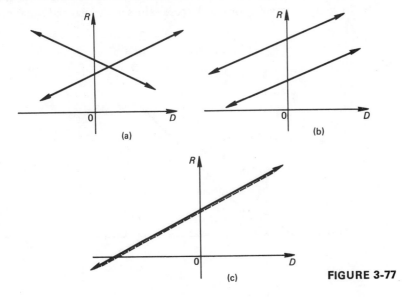

FIGURE 3-77

The necessary and sufficient conditions for a unique solution to exist are developed in linear algebra. It is found that the number of equations must be equal to the number of variables and that the equations must be linearly independent. However, a detailed discussion of these conditions is beyond the scope of this book.

Graphical Solution of Simultaneous Linear Equations

Consider the system of linear equations

$$x + 2y = 6$$
$$x - y = 0$$

In order to obtain the graphical solution, we graph both equations on the same set of axes. This can be done by setting up the usual table of x and y values, as shown in Table 3-1. We plot the points represented by the ordered

TABLE 3-1

x	$y = \dfrac{6 - x}{2}$	$y = x$
-2	4	-2
0	3	0
2	2	2
4	1	4
6	0	6

pairs in the DR plane. The completed graph is shown in Figure 3-78, and the coordinates of the point of intersection can easily be read from it as $(2, 2)$. To verify the results, we check these values in the original equations.

$$2 + 2(2) = 6 \qquad 2 - 2 = 0$$
$$2 + 4 = 6 \qquad 0 = 0$$

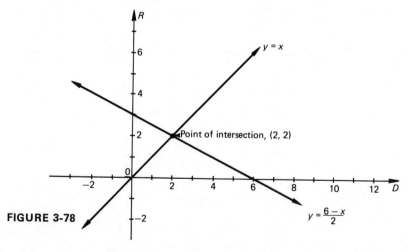

FIGURE 3-78

EXAMPLE 3-38 Find the graphical solution to the system

$$x + 3y = 12$$
$$x + 3y = -6$$

After graphing the two equations on the same set of axes (Figure 3-79), we see that no solution exists, since the lines do not intersect.

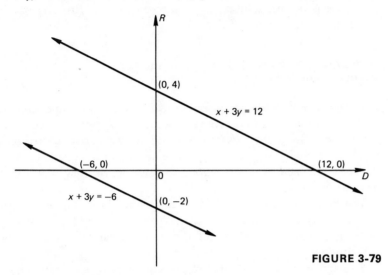

FIGURE 3-79

If we put both equations into slope–intercept form, we see that the lines have the same slope and different R axis intercepts, so they are parallel. In this form, the equations are

$$y = -\tfrac{1}{3}x + 4 \quad \text{and} \quad y = -\tfrac{1}{3}x - 2$$

respectively.

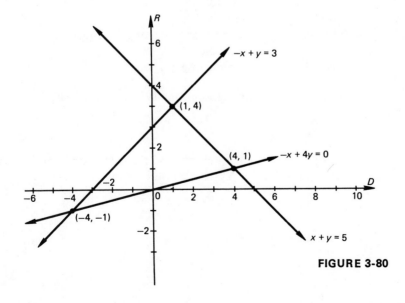

FIGURE 3-80

EXAMPLE 3-39 Find the graphical solution to the system

$$-x + y = 3$$
$$x + y = 5$$
$$-x + 4y = 0$$

From the graph of the system, shown in Figure 3-80, it is clear that there is no one solution to all three equations. However, there is a solution to any two of them.

Algebraic Solution of Simultaneous Linear Equations

A problem with the graphical method is that accurate nonintegral solutions are difficult to obtain from a graph. Algebraic methods, on the other hand, always yield exact answers, if answers exist. There are many algebraic techniques for solving systems of linear equations. We will illustrate the *method of elimination*, because it uses only the four basic arithmetic operations.

The basic idea of the method of elimination is to eliminate variables one at a time until only one is left. When the value of this variable has been determined, the values of the other variables can be found by substitution.

The steps in solving a system of two equations by elimination are:

1. Consider the equations and decide which of the variables is easiest to eliminate.
2. Multiply each of the equations by an appropriate value so that this variable has the same coefficient, but with opposite signs, in each equation.
3. Add the corresponding terms of the equations algebraically so that this variable is eliminated.
4. Solve for the remaining variable.
5. Substitute this result in either of the original equations.
6. Solve for the other variable.
7. Check the solutions in the original equations.

EXAMPLE 3-40 Solve the following system by elimination:

$$2x + y = 5$$
$$x - 3y = 6$$

Multiply the first equation by 3 and the second equation by 1. The result is

$$6x + 3y = 15$$
$$x - 3y = 6$$

Add these algebraically to get

$$7x = 21$$

Dividing by 7 yields

$$x = 3$$

Now, substitute this value of x into one of the original equations to find the value of y. If we choose the first equation, we obtain

$$2(3) + y = 5$$
$$6 + y = 5$$
$$y = 5 - 6$$
$$y = -1$$

Hence, the solution is the ordered pair $x = 3$, $y = -1$. Checking this solution in the remaining equation of the original set results in

$$3 - 3(-1) = 6$$
$$3 + 3 = 6$$
$$6 = 6$$

The elimination technique can become quite cumbersome if the coefficients of the unknown variables are not integers. In the following example, the method remains the same, but the arithmetic becomes more involved. It should be stressed that the solutions may not be exact but will be accurate to a number of decimal places determined by the accuracy and precision of the coefficients. (The concepts of accuracy and precision were discussed in Section 1-4.)

● **EXAMPLE 3-41** Find the solution of the system

$$7.853x - 27.9440y = 16.1038$$
$$16.4221x + 0.4276y = 9.4558$$

To eliminate the variable y, we multiply the first equation by 0.4276 and the second by 27.9440. The results are

$$3.358x - 11.94y = 6.886$$
$$458.899x + 11.94y = 264.23$$

The coefficients, which were obtained by multiplying values whose least accuracy was to four significant digits, have, therefore, been rounded off to the same number of significant digits. The sum of both equations yields

$$462.257x + 0y = 271.116$$

Solving for x, we get

$$x = 0.58651 = 0.5865$$

Again, this value is accurate to four significant digits. Substitution of this value into the first of the original equations yields

$$4.6060 - 27.9440y = 16.1038$$

Solving for y, we get

$$y = -0.41146$$

We use the remaining original equation as our check.

$$16.4221(0.58651) + 0.4276(-0.41146) = 9.4558$$
$$9.63173 - 0.17594 = 9.4558$$
$$9.45578 = 9.4558$$
$$9.4558 = 9.4558$$

Therefore, to four significant digits, our answers are $x = 0.5865$, $y = -0.4115$.

Systems of three equations in three variables can also be solved using the method of elimination. The following example shows how the technique is extended to more than two variables.

EXAMPLE 3-42   Solve the system

$$2x + y - z = -3$$
$$-x - y - z = -4$$
$$x + 3y + 4z = 17$$

Since there are three variables, the elimination must be carried out in two phases. First, we eliminate z by choosing any two equations and adding appropriate multiples of them together so that the sum has no z term. We then repeat this process with a different pair of equations. This results in two equations in two unknowns, x and y.

Multiplying the second equation by 4 and adding the result to the third equation yields

$$x + 3y + 4z = 17$$
$$-4x - 4y - 4z = -16$$
$$\overline{-3x - y = 1}$$

Multiplying the second equation by -1 and adding the result to the first equation yields

$$x + y + z = 4$$
$$2x + y - z = -3$$
$$\overline{3x + 2y = 1}$$

The equations $-3x - y = 1$ and $3x + 2y = 1$ are the result of the first phase of elimination.

Now take these equations and use the same process to eliminate another variable. In this particular case, simply adding them will eliminate x, and we can solve for y.

$$-3x - y = 1$$
$$3x + 2y = 1$$
$$\overline{ y = 2}$$

Now, we substitute $y = 2$ into one of the two equations to obtain a value for x.

$$3x + 2(2) = 1$$
$$3x + 4 \quad = 1$$
$$3x \qquad = -3$$
$$x \qquad = -1$$

Next, we substitute $x = -1$ and $y = 2$ into one of the three original equations to obtain a value for z. We choose the first equation.

$$2(-1) + 2 - z = -3$$
$$-2 + 2 - z = -3$$
$$-z = -3$$
$$z = 3$$

The solution is $x = -1$, $y = 2$, $z = 3$.

Finally, we check the three values obtained in the remaining two original equations. For the second equation, we have

$$-(-1) - 2 - 3 = -4$$
$$1 - 5 = -4$$
$$-4 = -4$$

For the third equation, we have

$$(-1) + 3(2) + 4(3) = 17$$
$$-1 + 6 + 12 = 17$$
$$-1 + 18 = 17$$
$$17 = 17$$

A system with four variables would require a three-step elimination procedure, but the process would remain the same. Note that in each example, no matter how trivial, the answer was checked in the original equations. It cannot be stressed too strongly that this is the *only* method of verifying the results. Careful work and consistent checking will help the student attain proficiency in solving systems of equations.

EXERCISES 3-4

Set A

1. Find the approximate solution to the given linear systems by graphing.
   (a) $x + 6y = 2$ (b) $6x + 5y = 5$
        $3x - 2y = -24$ $x + 10y = \frac{19}{3}$

2. Solve and check the linear systems in Exercise 1 by the method of elimination.

3. Solve and check the following systems of linear equations by the method of elimination:

(a)
$$x + y + z = 2$$
$$3x - y - z = 2$$
$$-4x + y - 2z = -1$$

(b)
$$2x - y - z = 0$$
$$x + 2y + z = \frac{9}{2}$$
$$3x + y - 2z = \frac{17}{2}$$

Set B

4. (a) The sum of two numbers is 233 and their difference is 99. Find the two numbers.

   (b) A club uses two types of mailings to advertise its functions. One costs 5¢ to post each piece and the other 10¢ each piece. If a total of 200 pieces of mail cost $15 to post, how many of each type were sent out?

5. A bottle manufacturer's plant can turn out bottles of two different sizes. The maximum output is 6000 bottles per day for both types. On a daily basis, the manufacturer can manufacture twice as many of the larger bottles as of the smaller bottles. If the plant operates at maximum capacity, how many of each bottle can be manufactured per day?

6. A farmer has 55 animals, consisting of pigs, steers, and chickens. Steers cost $10, pigs cost $3, and chickens cost 50¢. If the farmer bought all the animals for $125 and has six times as many chickens as steers, how many of each animal did the farmer purchase?

● 7. Use elimination techniques to solve for the variables in the following linear systems. Give the answers to the proper number of significant digits.
   (a)
$$-1.0043x + 6.9921y = 54.9887$$
$$21.1143x + 8.7535y = 93.0114$$
   (b)
$$0.0577x - 6.420y = -18.7790$$
$$1.1132x - 0.0376y = 0.8544$$

REVIEW EXERCISES FOR CHAPTER 3

1. Graph the following functions. Recall that $\mathcal{K}$ is a constant function, U is the unit step function, $\mathcal{G}$ is the ramp function, and sgn is the signum function.
   (a) $\mathcal{K}(t) = -4$
   (b) $v = 4U(s + 2)$
   (c) $y = -3\,\text{sgn}(x - 4) + 7$
   (d) $w = 2\mathcal{G}(t - 1) + 4$
   (e) $y = 3\mathcal{G}(t + 1) - U(t - 4)$
   (f) $y = 2\,\text{sgn}(t - 3) + U(t + 4)$

2. Graph the following functions:
   (a) $3x - 4y = 7$
   (b) $x + 6y = 8$
   (c) $(y + 4) = -2(3 - x)$
   (d) $y - 2 = 2(4 - x)$

3. Given the line $2y = 6x - 5$ and the point $(3, 5)$, find the equation of the line passing through the point and
   (a) parallel to the given line
   (b) perpendicular to the given line

4. Find and graph the solutions of the following inequalities:
   (a) $3 - 2x \leqslant 7$
   (b) $6x + 4 \geqslant 3$
   (c) $2x - 3 < 9$
   (d) $5 - 4x > 2$

5. Graph the region of solution of the following inequalities:
   (a) $y < |x - 4|$
   (b) $y \geqslant |x + 5|$

6. Find and graph the solutions of the following compound inequalities:
   (a) $4 - x > 3$ *and* $2x + 3 \geqslant -7$ (b) $3x - 2 \geqslant 7$ *or* $x + 1 < 4$
   (c) $|4 - x| \leqslant 3$ *or* $|x - 2| > 8$ (d) $|x| \geqslant 1$ *and* $|x| < 4$

7. Find the simultaneous solutions of the following systems of equations:
   (a) $2x + y = 8$ (b) $2x - y = 4$
       $3x + 4y = 15$ $6x + 5y = 13$
   (c) $x + 2y - z = 9$
       $-3x + y - 2z = -6$
       $x - 3y + 2z = 2$

8. For the following absolute value functions, state what restriction must be placed on the domain so that the inverse function exists. Then, find the inverse function.
   (a) $y = 2|x - 1|$ (b) $y = -|x + 1|$
   (c) $y = 4 - 2|x - 3|$

Quadratic Relations

4-1 QUADRATIC EQUATIONS—ROOTS AND ZEROS

Introduction

In Chapter 3, we discussed linear functions and some related special functions. The linear function, whose graph is a straight line, is an example of a first-degree equation. In general, for any algebraic expression in which the exponents of the variables are elements of $\mathbb{N}$, the *degree* of the expression is the greatest value of the sum of the exponents of all the variables in any single term. If the expression has only one variable, then the degree of the expression is the greatest exponent of that variable.

EXAMPLE 4-1

$5x^4$ is of degree 4.

$8x^3yz$ is of degree 5 in all three variables.

$5x^4 - 8x^3y^2z$ is of degree 6 in x, y, and z, but of degree 4 in x.

The equation of a straight line is

$$y = mx + b$$

141

Since the highest total power of the variables in any term is 1, linear functions are of degree 1, or of the *first degree*.

Relations whose graphs are neither straight lines nor the union of straight line segments are called *nonlinear relations*. The first class of nonlinear relations to be discussed in the class of second-degree, or *quadratic*, relations. The general second-degree relation in two variables is given by

▶ $Ax^2 + Bxy + Cy^2 + Dx + Ey + F = 0$

where $A, B, C, D, E, F \in \mathbb{R}$ and A, B, and C are not all 0. The curves associated with this general equation are called *conic sections* and are classified into four types: circles, parabolas, ellipses, and hyperbolas. These curves are discussed in detail in Section 4-2.

Zeros and Roots

In many instances, we wish to find the *zeros* of a second-degree relation.

DEFINITION Let F be an implicit relation given by the rule $F(x, y) = 0$. Then the elements of the domain of F that have image 0 are called the **zeros** of F.

EXAMPLE 4-2 The ordered pair $(x, y) = (-1, 0)$ satisfies the relation

$$x^2 + 3xy - 2y^2 - x + 5y - 2 = 0$$

and hence, $x = -1$ is a zero of this relation.

Graphing implicit relations often requires finding their D axis intercepts, which are the zeros of the relation. When we graph a nonhorizontal straight line, one of the critical points used is the D axis intercept, found by determining which value in the domain is mapped to the range value 0. For example, for the straight line $y = 2x + 3$, only one value in the domain, $x = -\frac{3}{2}$, is mapped to the range value $y = 0$. Therefore, the coordinates of the D axis intercept are $(-\frac{3}{2}, 0)$, and $-\frac{3}{2}$ is a zero of this relation.

If $F(x, y) = 0$ is an implicit relation, its zeros can be found by substituting $y = 0$ into the expression $F(x, y)$. This always results in an equation of the form

$$g(x) = 0$$

The values of x that satisfy this equation are called its *roots*.

DEFINITION Let $g(x) = 0$ be an equation in one variable, x. Then the values of $x \in \mathbb{C}$ that satisfy this equation are called the **roots** of the equation.

The student should not confuse the meanings of *zero* and *root*, since a root is not necessarily the result of the range variable of a relation being 0.

(For example, the equation $2x - 6 = 0$ has $x = 3$ as a root. However, this equation does not necessarily result from setting the range variable of a relation equal to 0. Note that it is possible to have roots that are not real numbers. Note as well that this sense of the word "root" is usually different from its sense in such phrases as "square root" and "cube root."

Again, consider the general equation of the second degree (the general quadratic equation),

$$Ax^2 + Bxy + Cy^2 + Dx + Ey + F = 0$$

where $A, B, C, D, E, F \in \mathbb{R}$ and $A, B,$ and C are not all 0. In order to find the zeros of this relation, assume that x represents the domain elements and y the range elements. By definition, therefore, we seek the values of x for which $y = 0$. If we set $y = 0$, the general quadratic equation becomes

$$Ax^2 + Dx + F = 0$$

where $A \neq 0$. A more familiar form of this equation is obtained by replacing $A, D,$ and F with $a, b,$ and c, respectively; the equation becomes

▶ $ax^2 + bx + c = 0, \qquad a \neq 0$

The roots of this equation are the zeros of the general quadratic equation.

Completing the Square

The next task is to develop a method of calculating the roots of the equation $ax^2 + bx + c = 0$ ($a \neq 0$). First, we review the algebraic technique used for this purpose, *completing the square*.

Consider the expression

$$x^2 + 6x$$

What must be added to this expression to make it a perfect square of the form

$$(x + q)^2$$

where q is some constant? If $(x + q)^2$ is expanded, the result is

$$(x + q)^2 = x^2 + 2qx + q^2$$

A term-by-term comparison with the original equation shows that

$$2q = 6 \quad \text{or} \quad q = \tfrac{6}{2} = 3$$

and that a quantity equal to

$$q^2 = 9$$

must be added to $x^2 + 6x$ to make it a perfect square. Thus,

$$x^2 + 6x = x^2 + 6x + 9 - 9$$
$$= (x + 3)^2 - 9$$

Note that a quantity equal to the amount added must be subtracted to preserve the value of the original expression. In general, the expression $ax^2 + bx$ can be rewritten as

$$ax^2 + bx = a\left[x^2 + \frac{b}{a}x\right]$$

$$= a\left[x^2 + \frac{b}{a}x + \frac{b^2}{4a^2}\right] - \frac{b^2}{4a}$$

$$= a\left[x + \frac{b}{2a}\right]^2 - \frac{b^2}{4a}$$

To summarize the process:

1. Factor the quadratic expression so that the coefficient of the second-degree term is 1.
2. Add the square of one-half the coefficient of the linear term to the expression.
3. Write this in the form of a perfect square, $(x + q)^2$, minus the quantity just added.

Quadratic Formula

It is now possible to develop an algebraic expression for the roots of the equation

$$ax^2 + bx + c = 0, \qquad a \neq 0$$

in terms of the constants a, b, and c. This expression is commonly called the quadratic formula.

THEOREM 4-1 Let $a, b, c \in \mathbb{R}$, with $a \neq 0$. Then the roots of the equation

$$ax^2 + bx + c = 0$$

are given by

$$\blacktriangleright \quad x = \frac{-b \pm \sqrt{b^2 - 4ac}}{2a}$$

PROOF Let

$$ax^2 + bx + c = 0, \qquad a \neq 0$$

Dividing by a yields

$$x^2 + \frac{b}{a}x + \frac{c}{a} = 0$$

and subtracting $\dfrac{c}{a}$ from each side gives

$$x^2 + \frac{b}{a}x = -\frac{c}{a}$$

Now, complete the square on the left side of the equation by squaring one-half the x coefficient and adding the result to both sides of the equation. This yields

$$x^2 + \frac{b}{a}x + \frac{b^2}{4a^2} = \frac{b^2}{4a^2} - \frac{c}{a}$$

The left side of the equation is now a perfect square, and the right side can be rewritten as a single fraction. The equation becomes

$$\left(x + \frac{b}{2a}\right)^2 = \frac{b^2 - 4ac}{4a^2}$$

Taking the square root of both sides yields

$$x + \frac{b}{2a} = \pm\sqrt{\frac{b^2 - 4ac}{4a^2}}$$

$$= \pm\frac{\sqrt{b^2 - 4ac}}{2a}$$

Subtracting $\frac{b}{2a}$ from both sides gives

$$x = \frac{-b \pm \sqrt{b^2 - 4ac}}{2a}$$

which was the formula to be derived. ∎

Because of the plus or minus sign in front of the radical, the quadratic formula yields two roots,

$$x_1 = \frac{-b + \sqrt{b^2 - 4ac}}{2a} \quad \text{and} \quad x_2 = \frac{-b - \sqrt{b^2 - 4ac}}{2a}$$

However, although this second-degree equation always has two roots, the roots are not always real-valued or distinct. The quantity that determines whether the roots are distinct and whether they are real is the value of the expression under the radical sign in the formula. This quantity,

$$b^2 - 4ac$$

is called the *discriminant* of the quadratic equation.

DEFINITION In the quadratic expression $ax^2 + bx + c$, $a \neq 0$, the quantity

$$b^2 - 4ac$$

is called the **discriminant**.

If

$$b^2 - 4ac > 0$$

then $\sqrt{b^2 - 4ac}$ is real, and two distinct real roots are obtained from the quadratic formula. This means that the graph of $y = ax^2 + bx + c$ intersects the D axis at two distinct points. If

$$b^2 - 4ac = 0$$

then $\sqrt{b^2 - 4ac} = 0$, and the formula yields two real roots with the same value. This means that the graph touches the D axis at exactly one point but does not cross the D axis. If

$$b^2 - 4ac < 0$$

then $\sqrt{b^2 - 4ac}$ is imaginary, and the formula yields two distinct complex roots. This means that the graph does not intersect the D axis.

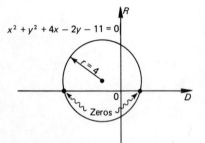

$x^2 + y^2 + 4x - 2y - 11 = 0$

FIGURE 4-1

EXAMPLE 4-3 Find the zeros of the second-degree relation given by

$$x^2 + y^2 + 4x - 2y - 11 = 0$$

By generating a set of ordered pairs, we can graph the relation as shown in Figure 4-1. From the graph, it can be seen that the relation has two distinct real zeros. If we set $y = 0$, the equation becomes

$$x^2 + 4x - 11 = 0$$

which is a quadratic equation in one variable with $a = 1$, $b = 4$, and $c = -11$. Using the quadratic formula and substituting for a, b, and c, we obtain

$$x = \frac{-b \pm \sqrt{b^2 - 4ac}}{2a}$$

$$= \frac{-(4) \pm \sqrt{(4)^2 - 4(1)(-11)}}{2(1)}$$

$$= \frac{-4 \pm \sqrt{16 + 44}}{2}$$

$$= \frac{-4 \pm \sqrt{60}}{2}$$

Since

$$\sqrt{60} = \sqrt{4}\,\sqrt{15} = 2\sqrt{15}$$

then

$$x = \frac{-4 \pm 2\sqrt{15}}{2} = -2 \pm \sqrt{15}$$

Since $\sqrt{15} \approx 3.873$, the two roots correct to three decimal places are

$$x_1 = -2 + 3.873 = 1.873$$

and

$$x_2 = -2 - 3.873 = -5.873$$

Therefore, the zeros of the relation, correct to three decimal places, are $x = 1.873$ and $x = -5.873$.

EXAMPLE 4-4 Find the zeros of the second-degree relation given by

$$x^2 + y^2 - 16y + 39 = 0$$

By generating a set of ordered pairs, we can graph the relation as shown in Figure 4-2. From the graph, it is evident that this relation has no real zeros. To prove this, let $y = 0$; then the equation becomes

$$x^2 + 39 = 0$$

For this equation, $a = 1$, $b = 0$, and $c = 39$. Substitution into the quadratic formula yields

$$x = \frac{-(0) \pm \sqrt{(0)^2 - 4(1)(39)}}{2(1)}$$

$$= \frac{\pm \sqrt{4} \sqrt{-39}}{2}$$

$$= \pm \sqrt{-39}$$

$$= \pm i\sqrt{39}$$

Thus, there are two roots, both of them imaginary. Since the roots are not real numbers, the circle does not cross the D axis, and the relation $x^2 + y^2 - 16y + 39 = 0$ has no real zeros. This confirms the conclusion we drew from Figure 4-2.

EXAMPLE 4-5   Find the zeros of the second-degree equation

$$x^2 - 6x + y + 9 = 0$$

By generating a set of ordered pairs, we can graph the relation as shown in Figure 4-3. From the graph, it seems that there is only one zero. This can be shown in another way. If we set $y = 0$, the equation becomes

$$x^2 - 6x + 9 = 0$$

which is a quadratic equation with $a = 1$, $b = -6$, and $c = 9$. Using the quadratic formula, we obtain its roots.

$$x = \frac{-(-6) \pm \sqrt{(-6)^2 - 4(1)(9)}}{2(1)}$$

$$= \frac{6 \pm \sqrt{36 - 36}}{2}$$

$$= \frac{6 \pm \sqrt{0}}{2}$$

Therefore, the roots are

$$x_1 = \frac{6 + 0}{2} = 3 \quad \text{and} \quad x_2 = \frac{6 - 0}{2} = 3$$

So there are two real roots, both equal to 3; hence, as the graph in Figure 4-3 indicates, the relation $x^2 - 6x + y + 9 = 0$ has only one real zero, whose value is 3.

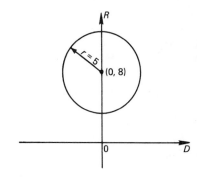

FIGURE 4-2

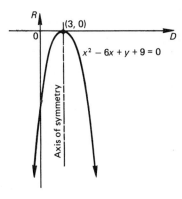

FIGURE 4-3

Factoring

Another method often used to find the zeros of a second-degree relation is *factoring*. Although sometimes easier than using the quadratic formula, factoring works well only when the zeros are rational and when the expression has obvious factors. The quadratic expression $ax^2 + bx + c$, $a \neq 0$, is factorable under certain specified conditions. In particular, if the discriminant, $b^2 - 4ac$, is a perfect square, the expression can be factored by inspection.

If the quadratic expression, which is a trinomial with leading coefficient not equal to 0, is factorable, then it can be rewritten as

$$ax^2 + bx + c = (Dx + E)(Gx + H)$$

where

$$DG = a, \quad EH = c, \quad \text{and} \quad GE + DH = b$$

In this case, the factored equation becomes

$$(Dx + E)(Gx + H) = 0$$

This can be true only if at least one of the factors is 0. Setting each factor equal to 0, we obtain the linear equations

$$Dx + E = 0 \quad \text{and} \quad Gx + H = 0$$

which can easily be solved for x. The values that result are the zeros of the relation. However, it must be stressed that when the roots are irrational or complex, this method is usually difficult to apply. The zeros obtained can be checked against the quadratic formula, which must yield the same values.

EXAMPLE 4-6   By factoring, find the roots of the equation

$$x^2 + 2x - 24 = 0$$

We have $a = 1$, so if the equation is factorable, it has the form

$$x^2 + 2x - 24 = (x + E)(x + H) = 0$$

where

$$EH = -24 \quad \text{and} \quad E + H = 2$$

The ways of factoring -24 with integers are as $-24 \times 1, -12 \times 2,$ $-8 \times 3, -6 \times 4, 6 \times -4, 8 \times -3, 12 \times -2,$ and $24 \times -1.$ The only pair whose sum is 2 is 6 and -4, so the answer is

$$(x + 6)(x - 4) = 0$$

Setting each factor equal to 0, we get

$$x + 6 = 0$$
$$x = -6$$

and

$$x - 4 = 0$$
$$x = 4$$

So the roots are

$$x_1 = -6 \quad \text{and} \quad x_2 = 4$$

EXAMPLE 4-7   Use factoring to find the roots of

$$12x^2 + 25x + 12 = 0$$

When factored, this becomes

$$(3x + 4)(4x + 3) = 0$$

Setting each factor equal to 0, we get

$$3x + 4 = 0$$
$$x = -\tfrac{4}{3}$$

and

$$4x + 3 = 0$$
$$x = -\tfrac{3}{4}$$

So the roots are

$$x_1 = -\tfrac{4}{3} \quad \text{and} \quad x_2 = -\tfrac{3}{4}$$

EXAMPLE 4-8   Use factoring to find the roots of

$$x^2 + x + 1 = 0$$

This equation has no obvious factorization. Since $b^2 - 4ac < 0$, the roots are not real numbers. Use of the quadratic formula shows that the roots are complex and are given by

$$x_1 = \frac{-1 + i\sqrt{3}}{2} \quad \text{and} \quad x_2 = \frac{-1 - i\sqrt{3}}{2}$$

The quadratic formula *always* works, so the student should learn it and apply it whenever possible.

A Use of the Quadratic Formula

The quadratic formula can be quite useful as an aid in graphing implicit relations where one of the variables is of degree 2. Example 4-9 illustrates the technique.

● **EXAMPLE 4-9**   Find a set of ordered pairs for

$$F(x, y) = x^2y + 2y^2 - 4 = 0$$

and graph the result.

The method used is to fix the value of x and then find the y values that satisfy the resulting one-variable equation. In the relation $x^2y + 2y^2 - 4 = 0$, if the variable x is held fixed, the equation becomes a quadratic function of y, and the y values can be found from the quadratic formula.

Since an exact numerical value for y will not be available when y is an irrational number, we must decide on an acceptable degree of accuracy for y. One possible criterion is to accept an approximation y_1 when the resulting value of $F(x_1, y_1)$ lies between two limits near 0. For example, the values x_1 and y_1 that result in

$$-0.01 < F(x_1, y_1) < 0.01$$

are close enough for the purposes of graphing. If the values of x and y are to be used for computation, a more stringent criterion might be needed.

The procedure is as follows. Select any value from the domain of the relation, say, $x = 2$. Then the relation becomes

$$F(2, y) = 2y^2 + 2^2y - 4$$
$$= 2y^2 + 4y - 4$$

Ideally, the values of y sought are those such that $F(2, y) = 0$. Using the quadratic formula, we can find the y values to three decimal places; this will assure that

$$-0.01 < F(2, y) < 0.01$$

The results for various integer values of x are listed in Table 4-1

TABLE 4-1   Values for $F(x, y) = 0$

x	y (First value)	y (Second value)
4	0.243	−8.243
3	0.408	−4.908
2	0.732	−2.732
1	1.186	−1.686
0	1.414	−1.414
−1	1.186	−1.686
−2	0.732	−2.732
−3	0.408	−4.908
−4	0.243	−8.243

(Note that there are two y values for each x value.) For each pair of x and y values in Table 4-1, the student should check that

$$-0.01 < F(x, y) < 0.01$$

The graph of $F(x, y) = x^2y + 2y^2 - 4 = 0$ is given in Figure 4-4.

FIGURE 4-4

Finally, note that the domain of this relation is the set of all real numbers, whereas the range is the set

$$\mathscr{R} = \{y \mid 0 < y \leqslant \sqrt{2} \quad \text{or} \quad y \leqslant -\sqrt{2}\}$$

EXERCISES 4-1

Set A

Find the zeros of the following second-degree relations. Answers may be left in radical form. $(x \in \mathscr{D}, y \in \mathscr{R})$.

1. $x^2 + y^2 - 8x + 12y + 3 = 0$
2. $x^2 - 4y^2 - 6x + 24y - 12 = 0$
3. $xy - 4x + 2y - 16 = 0$
4. $16x^2 + y^2 - 96x - 4y + 132 = 0$
5. $x^2 - 12x - y + 27 = 0$
6. $3y^2 - 4x^2 - 18y - 16x - 1 = 0$
7. $6x^2 + 4xy - 24 = 3y^2 - 4x + 2y$
8. $3xy - 5x^2 + 3y = 25x - 30$
9. $y^2 - 4x^2 = 2x + 6y$
10. $4y - 3x + 6xy = 8y^2$

Set B

11. By completing the square in both x and y, place the following equations in the form

$$A(x - h)^2 + B(y - k)^2 = C$$

where A, B, C, h, and k are constants.
(a) $x^2 + y^2 - 2x - 4y - 4 = 0$
(b) $3x^2 + 4y^2 + 6x + 4y = 0$
(c) $4x^2 - 3y^2 - 12x + 6y + 2 = 0$

● 12. Graph the relation

$$F(x, y) = 3x^2 - x^2y^2 - 3 = 0$$

by obtaining at least six ordered pairs that satisfy the relation.

Set C

13. You and a friend, traveling on motor scooters, start from the same point. You travel north, and your friend travels east. Your friend travels 14 miles per hour faster than you. After traveling for 5 hours, you are 170 miles apart on a straight line. At what speeds are you and your friend traveling?

14. A farmer, who has a rectangular stock pen that measures 20 feet wide and 32 feet long, wishes to double the area of the pen by increasing its length and width by the same amount. How much will it cost to fence in this new area on all sides if the fencing costs $8 per foot?

● 15. Use the quadratic formula to find the roots (real or complex) of the following quadratic equations:
(a) $17.47x^2 - 6.722x + 5.013 = 0$
(b) $0.942x^2 + 16.118x - 0.714 = 0$

(c) $2.588x^2 - 21.306x - 0.843 = 0$

(d) $0.0473x^2 + 6.172x + 5.988 = 0$

● 16. Follow the method developed in Example 4-9 to find at least ten ordered pairs that satisfy the implicit relations given below and graph the results.

(a) $x - 4y^2 + 3y = 0$ (b) $-x^2 + 6y^2 - 4xy = 0$

(c) $xy^2 + x^2y = 0$ (d) $xy^2 - x^2y = 0$

17. A biologist has determined that the rate of bacterial growth, r, and the temperature, T, of a specimen satisfy the implicit relation

$$2rT - 3T^2 + 4r^2T - 10 = 0$$

Find two ordered pairs (r, T) that satisfy this relation. Both r and T must be positive.

4-2 CONIC SECTIONS

In Section 4-1, we saw that the general second-degree equation is given by

$$Ax^2 + Bxy + Cy^2 + Dx + Ey + F = 0$$

where $A, B, C, D, E, F \in \mathbb{R}$ and $A, B,$ and C are not all 0. Depending on the values of $A, B,$ and C, the graph of this equation can be any of four nonlinear geometric curves, called a *circle*, an *ellipse*, a *parabola*, and a *hyperbola*. These curves are also called *conic sections*, because they are obtained by passing planar sections through a cone. A *cone* (see Figure 4-5) is a three-dimensional surface generated by circular rotation of a line, called the *generator*, about an axis, where the axis and generator intersect at a point called the *vertex*. The surface so generated, which is called a *right circular cone of two nappes*, is composed of an *upper nappe* and a *lower nappe*.

The following are the conditions under which the conic sections and their degenerate cases are obtained:

1. **Circle** A *circle* is any planar section perpendicular to the axis and not containing the vertex.
2. **Ellipse** An *ellipse* is any planar section that is not parallel to a generator, cuts only one nappe, and does not contain the vertex.
3. **Parabola** A *parabola* is any planar section parallel to a generator and not containing the vertex.
4. **Hyperbola** A *hyperbola* is any planar section that cuts both nappes and does not contain the vertex.
5. **Degenerate cases** Three degenerate cases occur when a planar section includes the vertex or the axis. These degenerate cases are a point, a pair of intersecting lines, or one line.

Another degenerate case occurs when the second-degree equation

$$Ax^2 + Bxy + Cy^2 = K$$

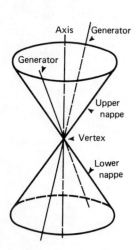

Axis   Generator

Generator

Upper nappe

Vertex

Lower nappe

FIGURE 4-5

for $A, B, C, K \in \mathbb{R}$, $K > 0$, is of the form

$$Ax^2 + Bxy + Cy^2 = (px + qy)^2 = K$$

This reduces to the equations of two parallel straight lines,

$$px + qy = \sqrt{K} \quad \text{and} \quad px + qy = -\sqrt{K}$$

However, this is *not* a degenerate conic section. Figures 4-6, 4-7, and 4-8 show the circle, ellipse, parabola, and hyperbola as conic sections.

As will be shown later, any given quadratic equation represents only one of these curves, translated and rotated in space. The Bxy term generally arises from an axis rotation, and the terms Dx and Ey and part of the constant F result from a translation. However, axis rotation is beyond the scope of the present discussion, so we consider the general equation only for the case $B = 0$. The rotational equations are presented in Appendix A, along with some examples illustrating how rotation affects the variables of the quadratic equation.

In analyzing the general second-degree equation, we will use the definitions of the conic sections to derive the equation form for each. We will also present some techniques that aid in graphing.

First, we will consider the curves in standard positions (this usually means centered at the origin); then the translation property will be used to develop the forms for the curves in other positions in the DR plane. Since the general second-degree equation cannot always be expressed in explicit form, the translation rule used in Section 3-2 must be altered slightly, as follows, to make it applicable to implicit relations.

DEFINITION Let F be an implicit relation, and let $h, k \in \mathbb{R}$. Then the **planar translation** of F by h units along the D axis and k units along the R axis is the relation $\hat{F}$ given by the rule

▶ $\hat{F}(x, y) = F[(x - h), (y - k)] = 0$

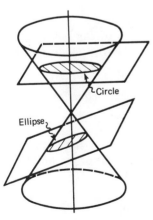

FIGURE 4-6

Circle

Ellipse

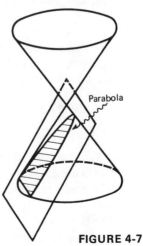

FIGURE 4-7

Parabola

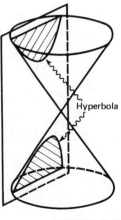

FIGURE 4-8

Hyperbola

The major difference in this definition is that now not only must all x terms be replaced by $x - h$, but also all y terms must be replaced by $y - k$. The method will be illustrated later.

The Circle

A circle is defined as a planar curve that has all its points at some fixed distance from a given point, called the *center* of the circle.

> **DEFINITION** Let $x_0, y_0, r \in \mathbb{R}$, $r > 0$. Then the **circle** with **center** (x_0, y_0) and **radius** r is the set of points (x, y) such that the distance from (x, y) to (x_0, y_0) is r.

A circle centered at the origin is shown in Figure 4-9. The equation of any circle of radius r centered at the origin will have the standard form

$$x^2 + y^2 = r^2$$

where x and y are the coordinates of any point on the circle.

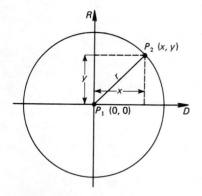

FIGURE 4-9

> **THEOREM 4-2** Let $x, y, r \in \mathbb{R}$, $r > 0$. Then the equation of the circle with radius r centered at the origin is given by
>
> ▶ $x^2 + y^2 = r^2$

PROOF Consider a circle of radius r centered at the origin, as shown in Figure 4-9. Let (x, y) be any point on the circle. From the distance equation and the definition of a circle,

$$r = \sqrt{(x - 0)^2 + (y - 0)^2}$$
$$= \sqrt{x^2 + y^2}$$

Squaring both sides yields

$$r^2 = x^2 + y^2$$

Since this equation describes the coordinates of any point whose distance from the origin is r, it is the equation of a circle of radius r centered at the origin. ∎

EXAMPLE 4-10 Describe the graph of the equation

$$x^2 + y^2 = 25$$

Comparing this to the standard form for the circle, we see that this is the equation of a circle centered at the origin with radius $r = 5$. The graph is shown in Figure 4-10.

EXAMPLE 4-11 Write the equation of the circle centered at $(2, 5)$ having a radius of 6.

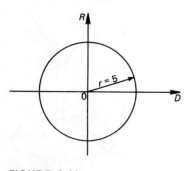

FIGURE 4-10

If centered at the origin, the circle would have the equation

$$x^2 + y^2 = 36$$

Written as an implicit relation F, this is

$$F(x, y) = x^2 + y^2 - 36 = 0$$

By the translation rule for implicit relations, the relation $\hat{F}$, which is the circle translated so that its center is $(2, 5)$, is given by the equation

$$\begin{aligned}\hat{F}(x, y) &= F[(x - 2), (y - 5)] = 0 \\ &= (x - 2)^2 + (y - 5)^2 - 36 = 0 \\ &= x^2 + y^2 - 4x - 10y - 7 = 0\end{aligned}$$

The circle with center $(2, 5)$ and radius 6 is graphed in Figure 4-11.

Some aspects of the last example are worth noting. First, the final equation has the general form of the second-degree equation with no rotation term (that is, with $B = 0$). Second, in the equations for both the standard and translated forms of the circle, the coefficients of x^2 and y^2 are equal. In fact, the graph of any general second-degree equation in which the coefficients of x^2 and y^2 (that is, A and C) are equal will be a circle, provided that $D^2 + E^2 > 4AF$. The following example illustrates why the latter condition is necessary.

EXAMPLE 4-12 Show that for the general quadratic equation

$$Ax^2 + Cy^2 + Dx + Ey + F = 0, \qquad \text{with } A = C > 0$$

the necessary condition for the equation to represent a circle is

$$D^2 + E^2 > 4AF,$$

Rearrangement of terms gives

$$Ax^2 + Dx + Cy^2 + Ey = -F$$

Completion of the squares on the left side gives

$$A\left(x^2 + \frac{D}{A}x + \frac{D^2}{4A^2}\right) + C\left(y^2 + \frac{E}{C}y + \frac{E^2}{4C^2}\right) = \frac{D^2}{4A} + \frac{E^2}{4C} - F$$

which simplifies to

$$A\left(x + \frac{D}{2A}\right)^2 + C\left(y + \frac{E}{2C}\right)^2 = \frac{CD^2 + AE^2 - 4ACF}{4AC}$$

This becomes, for $A = C$,

$$\left(x + \frac{D}{2A}\right)^2 + \left(y + \frac{E}{2C}\right)^2 = \frac{CD^2 + AE^2 - 4ACF}{4AC^2}$$

The left side represents the translation of the center from the origin, and the right side represents the square of the radius of the circle

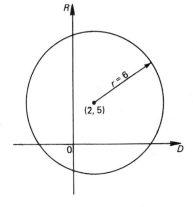

FIGURE 4-11

when $A = C$. Since the radius must be real, its square must be positive. Hence, for $A = C > 0$, $4AC^2 > 0$; therefore,

$$CD^2 + AE^2 - 4ACF > 0$$

which yields

$$CD^2 + AE^2 > 4ACF$$

for $A = C$, this becomes

$$D^2 + E^2 > 4AF$$

Note that if $D^2 + E^2 = 4AF$, the circle degenerates to a point; if $D^2 + E^2 < 4AF$, then no circle exists.

EXAMPLE 4-13 Describe the graph of the equation

$$4x^2 + 4y^2 - 16x + 24y - 48 = 0$$

Since the x^2 and y^2 coefficients are equal and $D^2 + E^2 > 4AF$, the curve is a circle. The terms $-16x$ and $24y$ indicate that the circle is not centered at the origin, because the standard equation derived in Theorem 4-2 does not contain terms of this type. To find the center and radius of this circle, we first divide all terms by 4, which yields

$$x^2 + y^2 - 4x + 6y - 12 = 0$$

After rearranging terms as follows

$$x^2 - 4x + y^2 + 6y = 12$$

we complete the square in the x and y terms:

$$x^2 - 4x + \underline{\quad} + y^2 + 6y + \underline{\quad} = 12 + \underline{\quad} + \underline{\quad}$$

or

$$(x^2 - 4x + 4) + (y^2 + 6y + 9) = 12 + 4 + 9$$

Note that in completing the squares, whatever is added on one side of the equation must also be added to the other side to keep the equation balanced. So we have

$$(x^2 - 4x + 4) + (y^2 + 6y + 9) = 25$$

or

$$(x - 2)^2 + (y + 3)^2 = 25$$

Clearly, this is the equation of the circle of radius 5 centered at the point $(2, -3)$, which is graphed in Figure 4-12.

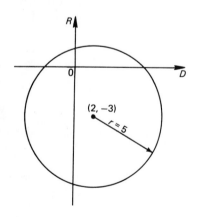

FIGURE 4-12

Graphing a circle is always simple. The procedure consists of determining the center and radius and then drawing the curve with a compass.

The Parabola

The circle is the simplest kind of nondegenerate quadratic curve, since it is defined entirely in terms of a given distance and a focal point, called the center. The next step in complexity is a curve defined in terms of its distance from a given focal point and a given line. A *parabola* is defined as a planar curve whose points are at the same distance from a given focal point as from a given line (called the *directrix*). Figure 4-13 shows a parabola; the particular curve shown is vertically oriented and concave upward.

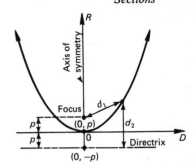

DEFINITION A **parabola** is the set of points equidistant from a fixed point and a fixed line.

FIGURE 4-13

In Figure 4-13, the focus is p units above the origin on the R axis, and the directrix is the line whose equation is $y = -p$, that is, the horizontal line p units below the D axis. For any point (x, y) on the curve, the definition requires that $d_1 = d_2$. The parabola shown has its *vertex*, or turning point, at the origin, and the R axis is the curve's axis of symmetry.

If a parabola has its vertex at the origin and is vertically oriented and concave upward, then its equation has the standard form

$$y = \frac{1}{4p} x^2 \quad \text{or} \quad 4py = x^2$$

THEOREM 4-3 Let $x, y, p \in \mathbb{R}$, $p > 0$. The equation of the parabola with focus at $(0, p)$ and directrix $y = -p$ is given by

▶ $$y = \frac{1}{4p} x^2 \quad \text{or} \quad 4py = x^2$$

PROOF The parabola is shown in Figure 4-14. By the definition of a parabola, the distances d_1 and d_2 must be equal. For any point (x, y) on the curve, $d_2 = y + p$. Using the distance formula, we can calculate d_1 as

$$d_1 = \sqrt{(x - 0)^2 + (y - p)^2}$$
$$= \sqrt{x^2 + (y - p)^2}$$

Since $d_1 = d_2$ for all x and y,

$$\sqrt{x^2 + (y - p)^2} = y + p$$

Squaring both sides yields

$$x^2 + (y - p)^2 = (y + p)^2$$

Simplifying, we obtain

$$x^2 + y^2 - 2py + p^2 = y^2 + 2py + p^2$$

which reduces to

$$x^2 = 4py \quad \text{or} \quad y = \frac{1}{4p} x^2$$

which is the required equation. ∎

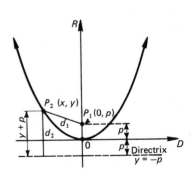

FIGURE 4-14

EXAMPLE 4-14 Describe the graph of

$$y = x^2$$

This equation is in the standard form for a parabola oriented as in Figure 4-13; that is, it is in the form $y = (1/4p)x^2$, where the coefficient of x^2 is 1. This yields

$$1 = \frac{1}{4p}$$

and therefore,

$$4p = 1 \quad \text{or} \quad p = \tfrac{1}{4}$$

So the graph of $y = x^2$ is a parabola whose focus is $(0, \tfrac{1}{4})$, whose directrix is the line $y = -\tfrac{1}{4}$, whose vertex is the origin, and whose axis of symmetry is the R axis. This parabola is graphed in Figure 4-15.

EXAMPLE 4-15 Find the equation of the parabola whose vertex is $(-2, -3)$ and whose focus is $(-2, -2)$.

From the information given, the distance from the focus to the curve is $p = 1$. If this curve had its vertex at the origin, its equation would be

$$y = \tfrac{1}{4}x^2 \quad \text{or} \quad F(x, y) = y - \tfrac{1}{4}x^2 = 0$$

Since the vertex is at the point $(-2, -3)$, we can use the definition of a planar translation to find the desired equation. The translated equation is

$$\hat{F}(x, y) = F[(x + 2), (y + 3)] = 0$$
$$= (y + 3) - \tfrac{1}{4}(x + 2)^2 = 0$$

Expanding, we obtain

$$(y + 3) - \tfrac{1}{4}(x^2 + 4x + 4) = 0$$

which can be simplified to

$$y + 3 - \frac{x^2}{4} - x - 1 = 0 \quad \text{or} \quad y = \tfrac{1}{4}x^2 + x - 2$$

This is the equation of the given parabola. We could also write this equation in the general second-degree form, as

$$\tfrac{1}{4}x^2 + x - y - 2 = 0 \quad \text{or} \quad x^2 + 4x - 4y - 8 = 0$$

The graph of this equation is shown in Figure 4-16.

Examples 4-14 and 4-15 suggest some general characteristics of the equations of parabolas. First, in the equation of a vertically oriented parabola, the variable x appears to the second degree, whereas y appears only to the first degree. Second, the equations could be written in explicit form. Third, as Example 4-15 suggests, any equation of the form

$$y = ax^2 + bx + c, \qquad a \neq 0$$

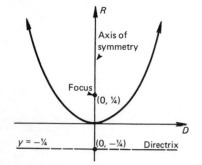

FIGURE 4-15

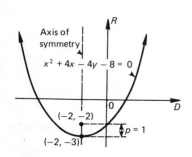

FIGURE 4-16

with b and c not both 0, is the equation of a vertically oriented parabola whose vertex is not at the origin.

EXAMPLE 4-16 Describe the graph of the equation

$$y = x^2 + 2x - 24$$

Write the equation in the form

$$y + 24 = x^2 + 2x$$

Completing the square on the right side of the equation yields

$$y + 24 + 1 = x^2 + 2x + 1 \quad \text{or} \quad y + 25 = (x + 1)^2$$

This is the equation of a vertically oriented parabola whose vertex is at the point $(-1, -25)$. The coefficient of the x^2 term is 1, so

$$1 = \frac{1}{4p} \qquad p = \tfrac{1}{4} = 0.25$$

where p is both the vertical distance from the vertex to the focus and the vertical distance from the vertex to the directrix. Since the vertex is at $(-1, -25)$, the focus is at $(-1, -24.75)$. The directrix, which is the horizontal line located p units below the vertex, has the equation

$$y = -25.25$$

The graph is shown in Figure 4-17.

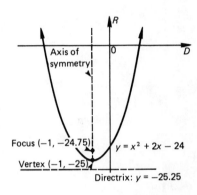

FIGURE 4-17

Figure 4-18 shows the four possible orientations of a parabola, along with standard equation forms both for parabolas with vertex at the origin

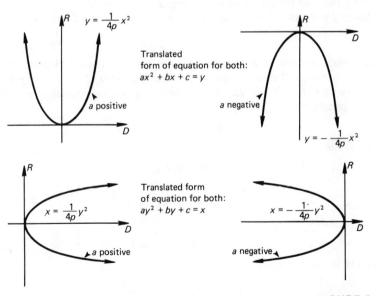

FIGURE 4-18

and for parabolas with vertex translated from the origin. (Note that in all four cases, the equation has no xy, or rotation, term.) The methods used in graphing and describing all parabolas are the same as those illustrated in the preceding examples, except that for the horizontal orientations the roles of x and y are interchanged.

Graphing Parabolas

We can simplify the graphing of a parabola by using the fact that in any of its orientations, a parabola has an axis of symmetry, which passes through the vertex. In order to identify the axis of symmetry, we must be able to find the coordinates of the vertex.

THEOREM 4-4 Let $x, y, a, b, c \in \mathbb{R}$. Then the vertically oriented parabola described by the equation

$$y = ax^2 + bx + c, \qquad a \neq 0$$

has its vertex at the point (x_v, y_v), where

$$\blacktriangleright \quad x_v = \frac{-b}{2a} \quad \text{and} \quad y_v = \frac{4ac - b^2}{4a}$$

PROOF We have already stated without proof that the second-degree equation of the form $y = ax^2 + bx + c$, $a \neq 0$, is the equation of a parabola, which is concave upward or downward depending on the sign of a. Figure 4-19 shows the two possible orientations. In either instance, the axis of symmetry is parallel to the R axis and passes through the vertex. The derivation of the formulas for the coordinates of the vertex is the same in both cases, so we show it only for the parabola that is concave upward.

Since the R axis intercept occurs when $x = 0$, its y coordinate is

$$y = c$$

The vertex, located at $x = x_v$, is also the point through which the axis of symmetry passes. Therefore, because of the symmetry of the curve, y should again be equal to c at $x = 2x_v$. So $x = 2x_v$ and $y = c$ must satisfy the equation of the parabola:

$$c = a(2x_v)^2 + b(2x_v) + c$$

This yields

$$a(2x_v)^2 + b(2x_v) = 0$$

or

$$4ax_v^2 + 2bx_v = 0$$

or

$$2x_v(2ax_v + b) = 0$$

Solving for x_v, we obtain

$$x_v = 0 \quad \text{and} \quad x_v = \frac{-b}{2a}$$

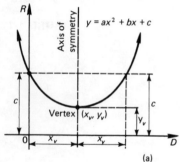

(a)

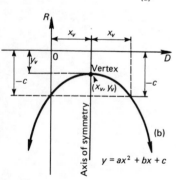

(b)

FIGURE 4-19

The solution $x_v = 0$ is not the general solution; it is the special case that arises when the parabola has its vertex on the R axis. Therefore, the general solution is

$$x_v = \frac{-b}{2a}$$

which also reduces to the special case when $b = 0$. When $x = x_v$, then $y = y_v$, so $x_v = -b/2a$ and $y = y_v$ must satisfy the equation of the parabola. This yields

$$y_v = a\left(\frac{-b}{2a}\right)^2 + b\left(\frac{-b}{2a}\right) + c$$

$$= \frac{ab^2}{4a^2} - \frac{b^2}{2a} + c$$

$$= \frac{b^2}{4a} - \frac{b^2}{2a} + c$$

$$= \frac{b^2 - 2b^2 + 4ac}{4a}$$

So,

$$y_v = \frac{4ac - b^2}{4a}$$

Therefore, we can give the coordinates of the vertex of the parabola whose equation is $y = ax^2 + bx + c$ ($a \neq 0$) in terms of a, b, and c. ∎

The reader can easily verify that the same equations result for a parabola that is concave downward and that when the parabola is horizontally oriented, the x and y variables interchange roles.

To sketch a parabola of the form $y = ax^2 + bx + c$, $a \neq 0$, we calculate the coordinates of the vertex from the equations just derived. The axis of symmetry is the vertical line passing through this point. If we plot two or three points on one side of this axis, then the symmetry of the curve automatically supplies the corresponding points on the other side of the axis. (A total of five to seven points is usually enough.) It is sometimes convenient to use the roots and intercepts in sketching the curve; however, these are not always the best choices, because there may be no real roots, and the R axis intercept may be the vertex itself.

If the parabola is horizontally oriented, then its equation has the form

$$x = ay^2 + by + c, \qquad a \neq 0$$

The coordinates of the vertex have the same form as for a vertically oriented parabola, except that the roles of x and y are interchanged:

$$y_v = \frac{-b}{2a} \quad \text{and} \quad x_v = \frac{4ac - b^2}{4a}$$

EXAMPLE 4-17   Sketch the graph of the equation

$$y = 2x^2 - 6x + 9$$

This is the equation of a vertically oriented parabola that is concave upward. The coordinates of the vertex are given by

$$x_v = \frac{-b}{2a} = \frac{6}{4} = \frac{3}{2}$$

$$y_v = \frac{4ac - b^2}{4a} = \frac{72 - 36}{8} = \frac{36}{8} = \frac{9}{2}$$

We choose two x values to the left of the axis of symmetry, such as $x = 0$ and $x = 1$. The y values calculated for these points are shown in Table 4-2, and the symmetry of the curve gives us the y values

TABLE 4-2

x	y
1	5
0	9
2	5
3	9

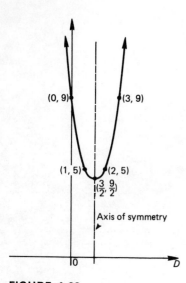

FIGURE 4-20

corresponding to $x = 2$ and $x = 3$. These points and the vertex are then used to sketch the curve, which is shown in Figure 4-20.

EXAMPLE 4-18 Sketch the graph of the equation

$$x = -3y^2 + 6y - 7$$

Since the equation contains a y^2 term with a negative coefficient, this is the equation of a horizontally oriented parabola that opens to the left. The coordinates of the vertex are

$$y_v = \frac{-b}{2a} = \frac{-6}{-6} = 1$$

$$x_v = \frac{4ac - b^2}{4a} = \frac{84 - 36}{-12} = \frac{48}{-12} = -4$$

Table 4-3 shows several y values (chosen to be symmetrical about the

TABLE 4-3

y	x
0	-7
-1	-16
2	-7
3	-16

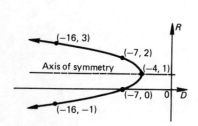

FIGURE 4-21

parabola's axis of symmetry) and the corresponding x values. Figure 4-21 shows a sketch of the curve.

The Ellipse

In defining the circle and the parabola, we used the concepts of the focus and of distances related to the focus. The next step in complexity is to define curves that have two focal points. The first such curve is the *ellipse*.

> **DEFINITION** Let $x, y \in \mathbb{R}$. An **ellipse** is the set of points (x, y) such that the sum of the distances between (x, y) and two fixed points, called the **foci**, is a positive constant.

Figure 4-22 shows an ellipse oriented in the horizontal direction and centered at the origin. As can be seen from the graph, an ellipse has two axes of symmetry. The *major axis* is the longer one (of length $2a$ in this case), and the *minor axis* is the shorter one (of length $2b$). The foci are located on the major axis, at a distance of c units from the center. An ellipse oriented as shown in Figure 4-22 will have the D axis as its major axis and the R axis as its minor axis, and its equation will have the standard form

$$\frac{x^2}{a^2} + \frac{y^2}{b^2} = 1$$

where $a^2 - b^2 = c^2$ and $a^2 > b^2$.

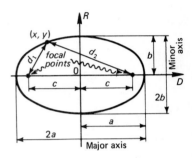

FIGURE 4-22

THEOREM 4-5 Let $x, y, a, b, c \in \mathbb{R}$, with $a^2 > b^2$. Then the equation of the ellipse centered at the origin with foci at $(c, 0)$ and $(-c, 0)$, major axis of length $2a$, and minor axis of length $2b$ is

$$\blacktriangleright \quad \frac{x^2}{a^2} + \frac{y^2}{b^2} = 1$$

if the ellipse is horizontally oriented.

PROOF Figure 4-23 shows the horizontally oriented ellipse centered at the origin, with major axis of length $2a$, minor axis of length $2b$, and foci located at $(c, 0)$ and $(-c, 0)$. By definition, for any point (x, y) on the curve, the sum of the distances d_1 and d_2 must be equal to a positive constant, K. The value of this constant can be found by considering a particular point on the curve, namely, $(a, 0)$. For this point, $d_1 = a - c$ and $d_2 = a + c$. The sum is

$$d_1 + d_2 = (a - c) + (a + c) = 2a$$

so

$$K = d_1 + d_2 = 2a$$

Using the distance formula, we obtain expressions for d_1 and d_2 in terms of an arbitrary point, (x, y), on the ellipse:

$$d_1 = \sqrt{(x - c)^2 + (y - 0)^2} = \sqrt{(x - c)^2 + y^2}$$

and

$$d_2 = \sqrt{[x - (-c)]^2 + (y - 0)^2} = \sqrt{(x + c)^2 + y^2}$$

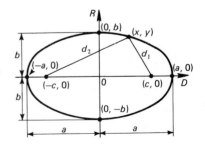

FIGURE 4-23

Hence,

$$\sqrt{(x - c)^2 + y^2} + \sqrt{(x + c)^2 + y^2} = K$$

or

$$\sqrt{(x - c)^2 + y^2} = K - \sqrt{(x + c)^2 + y^2}$$

Squaring both sides yields

$$(x - c)^2 + y^2 = K^2 + (x + c)^2 + y^2 - 2K\sqrt{(x + c)^2 + y^2}$$

Expanding, we have

$$x^2 - 2cx + c^2 + y^2 = K^2 + x^2 + 2xc + c^2 + y^2 - 2K\sqrt{(x + c)^2 + y^2}$$

Simplifying yields

$$\sqrt{(x + c)^2 + y^2} = \frac{4cx + K^2}{2K}$$

Squaring both sides again, we have

$$(x + c)^2 + y^2 = \left(\frac{4cx + K^2}{2K}\right)^2$$

or

$$x^2 + 2cx + c^2 + y^2 = \frac{16c^2x^2 + 8cK^2x + K^4}{4K^2}$$

Next, we clear fractions

$$4K^2x^2 + 8K^2cx + 4K^2c^2 + 4K^2y^2 = 16c^2x^2 + 8K^2cx + K^4$$

and combine like terms to obtain

$$(4K^2 - 16c^2)x^2 + 4K^2y^2 = K^4 - 4K^2c^2$$

Since $K = 2a$, this becomes

$$[4(2a)^2 - 16c^2]x^2 + 4(2a)^2y^2 = (2a)^4 - 4(2a)^2c^2$$

or

$$(16a^2 - 16c^2)x^2 + 16a^2y^2 = 16a^4 - 16a^2c^2$$

Dividing both sides by 16 and factoring the right side gives

$$(a^2 - c^2)x^2 + a^2y^2 = a^2(a^2 - c^2)$$

Dividing both sides by $a^2(a^2 - c^2)$ yields

$$\frac{x^2}{a^2} + \frac{y^2}{a^2 - c^2} = 1$$

To find what quantity $a^2 - c^2$ represents, let (x, y) be the point $(0, b)$, shown in Figure 4-23. For this point $d_1 = d_2$, since $(0, b)$ forms an isosceles triangle with $(c, 0)$ and $(-c, 0)$. So

$$d_1 + d_2 = 2d_1 = 2d_2 = K = 2a$$

and

$$d_1 = d_2 = a$$

Thus, a right triangle is formed with base c, height b, and hypotenuse a. By the Pythagorean Theorem,

$$c^2 + b^2 = a^2$$

so

$$a^2 - c^2 = b^2$$

and the equation of the horizontally oriented ellipse becomes

$$\frac{x^2}{a^2} + \frac{y^2}{b^2} = 1$$

where $c^2 = a^2 - b^2$ and $b^2 < a^2$. This is the equation that was to be derived. ∎

The student should show that a vertically oriented ellipse will have the equation

▶ $\dfrac{y^2}{a^2} + \dfrac{x^2}{b^2} = 1,$ where $a^2 > b^2, c^2 = a^2 - b^2$

Examples of Ellipses

EXAMPLE 4-19 Describe the graph of

$$x^2 + 9y^2 = 9$$

Divide each term by 9; the equation becomes

$$\frac{x^2}{9} + \frac{y^2}{1} = 1$$

Clearly, this is the standard form for the equation of a horizontally oriented ellipse, where

$$a^2 = 9, \qquad b^2 = 1$$

This yields

$$a = 3, \qquad b = 1$$

and

$$c^2 = a^2 - b^2 = 9 - 1 = 8$$
$$c = \sqrt{8} = 2\sqrt{2}$$

So the curve is an ellipse centered at the origin with major axis of length $2a = 6$, minor axis of length $2b = 2$, and foci located on the D axis, $2\sqrt{2}$ units from the origin. See Figure 4-24 for the graph.

EXAMPLE 4-20 Write the equation of the horizontally elongated ellipse with major axis of length 8, minor axis of length 4, and center at the point $(-4, 3)$.

Since the center is not at the origin, we use the translation rule. First, suppose the ellipse were centered at the origin. From the information given,

$$2a = 8, \qquad 2b = 4$$

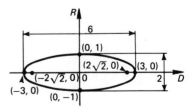

FIGURE 4-24

so $a = 4$ and $b = 2$. Then the ellipse centered at the origin would have the equation

$$\frac{x^2}{16} + \frac{y^2}{4} = 1$$

or, in implicit form,

$$F(x, y) = \frac{x^2}{16} + \frac{y^2}{4} - 1 = 0$$

By the translation rule, the equation for this ellipse translated to the new center, $(-4, 3)$, would be

$$\hat{F}(x, y) = \frac{(x + 4)^2}{16} + \frac{(y - 3)^2}{4} - 1 = 0$$

or

$$\frac{(x + 4)^2}{16} + \frac{(y - 3)^2}{4} = 1$$

By simplifying and rearranging terms, we can put this result in general second-degree form, as

$$x^2 + 4y^2 + 8x - 24y + 36 = 0$$

See Figure 4-25 for the graph.

As is suggested by Examples 4-19 and 4-20, in the general equation for an ellipse, the coefficients of x^2 and y^2 (that is, A and C) have the same sign but are not equal. The additional condition $CD^2 + AE^2 > 4ACF$ must also be met, as can be shown by the method of Example 4-12.

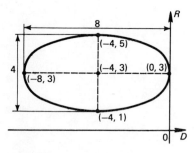

FIGURE 4-25

EXAMPLE 4-21 Describe the graph of the equation

$$4x^2 + 9y^2 - 32x + 18y + 37 = 0$$

Since the coefficients of x^2 and y^2 have the same sign but are not equal, the curve is an ellipse. As was the case with the equation of a circle, the presence of the terms $-32x$ and $18y$ indicates that the curve has been translated from the origin. Rewrite the equation as

$$4x^2 - 32x + 9y^2 + 18y = -37$$

and then as

$$4(x^2 - 8x) + 9(y^2 + 2y) = -37$$

Completing the squares on the left side of the equation gives

$$4(x^2 - 8x + 16) + 9(y^2 + 2y + 1) = 64 + 9 - 37$$

Care must be taken in completing squares when there are constants outside the parentheses. It would not be correct, in the above case, simply to add 16 and 1 to the right side. On the left, the term 16 is being multiplied by the 4 outside the parentheses, and the term 1 is being multiplied by 9. So we must add $16 \cdot 4 = 64$ and $9 \cdot 1 = 9$ to the right side, as indicated.

The equation becomes

$$4(x - 4)^2 + 9(y + 1)^2 = 36$$

Dividing each term by 36 yields

$$\frac{(x - 4)^2}{9} + \frac{(y + 1)^2}{4} = 1$$

Clearly, this is the equation of a horizontally oriented ellipse centered at $(4, -1)$, with major axis of length 6 and minor axis of length 4. See Figure 4-26 for the graph.

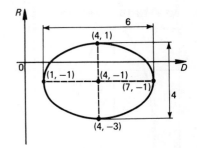

FIGURE 4-26

As was stated in Theorem 4-5, if the ellipse is vertically oriented (see Figure 4-27), then its standard equation is

$$\frac{y^2}{a^2} + \frac{x^2}{b^2} = 1$$

where, as before, $b^2 < a^2$ and $c^2 = a^2 - b^2$.

EXAMPLE 4-22 Sketch the graph of the equation

$$4x^2 + 9y^2 + 32x - 18y + 37 = 0$$

This equation can be put into the form

$$\frac{(x + 4)^2}{9} + \frac{(y - 1)^2}{4} = 1$$

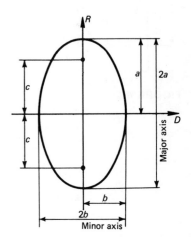

so its graph is an ellipse centered at $(-4, 1)$ with $a = 3$ and $b = 2$. Since the larger denominator appears in the x term, the ellipse is horizontally oriented with major axis of length $2a = 6$ and minor axis of length $2b = 4$. To sketch the ellipse, we proceed as follows. First, form a horizontally oriented rectangle $2a$ long by $2b$ high with its center at the center of the ellipse. Then sketch the ellipse so that it touches the rectangle at the points where the major and minor axes meet the rectangle. Figure 4-28 shows the completed sketch. If a more accurate sketch is required, some intermediate points can be calculated.

FIGURE 4-27

EXAMPLE 4-23 Sketch the graph of

$$9x^2 + y^2 + 36x + 4y + 31 = 0$$

This equation can be put into the form

$$\frac{(x + 2)^2}{1} + \frac{(y + 2)^2}{9} = 1$$

so it is the equation of a vertically oriented ellipse centered at

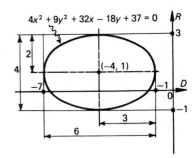

FIGURE 4-28

$9x^2 + y^2 + 36x + 4y + 31 = 0$

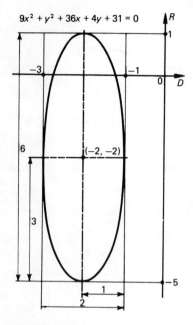

FIGURE 4-29

$(-2, -2)$ with major axis of length $2a = 6$ and minor axis of length $2b = 2$. The sketch of the graph is shown in Figure 4-29.

To graph an ellipse, we must know its center, the lengths of its major and minor axes, and its orientation.

As an interesting aside, note that if $a^2 = b^2$, then $c^2 = 0$. This means that both foci merge into the origin. Furthermore, $2a = 2b$, so the major and minor axes are equal. The standard equation becomes

$$\frac{x^2}{a^2} + \frac{y^2}{a^2} = 1 \quad \text{or} \quad x^2 + y^2 = a^2$$

This is precisely the standard form for the equation of the circle centered at the origin with radius a. The circle can then be considered an ellipse with major and minor axes of equal length and with its center at the single focal point.

The Hyperbola

If we substitute the words "absolute value of the difference" for the word "sum" in the definition of an ellipse, the definition of a *hyperbola* results.

> **DEFINITION** Let $x, y \in \mathbb{R}$. A **hyperbola** is the set of points (x, y) such that the absolute value of the difference of the distances between (x, y) and two fixed points, called the **foci**, is a positive constant.

The hyperbola is unusual in that it is a two-branched conic section and that it has asymptotes. Although we have encountered curves with asymptotes before, this is the first curve with asymptotes we will study in detail.

Figure 4-30 shows a horizontally oriented hyperbola centered at the origin. The distance between the vertices is the length of the *transverse axis*, $2a$. This distance is the difference $d_2 - d_1$ for the right branch of the

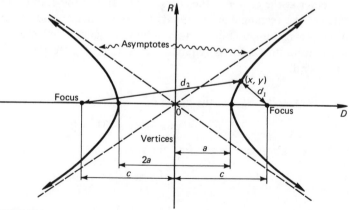

FIGURE 4-30

curve and $d_1 - d_2$ for the left branch of the curve. The value c is the distance from the origin to each of the two foci, which in this case are located on the D axis.

Any horizontally oriented hyperbola with center at the origin, foci at $(c, 0)$ and $(-c, 0)$, and vertices at $(a, 0)$ and $(-a, 0)$ has the equation

$$\frac{x^2}{a^2} - \frac{y^2}{b^2} = 1$$

where $c^2 = a^2 + b^2$. Furthermore, the asymptotes have the equations

$$y = \frac{b}{a}x \quad \text{and} \quad y = \frac{-b}{a}x$$

Thus, the asymptotes are straight lines passing through the origin with slopes of equal magnitude but opposite signs.

THEOREM 4-6 Let $x, y, a, b, c \in \mathbb{R}$, with $a \neq 0, b \neq 0$, and $c^2 = a^2 + b^2$. Then the equation of the hyperbola centered at the origin with foci at $(c, 0)$ and $(-c, 0)$ and vertices at $(a, 0)$ and $(-a, 0)$ is

$$\blacktriangleright \quad \frac{x^2}{a^2} - \frac{y^2}{b^2} = 1$$

if the hyperbola is horizontally oriented.

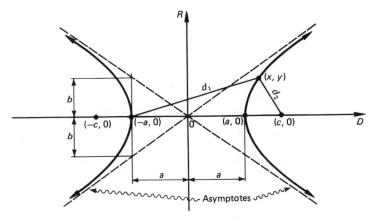

FIGURE 4-31

PROOF Figure 4-31 shows the horizontally oriented hyperbola centered at the origin with foci at $(-c, 0)$ and $(c, 0)$ and vertices at $(-a, 0)$ and $(a, 0)$. By definition, for any point (x, y) on the curve, the quantity $|d_1 - d_2|$ must be equal to a positive constant, K. The value of K can be calculated by considering a particular point on the curve, namely, $(a, 0)$. For this point, $d_1 = c + a$ and $d_2 = c - a$, so $|d_1 - d_2| = d_1 - d_2 = (c + a) - (c - a) = 2a$. (Note that this is the same value for K as in the case of the ellipse.) Using the distance formula, we obtain expressions for d_1 and d_2 in terms of an arbitrary point, (x, y), on the hyperbola:

$$d_1 = \sqrt{[x - (-c)]^2 + y^2} = \sqrt{(x + c)^2 + y^2}$$

and

$$d_2 = \sqrt{(x - c)^2 + y^2}$$

Hence,

$$d_1 - d_2 = \sqrt{(x + c)^2 + y^2} - \sqrt{(x - c)^2 + y^2} = 2a$$

or

$$\sqrt{(x + c)^2 + y^2} = 2a + \sqrt{(x - c)^2 + y^2}$$

Squaring both sides yields

$$(x + c)^2 + y^2 = 4a^2 + (x - c)^2 + y^2 + 4a\sqrt{(x - c)^2 + y^2}$$

Expanding, we have

$$x^2 + 2cx + c^2 + y^2 = 4a^2 + x^2 - 2cx + c^2 + y^2 + 4a\sqrt{(x - c)^2 + y^2}$$

which can be simplified to

$$\frac{4cx - 4a^2}{4a} = \sqrt{(x - c)^2 + y^2}$$

or

$$cx - a^2 = a\sqrt{(x - c)^2 + y^2}$$

Squaring both sides again yields

$$c^2x^2 - 2ca^2x + a^4 = a^2(x - c)^2 + a^2y^2$$

or

$$c^2x^2 - 2ca^2x + a^4 = a^2x^2 - 2ca^2x + c^2a^2 + a^2y^2$$

Collecting terms and simplifying, we obtain

$$(c^2 - a^2)x^2 - a^2y^2 = a^2(c^2 - a^2)$$

Dividing all terms by $a^2(c^2 - a^2)$ yields

$$\frac{x^2}{a^2} - \frac{y^2}{c^2 - a^2} = 1$$

If we define

$$c^2 - a^2 = b^2$$

then the equation becomes

$$\frac{x^2}{a^2} - \frac{y^2}{b^2} = 1$$

which is the equation that was to be defined. ∎

THEOREM 4-7 Let $x^2/a^2 - y^2/b^2 = 1$ be the equation of a horizontally oriented hyperbola in standard form. Then the equations of the asymptotes of this hyperbola are

$$\blacktriangleright \quad y = \pm\frac{b}{a}x$$

PROOF Rewrite the equation of the hyperbola as

$$y^2 = \frac{b^2 x^2}{a^2} - b^2 = \frac{b^2 x^2}{a^2}\left[1 - \frac{a^2}{x^2}\right]$$

As x becomes larger (either positively or negatively), the value of the expression within the bracket approaches 1. Thus, for very large x, the value of y^2 is approximated by

$$y^2 = \frac{b^2 x^2}{a^2}$$

Taking the square root of both sides yields

$$y = \pm \frac{bx}{a}$$

that is, $y = bx/a$ and $y = -bx/a$. These are the equations of two straight lines passing through the origin, one with slope b/a, the other with slope $-b/a$. Since the graph of $x^2/a^2 - y^2/b^2 = 1$ approaches these lines as x becomes large (positively or negatively), these lines are the asymptotes of the hyperbola. ∎

The derivation of the equation for a vertically oriented hyperbola is similar except that the equation becomes

$$\frac{y^2}{a^2} - \frac{x^2}{b^2} = 1, \quad \text{where} \quad a^2 + b^2 = c^2$$

and with asymptotes

▶ $$y = \frac{ax}{b} \quad \text{and} \quad y = \frac{-ax}{b}$$

Furthermore, by using the method of Example 4-12, it can be shown that a necessary condition for a hyperbola to exist is

$$CD^2 + AE^2 - 4ACF \neq 0$$

where A and C are of opposite sign.

Examples of Hyperbolas

EXAMPLE 4-24 Describe the graph of

$$\frac{x^2}{25} - \frac{y^2}{16} = 1$$

This is in the standard form for the equation of a hyperbola, where

$$a^2 = 25, \qquad b^2 = 16$$

That is, $a = 5$ and $b = 4$. Since

$$c^2 = a^2 + b^2$$

we have $c = \sqrt{41}$. Furthermore, the asymptotes have the equations

$$y = \frac{-4x}{5} \quad \text{and} \quad y = \frac{4x}{5}$$

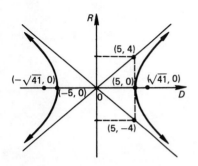

FIGURE 4-32

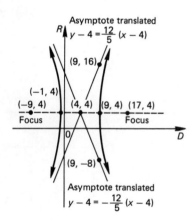

FIGURE 4-33

The curve is a horizontally oriented hyperbola with vertices located on the D axis, 5 units from the origin, and foci located on the D axis, $\sqrt{41}$ units from the origin. The graph is shown in Figure 4-32.

EXAMPLE 4-25 Write the equation of the horizontally oriented hyperbola centered at (4, 4), if the distance between its vertices, $2a$, is 10, and the distance between its foci, $2c$, is 26.

From the information given,

$$c = \tfrac{26}{2} = 13 \quad \text{and} \quad a = \tfrac{10}{2} = 5$$

Thus,

$$b^2 = c^2 - a^2 = 169 - 25 = 144$$

so $b = 12$. If this hyperbola were centered at the origin, its equation would be

$$\frac{x^2}{25} - \frac{y^2}{144} = 1$$

or

$$F(x, y) = \frac{x^2}{25} - \frac{y^2}{144} - 1 = 0$$

If we translate the graph of this equation to the center (4, 4), we obtain the equation

$$\hat{F}(x, y) = \frac{(x - 4)^2}{25} - \frac{(y - 4)^2}{144} - 1 = 0$$

or

$$\frac{(x - 4)^2}{25} - \frac{(y - 4)^2}{144} = 1$$

The graph is shown in Figure 4-33. The last equation can be expanded and rewritten in the general second-degree form as follows:

$$\frac{(x^2 - 8x + 16)}{25} - \frac{(y^2 - 8y + 16)}{144} = 1$$

or

$$144x^2 - 25y^2 - 1152x + 200y - 1696 = 0$$

The two preceding examples show that the equation of a horizontally oriented hyperbola cannot easily be written in explicit form. Moreover, in these examples the coefficients of x^2 and y^2 are opposite in sign; this is true for the equations of hyperbolas in all orientations except for one special case treated later in this section.

EXAMPLE 4-26 Describe the graph of

$$4x^2 - 3y^2 + 8x + 12y - 20 = 0$$

Since the coefficients of x^2 and y^2 are of opposite sign, the curve is a hyperbola. We rewrite the equation as

$$4x^2 + 8x - 3y^2 + 12y = 20$$

and collect similar terms:

$$4(x^2 + 2x) - 3(y^2 - 4y) = 20$$

Completion of the squares within the parentheses yields

$$4(x + 1)^2 - 3(y - 2)^2 = 12$$

Note that to obtain the value 12 on the right side of this equation, $4 \times 1 = 4$ and $(-3) \times 4 = -12$ were added to the value 20. These are the same values that were added to the left side to complete the squares.

Dividing each term by 12 yields

$$\frac{(x + 1)^2}{3} - \frac{(y - 2)^2}{4} = 1$$

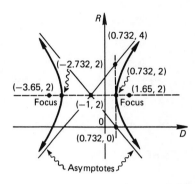

This is the equation of a horizontally oriented hyperbola whose center has been translated to $(-1, 2)$, where $a^2 = 3$, $b^2 = 4$, and $c^2 = 7$. So the vertices of the hyperbola are at a horizontal distance of $\sqrt{3}$ from $(-1, 2)$, and the foci are at a horizontal distance of $\sqrt{7}$ from $(-1, 2)$. See Figure 4-34 for the graph.

FIGURE 4-34

The equations of the asymptotes can be found by computing the asymptotes of the curve as if it were centered at the origin and then translating them so that their point of intersection is $(-1, 2)$. If the curve were centered at the origin, the asymptotes would have the equations

$$y = \frac{-2\sqrt{3}x}{3} \quad \text{and} \quad y = \frac{2\sqrt{3}x}{3}$$

Translating these to the center, $(-1, 2)$, we have

$$y - 2 = -\frac{2\sqrt{3}}{3}(x + 1) \quad \text{and} \quad y - 2 = \frac{2\sqrt{3}}{3}(x + 1)$$

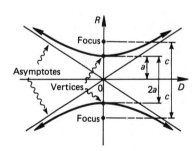

As mentioned earlier, the hyperbola can have a vertical orientation, as shown in Figure 4-35. The vertically oriented hyperbola centered at the origin with foci at $(0, c)$ and $(0, -c)$ and vertices at $(0, a)$ and $(0, -a)$ has the standard equation

FIGURE 4-35

$$\frac{y^2}{a^2} - \frac{x^2}{b^2} = 1$$

where $c^2 = b^2 + a^2$, and asymptotes $y = (a/b)x$ and $y = (-a/b)x$. The analysis and graphing of such equations are the same as shown in the preceding examples for the horizontal orientation.

In order to graph a hyperbola, its equation must be put into standard form. This form gives the slopes of the asymptotes, the orientation, and the location of the critical points.

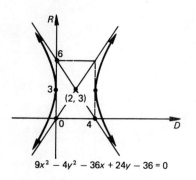

$$9x^2 - 4y^2 - 36x + 24y - 36 = 0$$

FIGURE 4-36

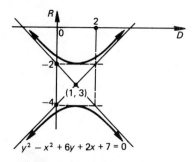

$$y^2 - x^2 + 6y + 2x + 7 = 0$$

FIGURE 4-37

EXAMPLE 4-27 Sketch the graph

$$9x^2 - 4y^2 - 36x + 24y - 36 = 0$$

In standard form after completion of the square, the equation becomes

$$\frac{(x - 2)^2}{4} - \frac{(y - 3)^2}{9} = 1$$

This is the equation of a horizontally oriented hyperbola centered at $(2, 3)$, with $a^2 = 4$ and $b^2 = 9$ (and thus, $a = 2$ and $b = 3$). To graph this hyperbola, the following steps are used:

1. Form a rectangle centered at the point $(2, 3)$ with height $2b = 6$ and width $2a = 4$.
2. Draw the asymptotes. They automatically will be the diagonals of the rectangle.
3. Sketch the curve using the asymptotes and the vertices, which are located on either side of the center, at a distance of a units from it.

Figure 4-36 shows the construction of the sketch.

EXAMPLE 4-28 Sketch the graph of

$$y^2 - x^2 + 6y + 2x + 7 = 0$$

In standard form, the equation becomes

$$\frac{(y + 3)^2}{1} - \frac{(x - 1)^2}{1} = 1$$

This is the equation of a vertically oriented hyperbola centered at $(1, -3)$, with $a = 1$ and $b = 1$. The construction of the sketch is shown in Figure 4-37.

Special Hyperbolas

Two special hyperbolas that frequently occur in problems, in either horizontal or vertical orientation, arise when $a^2 = b^2$ (that is, $a = b$). This condition results in the equations

$$\blacktriangleright \quad \frac{x^2}{a^2} - \frac{y^2}{a^2} = 1$$

and

$$c^2 = a^2 + a^2$$
$$= 2a^2$$

for the horizontally oriented case. (What is said of this case also carries over to the vertically oriented case.) The asymptotes, which have the equations

$$\blacktriangleright \quad y = -x \quad \text{and} \quad y = x$$

meet at right angles. This is called the *equilateral hyperbola*. The vertically oriented hyperbola that results from the same condition ($a = b$) is completely analogous to the horizontally oriented one. Figure 4-38 shows the horizontally oriented equilateral hyperbola.

A general discussion of rotation of axes appears in Appendix A; however, we can now consider the special case of the equilateral hyperbola rotated counterclockwise, as shown in Figure 4-39. The asymptotes of the rotated curve are the D and R axes, and the foci are now located on the line $y = x$. The equation of the hyperbola in this orientation is

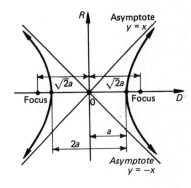

$$\blacktriangleright \quad xy = K, \quad \text{where} \quad K = \frac{a^2}{2}, \quad K \neq 0$$

Hyperbolas of this type are often called *rectangular hyperbolas*. Their graphs are quite simple. Since the axes are the asymptotes, only a few additional points need be calculated to sketch the curve.

FIGURE 4-38

EXAMPLE 4-29 Sketch the graph of

$$xy = 4$$

This is the equation of a rectangular hyperbola whose asymptotes are the D and R axes. We calculate a few additional points for values of x near 0. Table 4-5 gives the data used in drawing the sketch, which is shown in Figure 4-40.

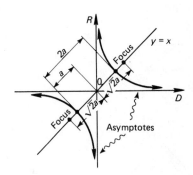

FIGURE 4-39

TABLE 4-5

x	y
1	4
2	2
4	1
−1	−4
−2	−2
−4	−1

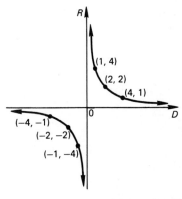

FIGURE 4-40

The equation of a translated rectangular hyperbola is

$$(x - h)(y - k) = K$$

where K is a constant and the point (h, k) is the new center of the curve. Functions of the form

$$\blacktriangleright \quad y = \frac{Ax + B}{Cx + D}$$

where A, B, C, and D are real constants and $x \neq -D/C$, can be rewritten in the form for a translated rectangular hyperbola.

EXAMPLE 4-30 Sketch the curve of the function

$$y = \frac{x - 4}{x + 2}$$

Rewrite this as

$$xy + 2y - x + 4 = 0$$

which becomes

$$y(x + 2) - x + 4 = 0$$

To get a second term of $x + 2$ from the last two terms on the left, add and subtract 2.

$$y(x + 2) - x - 2 + 6 = 0$$

This becomes

$$y(x + 2) - (x + 2) = -6$$

which can be rewritten as

$$(x + 2)(y - 1) = -6$$

This is the equation of the rectangular hyperbola

$$xy = -6$$

translated from the origin to the center $(-2, 1)$. The asymptotes are the two lines through the point $(-2, 1)$ parallel to the D and R axes.

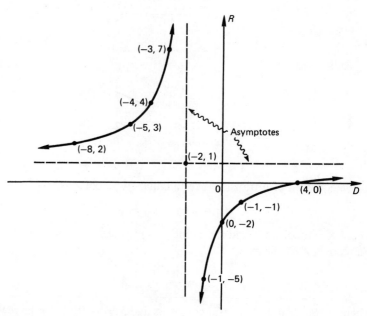

FIGURE 4-41

TABLE 4-6

4-2 *Conic* **177**
Sections

x	y
-1	-5
0	-2
1	-1
-3	7
-4	4
-5	3
4	0
-8	2

Table 4-6 shows some of the calculated points used in the sketch of the curve, and Figure 4-41 is the required sketch. Note that the data points chosen for the calculation are symmetrically located about the new center.

Summary

Below is a summary of the conditions that identify the type of curve represented by the general second-degree equation (assuming that the curve is not degenerate). For the equation

$$Ax^2 + Cy^2 + Dx + Ey + F = 0$$

A and C not both 0, the following is true:

(a) If $A = C$, then the curve is a circle.
(b) If A and C have the same sign but $A \neq C$, then the curve is a horizontally oriented ellipse if $A < C$, and a vertically oriented ellipse if $A > C$.
(c) If $A = 0, C \neq 0$, then the curve is a horizontally oriented parabola; if $C = 0, A \neq 0$, then the curve is a vertically oriented parabola.
(d) If A and C have opposite signs, then the curve is a hyperbola. The orientation cannot be easily determined until the squares are completed.

Except for rotations and degenerate cases, these are the *only* possibilities. Note that for the circle and the ellipse, there is the additional requirement that

$$CD^2 + AE^2 > 4ACF$$

and for the hyperbola

$$CD^2 + AE^2 - 4ACF \neq 0$$

EXERCISES 4-2

Set A

1. Describe the curves given by the following equations in as much detail as possible, with reference to foci, vertices, asymptotes, and centers. Graph all results.
   (a) $10x^2 + 10y^2 = 80$
   (b) $25x^2 + 9y^2 = 225$
   (c) $16x^2 - 4y^2 = 16$
   (d) $xy = 8$
   (e) $6y^2 - 4x^2 = 24$
   (f) $y = -4x^2$

2. Graph the following circles.
   (a) $x^2 + y^2 = 49$
   (b) $(x - 4)^2 + y^2 = 64$
   (c) $(x + 3)^2 + (y - 2)^2 = 25$

3. Graph the following parabolas.
   (a) $y = \frac{1}{8}x^2$
   (b) $y - 4 = (x + 1)^2$
   (c) $8(y + 2) = x^2$

4. Graph the following ellipses.
   (a) $\dfrac{x^2}{49} + \dfrac{(y - 1)^2}{4} = 1$
   (b) $\dfrac{(x + 1)^2}{16} + \dfrac{(y + 1)^2}{25} = 1$
   (c) $\dfrac{(x - 3)^2}{4} + y^2 = 1$

5. Graph the following hyperbolas.
   (a) $\dfrac{(y + 2)^2}{4} - x^2 = 1$
   (b) $\dfrac{x^2}{9} - \dfrac{(y + 1)^2}{16} = 1$
   (c) $\dfrac{(x - 4)^2}{25} - \dfrac{(y - 5)^2}{36} = 1$

Set B

The following curves have been translated from the origin. Completely describe the curves in terms of their foci, vertices, asymptotes, and centers.

6. $6x^2 + 6y^2 + 48x - 12y + 66 = 0$

7. $3x^2 + 3x - y - 10 = 0$

8. $x^2 - 4y^2 + 2x - 16y - 31 = 0$

9. $5x^2 + 3y^2 - 40x - 6y + 68 = 0$

10. Using the techniques of Section 4-1, approximate to two decimal places the real zeros of the following.
    (a) $4x^2 + 25y^2 = 25$
    (b) $8x^2 - y^2 = 32$
    (c) $(x - 6)^2 = 8(y + 1)$

11. Let a parabola exist with focal point at $(p, 0)$ and with directrix $x = -p$. Show that the equation of this parabola is $y^2 = 4px$.

Set C

12. Show that for the quadratic equation $Ax^2 + Cy^2 + Dx + Ey + F = 0$,

(a) if $CD^2 + AE^2 = 4ACF$, and A and C are of the same sign, then the conic degenerates to a point;

(b) if $CD^2 + AE^2 = 4ACF$, and A and C are of opposite signs, then the conic degenerates into two straight lines;

(c) if $CD^2 + AE^2 < 4ACF$, and A and C are of the same sign, then no conic exists.

13. Figure 4-42 shows the orbit of a satellite of the earth. The orbit is elliptical, and the center of the earth acts as one of the foci of this ellipse. Assume that the earth is a perfect sphere with diameter 8000 miles. The minimum altitude (perigee) of the satellite is 100 miles, and the maximum altitude (apogee) is 1200 miles. Write the equation of this orbit, assuming that the center of the earth is the origin of the coordinate system.

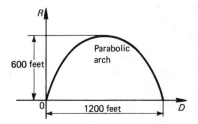

FIGURE 4-43

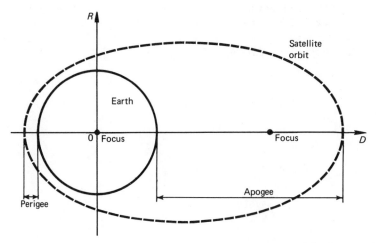

FIGURE 4-42

14. An architect wishes to design a parabolic arch that will be 600 feet tall and be 1200 feet wide at its base (see Figure 4-43). Using the ground as one reference axis and the bottom of the left leg as the origin, write the equation of this arch.

15. Consider the parabola

$$y = \frac{1}{4\sqrt{2}} x^2$$

whose graph is shown in Figure 4-44(a). By a combination of translation and rotation (see Appendix A), the graph of the parabola has been moved as shown in Figure 4-44(b). Note that the curve touches, but does not cross, the D and R axes at the points $(d, 0)$ and $(0, d)$, respectively. If the rotation angle is $-\pi/4$ radians and if the line from $(d, 0)$ to $(0, d)$ goes through the focus of the parabola, find

(a) the coordinates of the points $(d, 0)$ and $(0, d)$

(b) the point (h, k) to which the vertex has been translated

(c) the equation of the rotated and translated parabola.

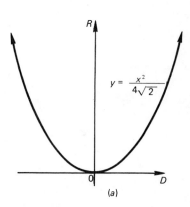

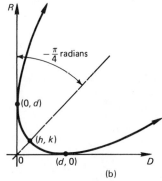

FIGURE 4-44

REVIEW EXERCISES FOR CHAPTER 4

1. Find the roots of the following equations:
   (a) $x^2 - 2x - 1 = 0$ (b) $x^2 + x - 1 = 0$
   (c) $x^2 + x + 1 = 0$ (d) $-x^2 + x + 3 = 0$
   (e) $3x^2 + 2x - 4 = 0$ (f) $8x^2 - 6x + 7 = 0$

2. Find the zeros of the following relations ($x \in \mathcal{D}, y \in \mathcal{R}$):
   (a) $x^2 - 9x - y - 10 = 0$ (b) $x^2 - 3y^2 = 4$
   (c) $5x^2 - 3xy + 6y + 25x + 30 = 0$ (d) $x^2 - 9y^2 + 3y - 7x = 0$

3. Graph the following conic sections:
   (a) $x^2 + (y + 1)^2 = 4$ (b) $4(x - 1)^2 + 9y^2 = 36$
   (c) $6(y + 4) = x^2$ (d) $x^2 - 4y^2 = 16$

4. Describe the following conic sections fully and sketch their graphs:
   (a) $2x^2 + 2y^2 - 8x + 6y - 7 = 0$ (b) $x^2 + 3y^2 - x - 6y - 12 = 0$
   (c) $y^2 + x^2 - 7x + 3y - 4 = 0$ (d) $y^2 - 2x^2 + 4x - 3y - 8 = 0$
   (e) $6x^2 - 2y^2 + 3x - 4y - 10 = 0$

Circular (Trigonometric) Functions

5-1 TRIGONOMETRIC ANGLES

Introduction

The relations and functions discussed in Chapters 2 and 3 were expressed in algebraic form. That is, their equations were made up of expressions such as x^2, $4x^3$, and $1/x^2$.

> **DEFINITION** The relation ρ is an **algebraic relation** if its rule of correspondence can be described in terms of real numbers and variables combined by the operations of addition, subtraction, multiplication, division, and raising variables to a rational power a finite number of times.

However, many relations cannot be expressed in this way. These relations are said to be *nonalgebraic* or *transcendental*.

> **DEFINITION** A **transcendental relation** is one that is not algebraic.

The first transcendental relations we will discuss are the circular, or trigonometric, functions. In solving problems involving these functions (or any other transcendental functions), we find that the real number laws, which are so important in working with algebraic functions, are of little use. The major source of numerical data will be trigonometric tables, which

181

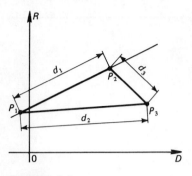

FIGURE 5-1

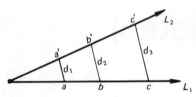

FIGURE 5-2

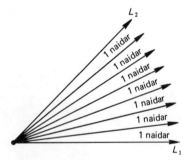

FIGURE 5-3

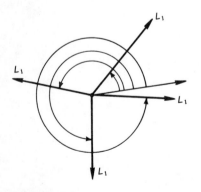

FIGURE 5-4

have been developed with the techniques of the calculus. The functional concepts developed in Chapter 2 are still valid but are more difficult to visualize. For this reason, we make more use of graphical techniques to illustrate the properties of the transcendental functions.

The Concept of Angle

Consider two points, P_1 and P_2, in the DR plane, as shown in Figure 5-1. What relationships exist between the two points? There are a variety of ways in which the points can be described in relation to each other. For example, we could write the equation of the line that passes through both points or calculate the distance between them.

Now suppose a third point is added. Then the three points form a triangle, which is uniquely determined (except for its position in the DR plane) by the lengths of its sides. This concept of distance is one of the basic quantities used to define mathematical systems. To most people, distance means length as measured with a ruler. This type of distance is said to be *invariant*; that is, the actual physical distance never changes, although it may have different values in different systems (for example, a distance of 10 inches is the same as 25.4 centimeters or 254 millimeters).

But this is the only kind of distance that can be considered. Figure 5-2 shows two half lines (rays), L_1 and L_2, which have the same endpoint, called the vertex. This configuration is called an *angle*. How may the separation between rays L_1 and L_2 be characterized so that it is invariant? Here, the usual concept of distance fails. For even if we start at a point on L_1 and measure the shortest distance to a point on L_2 (see Figure 5-2), the distance obtained will vary depending on the particular starting point chosen. So this type of distance is not invariant, and another way of measuring an angle must be considered.

The two rays, L_1 and L_2, form a wedge. Suppose the region between L_1 and L_2 is divided into smaller elemental wedges, as shown in Figure 5-3. Let us call each of these small wedges an angle of 1 "naidar"; then no matter where the measurement is taken, the angle always measures 7 "naidars." This is the concept of angle measure. The size of the elemental wedge does not matter, because once this size is fixed, all angle values can be expressed as some multiple or fractional part of it.

Figure 5-4 shows a sequence of angles being generated. The fixed reference line (or *initial side*) has been arbitrarily chosen as the horizontal ray to the right. The generating line (or *terminal line*) is considered to be hinged at the vertex and is rotated counterclockwise to generate an angle. Clearly, once the hinged line has rotated through a complete circular revolution, any further rotations will end with the terminal line in a position that it has previously occupied. Thus, we will first consider the angle values that are generated by rotations through no more than one complete revolution. Study of the angles contained within the circle will help to establish the circular functions, which are the basis of the branch of mathematics called trigonometry.

Angle Measure: Radians

Figure 5-5 shows one way of arriving at the most natural angle measure. Consider the analogy of an automobile positioned on a circular race track of radius 1 kilometer, at a point that has been marked by a flag numbered 0. The car's mileage meter is set to 0, and the car is driven counterclockwise along the circular track. Whenever the meter reads an integer value (in kilometers), the driver stops and places a flag labeled with the same integer on the track. Since a circle of radius 1 kilometer has a circumference of $2\pi \approx 6.28$ kilometers, the driver sets up six flags, after which the car requires approximately 0.28 additional kilometers to return to the initial starting position. Thus, the circle has been divided into 2π (approximately 6.28) sectors, each cutting off an arc of length equal to the radius of the circle.

Now consider any circle of radius r, as shown in Figure 5-6. Since this circle has a circumference of $2\pi r \approx 6.28r$, the circumference can be divided into 2π arcs of length r. The central angle that cuts off an arc of length r is said to have measure 1 *radian*.

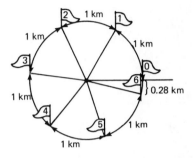

FIGURE 5-5

> **DEFINITION** One **radian** is the measure of the central angle formed by a sector of a circle that cuts off an arc of length equal to the radius of that circle.

Hence, any circle contains a total of 2π radians; similarly, a straight angle, which cuts off a semicircle, has measure $2\pi/2 = \pi$ radians.

It can be shown that the radian measure of an angle is independent of the length of the circle's radius. Exercise 11 at the end of this section indicates how to prove this.

Figure 5-7 shows a central angle of θ (radians) cutting off an arc of length s. The central angle, θ (in radians), must be in the same ratio to the total angle in a circle, 2π radians, as its subtended arc length, s, is to the total circumference, $2\pi r$. Hence,

$$\frac{\theta}{2\pi} = \frac{s}{2\pi r}$$

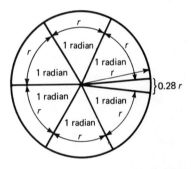

FIGURE 5-6

Solving for s yields

$$s = r\theta$$

and we make the following definition:

> **DEFINITION** The **circular arc length**, s, of any sector whose central angle is θ radians and whose radius is r is given by the equation
>
> ▶ $s = r\theta$

EXAMPLE 5-1 What is the distance traveled by a particle along a circle of radius 3 centimeters if the particle moves through an angle of 6 radians?

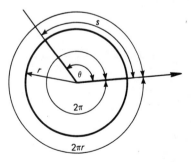

FIGURE 5-7

We have

$$s = r\theta$$
$$= 3(6)$$
$$= 18$$

So the distance traveled is 18 centimeters.

EXAMPLE 5-2 A bicycle wheel having a radius of 14 inches rolls along the ground making 7 complete revolutions. How far has a particular point on the circumference of the wheel traveled?

One revolution is 2π radians. Therefore, after 7 complete revolutions, the wheel will have rotated through an angle of $7(2\pi)$ radians or, to two decimal places, 43.96 radians. The distance traveled in inches will be

$$s = r\theta$$
$$= 14(43.96)$$
$$= 613.44$$

which is the same as 51.12 feet.

If the equation for arc length is rewritten to solve for θ, then

$$\blacktriangleright \quad \theta = \frac{s}{r}, \quad r \neq 0$$

Since the radian value of θ is the ratio of two real-valued lengths, the radian value is a dimensionless real number. The following examples illustrate this property.

EXAMPLE 5-3 Find the radian measure of an angle formed by an arc of length 6.3 inches in a circle of radius 3 inches.

The radian measure of the angle is

$$\theta = \frac{s}{r} = \frac{6.3}{3} = 2.1$$

EXAMPLE 5-4 Find the radian measure of an angle formed by an arc of length 3 feet in a circle of radius 18 inches.

The angle in radians is

$$\theta = \frac{3 \text{ feet}}{18 \text{ inches}} = \frac{36 \text{ inches}}{18 \text{ inches}} = 2$$

Angle Measure: Degrees

An alternative system of measuring angles is by the use of the familiar units: degrees, minutes, and seconds. In this system, one complete circular revolution is partitioned into 360 equal units, called *degrees*. Each degree is subdivided into 60 equal units, called *minutes*, and each minute is further subdivided into 60 equal units, called *seconds*. The degree system was artificially created by the early Babylonian astronomers for use in locating celestial bodies, and the subdivisions into minutes and seconds resulted from the use of geared clockwork mechanisms to subdivide the degree.

Angles of 1 degree, 1 minute, and 1 second are usually denoted by 1°, 1′, and 1″, respectively. Thus,

$$1° = 60′ \quad \text{and} \quad 1′ = 60″$$

and the angle

$$28°15′22″$$

is read "28 degrees, 15 minutes, and 22 seconds." Since this is a rather contrived system, there is no simple way to relate the degree measure of an angle to the length of the arc it cuts off in a circle or to the length of the circle's radius. However, the degree measure of an angle can be converted to radian measure. This is done by putting the angle measure in decimal form and then using a conversion formula to obtain the radian value.

EXAMPLE 5-5 Express the angle 31°15′24″ in decimal form.
First, since 1′ = 60″, we have

$$24″ = \frac{24′}{60} = 0.4′$$

so 15′24″ = 15.4′. Now, since 1° = 60′, we have

$$15.4′ = \frac{15.4°}{60} = 0.25666\cdots°$$

$$= 0.25\overline{6}°$$

Finally,

$$31°15′24″ = 31.25\overline{6}°$$

An angle expressed in radian measure is always distinguishable from one in degree measure by the absence of the degree system symbology. Since the radian measure is a dimensionless quantity, an angle measure expressed as $\theta = 2$ is taken to mean 2 radians, whereas $\theta = 30°$ is taken to mean an angle measure of 30 degrees by virtue of the presence of the degree symbol. Thus, to write $\theta = 3$ radians is superfluous, since any angle measured in radians is always expressed by a real number. It is enough to write $\theta = 3$.

Angle Measure Conversions

Both the degree measure and the radian measure of an angle are useful, but the radian measure has the advantage of being a dimensionless real value. Since the domain elements of some transcendental functions are angle measures, the use of radian measure will place the domain of these transcendental functions within the set of real numbers $\mathbb{R}$.

There is a simple conversion formula that gives the relationship between angle measures in radians and in degrees. For a full circle,

$$360 \text{ degrees} = 2\pi \text{ radians}$$

or

$$180 \text{ degrees} = \pi \text{ radians}$$

Therefore,

$$1 \text{ degree} = \frac{\pi}{180} \text{ radians} \quad \text{or} \quad 1 \text{ radian} = \frac{180}{\pi} \text{ degrees}$$

A convenient way to remember this relationship is to form a proportion involving radians and degrees as follows:

$$\blacktriangleright \quad \frac{\theta_r}{\pi} = \frac{\theta_d}{180}$$

where θ_r and θ_d are, respectively, the decimal measures of the angle in radians and degrees. Table 5-1 gives the measurements of some common angles in the two systems.

TABLE 5-1

Angle	
Radian	Degree
0	0°
$\pi/6$	30°
$\pi/4$	45°
$\pi/3$	60°
$\pi/2$	90°
π	180°
$3\pi/2$	270°
2π	360°

For convenience we can approximate 1 radian as 57.3° and 1° as 0.01745 radians. For a more precise conversion formula, we can evaluate the constants $\pi/180$ and $180/\pi$ using the value of π to twelve decimal places, which is

$$\pi = 3.141592653590$$

This value for π yields the conversion equations

$$\theta_d = 57.29577951308 \, \theta_r \quad \text{and} \quad \theta_r = 0.0174532925199 \, \theta_d$$

Although these equations are carried to 13 significant digits, the student can terminate the coefficients at whatever accuracy is appropriate to the problem at hand.

EXAMPLE 5-6 Convert 327.2° into radians.

$$\theta_r = \frac{\pi}{180}\, \theta_d$$

$$= (0.01745)(327.2)$$
$$= 5.7107$$

EXAMPLE 5-7 Convert the angle −27.4 into degrees.

$$\theta_d = \frac{180}{\pi}\, \theta_r$$

$$= (57.3)(-27.4)$$
$$= -1570° \text{ (to three significant digits)}$$

Circular Motion

The uniform motion of a particle along the circumference of a circle is related to the time the particle travels. The total distance divided by the total time is the average velocity of a particle. In terms of the arc length, we know that

$$s = r\theta$$

If both sides of this equation are divided by time, given by the variable t, then

$$\frac{s}{t} = \frac{r\theta}{t} \quad \text{or} \quad \frac{s}{t} = \left(\frac{\theta}{t}\right)r$$

The value expressed by the ratio s/t is distance divided by time, or velocity, symbolized by v. The quantity θ/t is the ratio between the angle (in radians) and time. This ratio is called the *angular velocity* of the particle and is symbolized by ω. In brief,

$$\blacktriangleright \quad v = \frac{s}{t}, \qquad \omega = \frac{\theta}{t}$$

Therefore, the equation $s/t = (\theta/t)r$ can be rewritten as

$$\blacktriangleright \quad v = \omega r$$

EXAMPLE 5-8 A wheel is spinning at the rate of 4 radians per second. If a particle at the edge of the wheel is moving at 32 centimeters per second, what is the radius of the wheel?

In this case, we know that

$$v = 32, \qquad \omega = 4$$

and that

$$v = \omega r$$

Therefore,

$$r = \frac{v}{\omega}$$
$$= \frac{32}{4}$$
$$= 8 \text{ centimeters}$$

EXAMPLE 5-9   An electric motor is rotating at a speed of 1800 revolutions per minute. A disc attached to this motor has a radius of 4 inches. How fast is a particle at the edge of the disc moving?

In this case, $r = 4$. The value of ω cannot be directly expressed, since ω must be measured in angular radians per unit of time. Therefore, it is necessary to convert revolutions to radians. Since each revolution contains an angle of 2π radians, 1800 revolutions $= 3600\pi$. Hence, $\omega = 3600\pi$ radians per minute. Substituting these values in the equation for v, we obtain

$$v = \omega r$$
$$= (3600\pi)(4)$$
$$= 14400\pi \text{ inches per minute}$$

This is an exact answer, because the value of π has not been approximated.

In many of these problems, a change to an approximate value might be useful. If the answer is to be expressed in seconds rather than minutes, then a division by 60 second/minute is required. Therefore,

$$v = 14400\pi \text{ inches per minute}$$
$$= 240\pi \text{ inches per second}$$
$$= 20\pi \text{ feet per second}$$

Naturally, this process can go on indefinitely, depending on the desired units. The velocity in feet per second for this problem is approximately

$$v = 20(3.14)$$
$$= 62.8 \text{ feet per second}$$

EXERCISES 5-1

Set A

1. Convert, to two decimal places, the following angles from radians to decimal degrees or from decimal degrees to radians:
   (a) 2.43   (b) 0.72
   (c) 9.61   (d) 1.1
   (e) 3.44   (f) 4.43
   (g) 27°   (h) 176°
   (i) 32.6°   (j) 472.7°

2. Using the equations $1' = 60''$ and $1° = 60'$, convert the following angles to radians (to two decimal places):

(a) 50°20'   (b) 68°44'
(c) 983°27'40"   (d) 146°36'15"
(e) 527°15'15"   (f) 250°52'30"
(g) 372°30'45"   (h) 16°12'48"

3. For the data given, calculate the missing angle, radius, or arc length to three decimal places.
    (a) $s = 4$ inches, $\theta = 2.6$
    (b) $r = 2$ inches, $\theta = 1.14$
    (c) $s = 6$ feet, $r = 44$ inches
    (d) $r = 19.2$ inches, $\theta = 3.4$
    (e) $s = 28$ inches, $r = 0.5$ feet
    (f) $s = 29$ centimeters, $\theta = 4.3$

4. For the data given, calculate the missing velocity, angular velocity, or radius to three decimal places.
    (a) $v = 6$ feet/second, $r = 2$ feet
    (b) $\omega = 2$ radians/minute, $r = 3$ centimeters
    (c) $v = 100$ inches/minute, $\omega = 4$ radians/second
    (d) $v = 44$ feet/second, $\omega = 10$ revolutions/minute
    (e) $v = 36$ feet/minute, $r = 18$ inches
    (f) $\omega = 60°$/second, $r = 15$ centimeters

● 5. Convert the following angle measures to decimal degrees or radians to the same number of significant digits.
    (a) 4.38172   (b) 127.8143°
    (c) 0.00273°   (d) 0.000143
    (e) 427.6113°   (f) 8.77231
    (g) 6.11485°   (h) 39.0047°
    (i) 15.9644   (j) 893.455°

Set B

6. Suppose you wish to measure your speed as you ride on a merry-go-round. You estimate that it takes 12 seconds for the ride to make one complete turn. Find your linear velocity if you are sitting 20 feet from the center of the ride. Give the velocity in feet per minute.

7. Using commonly known facts about the moon, determine the speed at which the moon travels around the earth. Assume a circular orbit. (*Hint:* Use the average distance to the moon and time needed for one revolution.)

8. A person wishes to travel 8 miles in 40 minutes on a bicycle that has wheels of diameter 2 feet. If the pedal-to-wheel speed ratio is 1 to 4, how fast should the person pedal (in pedal rotations per minute)?

Set C

9. Suppose a planet rotates about its sun in a circular orbit of radius 60 million miles. (In reality, planetary orbits are ellipses.) Assuming a constant velocity along the orbit, how many miles does the planet travel in one-fourth of its year? (A planetary year is one revolution around its orbit.) If in one "earth day" this planet sweeps out an angle of 0.0314

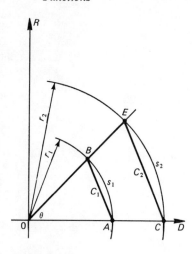

FIGURE 5-8

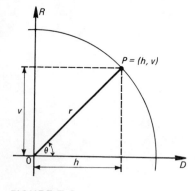

FIGURE 5-9

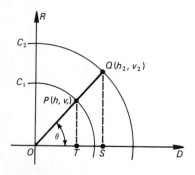

FIGURE 5-10

radians, how many "earth days" are there in one of the planet's years? Find the velocity of the planet in miles per second.

10. A biologist uses a small centrifuge to help separate out the heavier particles in a solution. The test tubes are placed at a distance of 10 inches from the center, and the centrifuge spins at 72,000 revolutions per minute.
(a) Find the angle swept out by a test tube, in one second, in radians and degrees.
(b) Find the velocity of a test tube in feet per second.
(c) If the centrifugal force is given by the equation

$$F = \frac{mv^2}{r}$$

where v is in feet per second and r is in feet, calculate the force exerted on the test tube if the total mass (test tube plus solution) is 0.004 pounds.

11. Use the arc length formula and the diagram in Figure 5-8 to show that the radian measure of an angle is independent of the radius of the circle; i.e., show that

$$\frac{s_2}{r_2} = \frac{s_1}{r_1} = \theta$$

5-2 CIRCULAR FUNCTIONS

Introduction

Consider the problem of describing the location of a point P on the circumference of a circle. Since the circle is a two-dimensional curve, any point on its circumference would be located by giving the horizontal distance, h, and the vertical distance, v, from the center of the circle. If the center of the circle is placed at the origin of the DR plane, as shown in Figure 5-9, the distances h and v become the coordinates of point P.

If $P = (h, v)$ is moved along the circumference of the circle, the values of h and v do not vary in the same manner. Furthermore, if r is the radius of the circle and θ the angle between the line that joins P to the origin and the D axis, then h and v must depend on both r and θ. Thus, we can write

$$h = F(r, \theta) \quad \text{and} \quad v = G(r, \theta)$$

where F and G are different relations. Moreover, since a circle has a central angle of measure 2π radians, it is sufficient to consider values of $\theta \in [0, 2\pi]$.

Now consider two concentric circles, C_1 and C_2, centered at the origin as shown in Figure 5-10. Let $\overline{OP} = r_1$, $\overline{OQ} = r_2$, $P = (h_1, v_1)$, and $Q = (h_2, v_2)$, where O, P, and Q are collinear. Then $\overline{OT} = h_1$, $\overline{OS} = h_2$, $\overline{TP} = v_1$, and $\overline{SQ} = v_2$. Triangles OPT and OQS are similar, so their corresponding sides must be proportional. Therefore,

$$\frac{\overline{SQ}}{\overline{TP}} = \frac{\overline{OQ}}{\overline{OP}}$$

which by substitution becomes

$$\frac{v_2}{v_1} = \frac{r_2}{r_1}$$

Since θ is the same for both triangles,

$$v_1 = G(r_1, \theta) \quad \text{and} \quad v_2 = G(r_2, \theta)$$

Substituting these expressions into the proportion yields

$$\frac{G(r_2, \theta)}{G(r_1, \theta)} = \frac{r_2}{r_1}$$

This shows that the ratio $G(r_2, \theta)/G(r_1, \theta)$ depends only on the ratio of the respective radii. Therefore, the portion of G that involves θ has canceled from the numerator and denominator of the ratio on the left. Then the portion of G that involves θ must be a factor of both numerator and denominator. Since the value of θ was unspecified, this must be true for any $\theta \in \mathbb{R}$. If we write the portion of G that involves θ as $g(\theta)$, then we have

$$G(r_1, \theta) = r_1 g(\theta)$$
$$G(r_2, \theta) = r_2 g(\theta)$$

and for any radius r,

$$G(r, \theta) = rg(\theta)$$

A similar argument shows that

$$F(r, \theta) = rf(\theta)$$

Finally, since $h = F(r, \theta)$ and $v = G(r, \theta)$, the original expressions for h and v become

$$h = rf(\theta) \quad \text{and} \quad v = rg(\theta)$$

Any fixed nonzero value of r, and any given value of θ, determine a unique point, $P = (h, v)$, on the circle. Hence, the ratios

$$\frac{h}{r} \quad \text{and} \quad \frac{v}{r}, \qquad r \neq 0$$

have unique values corresponding to each value of θ. This means that both $f(\theta) = h/r$ and $g(\theta) = v/r$ are functions, and we can write

$$f: \theta \to f(\theta)$$
$$g: \theta \to g(\theta)$$

where θ is the real argument of f and g. Furthermore, it is clear from the

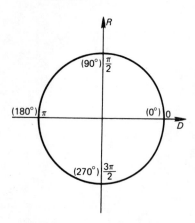

FIGURE 5-11

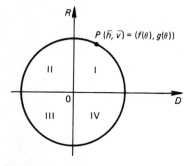

FIGURE 5-12

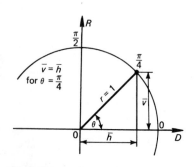

FIGURE 5-13

graph of the circle that the possible values of h and v fall in the regions

$$-r \leqslant h \leqslant r \quad \text{and} \quad -r \leqslant v \leqslant r$$

Hence

$$f: [0, 2\pi] \twoheadrightarrow [-1, 1] \quad \text{and} \quad g: [0, 2\pi] \twoheadrightarrow [-1, 1]$$

that is, both f and g map the set of real values in the interval $[0, 2\pi]$ *onto* the real interval $[-1, 1]$.

The Cosine and Sine Functions

To study the behavior of the functions f and g, we consider the *unit circle*, the circle for which $r = 1$. Let the coordinates of point P on the unit circle be $(\bar{h}, \bar{v})$. Then

$$\frac{h}{r} = \frac{\bar{h}}{1} = f(\theta) \quad \text{and} \quad \frac{v}{r} = \frac{\bar{v}}{1} = g(\theta)$$

Therefore, $\bar{h} = f(\theta)$ and $\bar{v} = g(\theta)$ for $0 \leqslant \theta \leqslant 2\pi$. We will evaluate these two functions for particular values of the argument θ, as shown in Figure 5-11.

For $\theta = 0$ (0°), the point on the circle is the intersection of the circle with the positive D axis. Hence, $\bar{h} = f(0) = +1$ and $\bar{v} = g(0) = 0$.

For $\theta = \pi/2$ (90°), the point on the circle is the intersection of the circle with the positive R axis. Hence, $\bar{h} = f(\pi/2) = 0$ and $\bar{v} = g(\pi/2) = +1$.

For $\theta = \pi$ (180°), the point on the circle is the intersection of the circle with the negative D axis. Hence, $\bar{h} = f(\pi) = -1$ and $\bar{v} = g(\pi) = 0$.

For $\theta = 3\pi/2$ (270°), the point on the circle is the intersection of the circle with the negative R axis. Hence, $\bar{h} = f(3\pi/2) = 0$ and $\bar{v} = g(3\pi/2) = -1$.

For $\theta = 2\pi$ (360°), the point is the same as for $\theta = 0$. Hence, $\bar{h} = f(2\pi) = 1$ and $\bar{v} = g(2\pi) = 0$.

The values $\theta = 0$, $\pi/2$, π, $3\pi/2$, and 2π are called *quadrantal angles*, because they divide the circle into four quadrants. (See Figure 5-12.) Any point in the first quadrant has both its components positive. Three special angles in the first quadrant are of importance because of their geometric properties; they are $\pi/4$, $\pi/6$, and $\pi/3$ (45°, 30°, and 60°, respectively). We now derive the components of the points on the unit circle corresponding to these angles.

For $\theta = \pi/4$ (45°), consider Figure 5-13. The components $(\bar{h}, \bar{v})$ are the magnitudes of the legs of an isosceles right triangle. In this case $\bar{h} = \bar{v}$, and by the Pythagorean Theorem,

$$\bar{h}^2 + \bar{h}^2 = 1$$
$$2\bar{h}^2 = 1$$
$$\bar{h}^2 = \tfrac{1}{2}$$

Thus, $\bar{h} = \pm 1/\sqrt{2} = \pm\sqrt{2}/2$. Since $\bar{h} \geqslant 0$ in the first quadrant, we choose $\bar{h} = +\sqrt{2}/2$ and $\bar{v} = \bar{h} = +\sqrt{2}/2$. Hence, $\bar{h} = f(\pi/4) = \sqrt{2}/2$ and $\bar{v} = g(\pi/4) = \sqrt{2}/2$.

For $\theta = \pi/6$ (30°), consider Figure 5-14. The triangle shown includes angle $\theta = \pi/6 = 30°$, a right angle, and, consequently, an angle of $\pi/3 = 60°$. In a 30°–60°–90° triangle, the length of the side opposite the 30° angle is one-half the length of the hypotenuse. Thus, $\bar{v} = \frac{1}{2}$, and by the Pythagorean Theorem,

$$\bar{h}^2 = 1 - \bar{v}^2 = 1 - (\tfrac{1}{2})^2 = 1 - \tfrac{1}{4} = \tfrac{3}{4}$$

so

$$\bar{h} = \pm\sqrt{\frac{3}{4}} = \pm\frac{\sqrt{3}}{2}$$

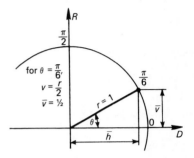

Since $\bar{h} \geqslant 0$ in the first quadrant, we choose $\bar{h} = +\sqrt{3}/2$. Hence, $\bar{h} = f(\pi/6) = \sqrt{3}/2$ and $\bar{v} = g(\pi/6) = \frac{1}{2}$.

For $\theta = \pi/3$ (60°), consider Figure 5-15. Here, another 30°–60°–90° triangle is formed, with $\bar{v} = \sqrt{3}/2$ and $\bar{h} = \frac{1}{2}$. Hence, $\bar{h} = f(\pi/3) = \frac{1}{2}$ and $\bar{v} = g(\pi/3) = \sqrt{3}/2$.

The symmetry of the circle allows us to obtain components for the points in the second, third, and fourth quadrants corresponding to the angles $\pi/4$, $\pi/6$, and $\pi/3$, as shown in Figure 5-16. Table 5-2 gives the corresponding angle values in each of the four quadrants. The components $(\bar{h}, \bar{v})$ in the second, third, and fourth quadrants are similar to those in the first quadrant; the magnitudes are identical, but the signs may

FIGURE 5-14

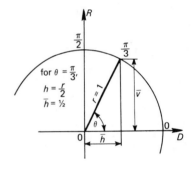

FIGURE 5-15

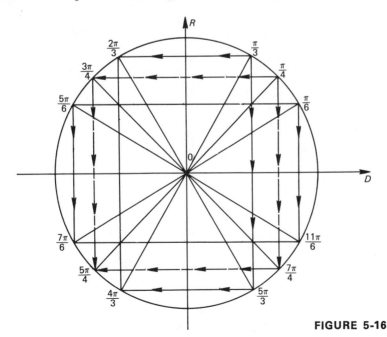

FIGURE 5-16

TABLE 5-2

	Quadrant		
I	II	III	IV
$\pi/4(45°)$	$3\pi/4(135°)$	$5\pi/4(225°)$	$7\pi/4(315°)$
$\pi/6(30°)$	$5\pi/6(150°)$	$7\pi/6(210°)$	$11\pi/6(330°)$
$\pi/3(60°)$	$2\pi/3(120°)$	$4\pi/3(240°)$	$5\pi/3(300°)$

be different. For example, if $(\bar{h}_2, \bar{v}_2)$ in the second quadrant is symmetrically opposite $(\bar{h}_1, \bar{v}_1)$ in the first quadrant, then $\bar{h}_2 = -\bar{h}_1$ and $\bar{v}_2 = \bar{v}_1$.

The usual names for the functions f and g are respectively cosine and sine, abbreviated cos and sin. Thus,

$$\bar{h} = f(\theta) = \cos\theta, \qquad \bar{v} = g(\theta) = \sin\theta$$

Table 5-3 lists the values of $\bar{h} = f(\theta) = \cos\theta$ and $\bar{v} = g(\theta) = \sin\theta$ for the special values of θ, $0 \leqslant \theta \leqslant 2\pi$.

TABLE 5-3

θ (radians)	$\cos\theta$ $\bar{h} = f(\theta)$	$\sin\theta$ $\bar{v} = g(\theta)$	θ (radians)	$\cos\theta$ $\bar{h} = f(\theta)$	$\sin\theta$ $\bar{v} = g(\theta)$
0	1	0	$\dfrac{7\pi}{6}$	$-\dfrac{\sqrt{3}}{2}$	$-\dfrac{1}{2}$
$\dfrac{\pi}{6}$	$\dfrac{\sqrt{3}}{2}$	$\dfrac{1}{2}$	$\dfrac{5\pi}{4}$	$-\dfrac{\sqrt{2}}{2}$	$-\dfrac{\sqrt{2}}{2}$
$\dfrac{\pi}{4}$	$\dfrac{\sqrt{2}}{2}$	$\dfrac{\sqrt{2}}{2}$	$\dfrac{4\pi}{3}$	$-\dfrac{1}{2}$	$-\dfrac{\sqrt{3}}{2}$
$\dfrac{\pi}{3}$	$\dfrac{1}{2}$	$\dfrac{\sqrt{3}}{2}$	$\dfrac{3\pi}{2}$	0	-1
$\dfrac{\pi}{2}$	0	1	$\dfrac{5\pi}{3}$	$\dfrac{1}{2}$	$-\dfrac{\sqrt{3}}{2}$
$\dfrac{2\pi}{3}$	$-\dfrac{1}{2}$	$\dfrac{\sqrt{3}}{2}$	$\dfrac{7\pi}{4}$	$\dfrac{\sqrt{2}}{2}$	$-\dfrac{\sqrt{2}}{2}$
$\dfrac{3\pi}{4}$	$-\dfrac{\sqrt{2}}{2}$	$\dfrac{\sqrt{2}}{2}$	$\dfrac{11\pi}{6}$	$\dfrac{\sqrt{3}}{2}$	$-\dfrac{1}{2}$
$\dfrac{5\pi}{6}$	$-\dfrac{\sqrt{3}}{2}$	$\dfrac{1}{2}$	2π	1	0
π	-1	0			

The angles we have investigated are sufficient to graph the sine and cosine functions. (Note that a value such as $\pi/4$ is a real number approxi-

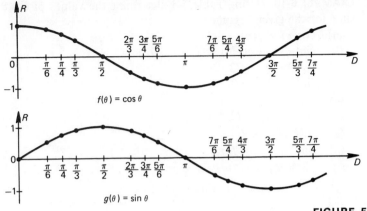

$f(\theta) = \cos \theta$

$g(\theta) = \sin \theta$

FIGURE 5-17

mately equal to $3.1416/4 = 0.7854$.) The graphs of the sine and cosine functions are shown in Figure 5-17.

Earlier, we saw that for any circle with radius r centered at the origin, $h/r = f(\theta)$ and $v/r = g(\theta)$. If we replace h and v by x and y, respectively, and f and g by cos and sin, respectively, then

$$\frac{x}{r} = \cos \theta \quad \text{and} \quad \frac{y}{r} = \sin \theta$$

or equivalently,

$$x = r \cos \theta \quad \text{and} \quad y = r \sin \theta$$

Hence, any point $P = (x, y)$ in the DR plane is represented by $P = (r \cos \theta, r \sin \theta)$. For the case $r = 1$, P has coordinates $(\cos \theta, \sin \theta)$ and is called a *circular point*. This leads to the following definition:

DEFINITION Let $P = (x, y)$ be a point on a circle of radius $r > 0$ centered at the origin, and let $\theta \in [0, 2\pi]$ be the angle between the positive D axis and the radius to P. Then the *cosine* function of θ, cos θ, is a mapping $\theta \rightarrow \cos \theta$ such that

$$\blacktriangleright \quad \cos \theta = \frac{x}{r}$$

and the *sine* function of θ, sin θ, is a mapping $\theta \rightarrow \sin \theta$ such that

$$\blacktriangleright \quad \sin \theta = \frac{y}{r}$$

In set notation, these mappings are

$$\blacktriangleright \quad \cos: [0, 2\pi] \twoheadrightarrow [-1, 1]$$

$$\blacktriangleright \quad \sin: [0, 2\pi] \twoheadrightarrow [-1, 1]$$

EXAMPLE 5-10 Using Table 5-3, determine the values of cos θ and sin θ for the given arguments.

(a) $\cos(\pi) = f(\pi) = -1$

(b) $\sin(\pi/2) = g(\pi/2) = 1$

(c) $\cos(3\pi/2) = f(3\pi/2) = 0$

(d) $\sin(3\pi/2) = g(3\pi/2) = -1$

(e) $\sin(\pi) = g(\pi) = 0$

(f) $\cos(2\pi/3) = f(2\pi/3) = -\frac{1}{2}$

(g) $\cos(7\pi/4) = f(7\pi/4) = \sqrt{2}/2$

(h) $\sin(7\pi/6) = g(7\pi/6) = -\frac{1}{2}$

(i) $\sin(3\pi/4) = g(3\pi/4) = \sqrt{2}/2$

(j) $\cos(11\pi/6) = f(11\pi/6) = \sqrt{3}/2$

Periodicity of the Sine and Cosine Functions

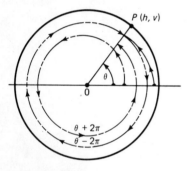

FIGURE 5-18

Until now, we have considered only angles such that $0 \leqslant \theta \leqslant 2\pi$. The angles were always measured counter-clockwise between the positive D axis and the terminal line. One full counter-clockwise revolution of the terminal line generates all θ values such that $0 \leqslant \theta \leqslant 2\pi$. However, θ can take on all real values. Clearly, if the terminal line is rotated counter-clockwise once beyond the positive D axis to some point $P = (r \cos \theta, r \sin \theta)$, then the total angle generated is 2π plus the angle, θ. (See Figure 5-18.) Thus, the coordinates of the point where the terminal line intersects the circle are exactly the same for θ and $\theta + 2\pi$. Hence, for any circle of radius r, we have

$$\cos(\theta + 2\pi) = \cos \theta \quad \text{and} \quad \sin(\theta + 2\pi) = \sin \theta$$

Since angles with positive measures are generated by counterclockwise rotation of the terminal line, clockwise rotation of the terminal line defines angles with negative measures. If the terminal line of an angle of measure θ meets the circle at a point P, then a clockwise rotation of 2π will bring the terminal line back to the same position. (See Figure 5-18.) The angle generated by this rotation has measure $\theta - 2\pi$. Hence, if the terminal line meets the circle of radius r at $P = (r \cos \theta, r \sin \theta)$, then

$$\cos(\theta - 2\pi) = \cos \theta \quad \text{and} \quad \sin(\theta - 2\pi) = \sin \theta$$

A rotation of the terminal line of any angle θ by a nonzero integer multiple of 2π will always return the terminal line to its original position. Hence,

▶ $\cos(\theta + 2n\pi) = \cos \theta \quad \text{and} \quad \sin(\theta + 2n\pi) = \sin \theta, \qquad n \in \mathbb{J}, n \neq 0$

Functions whose values repeat after a given interval in the domain are called *periodic functions*.

DEFINITION A function F is **periodic** with **fundamental period** p if there exists a smallest $p > 0$ such that

▶ $F(t + np) = F(t)$

for every t in the domain of F and every $n \in \mathbb{J}$.

Any portion of a periodic function obtained by restricting its domain to an interval of length equal to one fundamental period is called one *cycle* of the function. Figure 5-19 shows four cycles of the cosine and sine functions, which have a fundamental period of 2π.

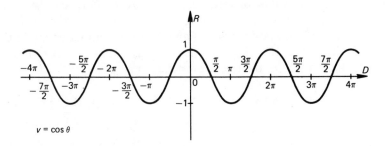

$v = \cos \theta$

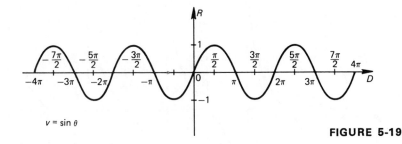

$v = \sin \theta$

FIGURE 5-19

EXAMPLE 5-11 Use the fact that the cosine function is periodic to evaluate $\cos(64\pi/3)$.

The argument $64\pi/3$ can be broken down as follows:

$$\frac{64\pi}{3} = 21\pi + \frac{\pi}{3} = 20\pi + \pi + \frac{\pi}{3} = \frac{4\pi}{3} + 20\pi = \frac{4\pi}{3} + 2(10)\pi$$

Therefore, by the periodicity of the cosine function,

$$\cos\frac{64\pi}{3} = \cos\left[\frac{4\pi}{3} + 2(10)\pi\right] = \cos\frac{4\pi}{3}$$

Hence, using Table 5-3, we obtain the value

$$\cos\frac{64\pi}{3} = -\frac{1}{2}$$

The Tangent Function

Another very important function is the *tangent* function.

> **DEFINITION**   Let $\theta \in \mathbb{R}$. Then the **tangent** of θ, tan θ, is defined by
> the equation

$$\blacktriangleright \quad \tan \theta = \frac{\sin \theta}{\cos \theta}, \quad \cos \theta \neq 0$$

The graph of the tangent function is shown in Figure 5-20. As can be seen,
the tangent function is periodic with period π and has infinite discontinuities at odd integer multiples of $\pi/2$ $(-\pi/2, \pi/2,$ etc.). The discontinuities are at the points for which cos $\theta = 0$. As cos θ approaches zero,
the tangent curve increases without bound in the positive direction if the
ratio $\sin(\theta)/\cos(\theta)$ has positive values and increases without bound in the
negative direction if the ratio $\sin(\theta)/\cos(\theta)$ has negative values. Hence,
the periodic relation for the tangent function is given by

$$\tan(\theta + n\pi) = \tan \theta, \quad \text{for } n \in \mathbb{J},\ \theta \neq (2n + 1)\frac{\pi}{2}$$

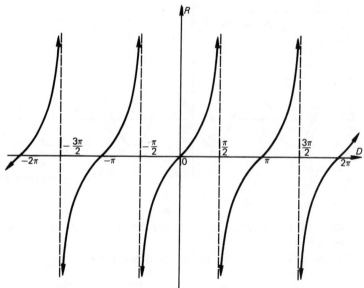

FIGURE 5-20

Other Related Functions

There are three other functional ratios that can be defined in terms of
sin θ and cos θ. The *cotangent* function is defined by the equation

$$\blacktriangleright \quad \cot \theta = \frac{\cos \theta}{\sin \theta} = \frac{1}{\tan \theta}, \quad \sin \theta \neq 0$$

The *secant* function is defined by the equation

$$\blacktriangleright \quad \sec \theta = \frac{1}{\cos \theta}, \qquad \cos \theta \neq 0$$

The *cosecant* function is defined by the equation

$$\blacktriangleright \quad \csc \theta = \frac{1}{\sin \theta}, \qquad \sin \theta \neq 0$$

Although all of these functions are useful, the most important are the cosine, sine, and tangent. The properties and interrelationships of these functions will be discussed in later sections. For the present, the reader should become thoroughly familiar with the graphical behavior of these functions.

Further Considerations

The discussion of the sine, cosine, and their related functions has been based on the unit circle and the behavior of points on this circle. For this reason, these functions are called the *circular functions*. In addition, we have used geometric considerations (primarily, angle relationships) to ascertain and describe the basic behavior of these functions. However, the importance and uses of the circular functions go far beyond applications to the unit circle and polygons; some other applications are to electromagnetic theory, acoustics, and harmonic motion.

The key element in the development of these functions is the manner in which the argument of the functions is defined. The radian is a dimensionless *real* number and, as such, need not relate to an angle in the unit circle or in a polygon. To illustrate this, consider the following population problem.

Suppose there are two populations, one a predator and the other a prey. As the prey population grows, the predator population increases. At some point, the prey population will reach a maximum and begin to decrease (due to limited food supply, being eaten, disease, etc.). A decrease in the prey population will cause an eventual peak and then a decrease in the predator population, due mainly to lack of food. The prey population decreases until the number of predators falls to a level at which more prey are born than die. The cycles of buildup and decrease will then recur in a periodic manner. These variations in the population sizes can be described by trigonometric functions of the form

$$f(t) = A \cos kt + B \sin kt$$

where A, B, and k are real constants and t represents time in years.

In this case, no geometric angle is involved. The argument is simply a real number that varies with time. When the argument of a circular function relates to a geometric angle, the circular function is often called a *trigonometric* function.

Let $t \in \mathbb{R}$, $B = \{b \mid -1 \leqslant b \leqslant 1\}$, and $S = \{s \mid |s| \geqslant 1\}$. Then in terms of individual points, we can write

$$\cos: t \to \cos t \qquad \sin: t \to \sin t$$
$$\tan: t \to \tan t \qquad \sec: t \to \sec t$$
$$\csc: t \to \csc t \qquad \cot: t \to \cot t$$

In terms of the domains and ranges of these functions, we can write

▶ $\cos: \mathbb{R} \twoheadrightarrow B$

▶ $\sin: \mathbb{R} \twoheadrightarrow B$

▶ $\tan: \mathbb{R} - \left\{ (2n+1)\dfrac{\pi}{2} \right\} \twoheadrightarrow \mathbb{R}$

▶ $\sec: \mathbb{R} - \left\{ (2n+1)\dfrac{\pi}{2} \right\} \twoheadrightarrow S$

▶ $\csc: \mathbb{R} - \{n\pi\} \twoheadrightarrow S$

▶ $\cot: \mathbb{R} - \{n\pi\} \twoheadrightarrow \mathbb{R}$

where n takes on all integer values. (The set complementation with respect to $\mathbb{R}$ in the last four cases results from the fact that the indicated values are not part of the domains.) Although we will continue to use the unit circle to develop further circular relationships, the arguments of the circular functions are always understood to be real numbers. This holds even if the argument is given in degrees, since a degree measure can always be converted to a radian measure, which is a real number.

EXERCISES 5-2

Set A

1. For the data below, use the Pythagorean Theorem to calculate the value of the missing letter shown in Figure 5-21. Then calculate the sine, cosine, tangent, cotangent, secant, and cosecant of θ. (Assume that θ is the counterclockwise angle formed by the positive D axis and the line joining the origin to the terminal point given below.)

(a) $x = -3, y = 4$ (b) $x = 5, y = -2$
(c) $r = 17, y = -8, x < 0$ (d) $r = 9, x = 4, y < 0$
(e) $y = 6, x = 9$ (f) $x = -4, y = -7$

2. For each set of data in Exercise 1, identify the trigonometric function that can immediately be evaluated from the information given, without using the Pythagorean Theorem to calculate the unknown side.

3. Using the periodic properties of the circular functions, evaluate the following (use Table 5-3):

(a) $\sin \dfrac{47\pi}{3}$ (b) $\cos \dfrac{35\pi}{4}$

(c) $\tan \dfrac{31\pi}{3}$ (d) $\sin -\dfrac{17\pi}{2}$

(e) $\cos -\dfrac{41\pi}{3}$ (f) $\tan -\dfrac{29\pi}{4}$

(g) $\cos \dfrac{53\pi}{4}$ (h) $\cos -\dfrac{35\pi}{4}$

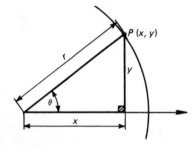

FIGURE 5-21

(i) $\sin -\dfrac{39\pi}{2}$

(j) $\tan \dfrac{56\pi}{3}$

(k) $\tan -\dfrac{35\pi}{4}$

(l) $\sin \dfrac{125\pi}{4}$

Set B

4. Sketch the graphs of cot θ, sec θ, and csc θ, using the definitions, Table 5-3, and the periodic properties of the sine and cosine functions. (Sketch at least two cycles of each function.) What are the fundamental periods of each of these functions?

5. The graphs of the circular functions exhibit odd and even symmetries. Classify each of the six circular functions as odd or even. Use the definitions of odd and even functions to develop the equations that relate the values of each circular function for arguments θ and $-\theta$.

6. On graph paper, carefully draw a circle of radius 3 inches. Using the positive D axis as $0°$, draw the terminal sides of angles of $30°$, $45°$, $60°$, $90°$, and all multiples of these angles up to $360°$. (Construct the angles with a protractor or a compass.) By measuring the coordinates of the intersection of each angle with the circle, develop a table of values for $\sin \theta$ and $\cos \theta$; then, on separate pieces of graph paper, draw the curves $y = \sin \theta$ and $y = \cos \theta$. Let the D axis represent θ, scaled to $\frac{1}{4}$ inch $= 15°$, and the R axis represent y, scaled to 3 inches $= 1$. In the construction, carefully connect all data points with a smooth curve.

7. Using the data in Table 5-3, sketch the graphs of the following circular functions:
    (a) $f(t) = \sin 3t,\ 0 \leqslant t \leqslant \pi$
    (b) $g(t) = 2 \cos t,\ -\pi \leqslant t \leqslant \pi$
    (c) $h(t) = 3 \cos 2t,\ 0 \leqslant t \leqslant 2\pi$

8. Use the planar translation property to sketch the graphs of the following circular functions for $t \in [0, 2\pi]$:
    (a) $y + 1 = 2 \cos t$ (b) $y - 3 = \sin(t - \pi/3)$
    (c) $y - 1 = 2 \cos(t + \pi/4)$

9. For the following functions let $t \in [-2\pi, 2\pi]$. Find the fundamental period, the region(s) for which the mapping is one to one, and the image set that results in an onto mapping.
    (a) $f(t) = 2 \sin t$ (b) $g(t) = 3 \cos(t/2)$
    (c) $h(t) = \tan(t/2)$

Set C

10. Let $f(t) = \sin t$, $g(t) = \cos t$, and $h(t) = t^2 + 1$. Find
    (a) $(f \circ g)(t)$ (b) $(g \circ h)(t)$
    (c) $(f/g)(\pi/3)$ (d) $(f \cdot g)(\pi/4)$
    (e) $(h \circ f)(2\pi/3)$ (f) $(h \cdot f + g)(t^2)$

11. For the functions in Exercise 10, find the range of
    (a) $f \circ g$ (b) $g \circ h$ (c) $h \circ f$

12. Use Table 5-3 to graph the following product functions for t in radians, $-\pi \leqslant t \leqslant 2\pi$, in increments of $\pi/6$:

(a) $y = \sin t \cos t$ (b) $y = (\sin t)^2$

(c) $y = (\cos t)^2$ (d) $y = (\sin t)^3$

(e) $y = (\sin t)(\cos t)^2$ (f) $y = t \sin t$

What are the periods of the functions in (a), (b), and (c)? In Exercise 5, it was seen that $\sin \theta$ is an odd function and $\cos \theta$ an even function. What conclusions can you draw about products of odd and even functions? What real number operations do these products resemble?

5-3 TRIGONOMETRIC TABULATIONS

The Trigonometric Tables

In Section 5-2, we developed a table of values for the sine and cosine functions. More complete tables are presented in Appendix C (Tables C-3 and C-4). The symmetry of the trigonometric functions allows us to evaluate them for any angle using only the values of these functions for angles between 0 and $\pi/2$ (90°). (Note that in the following discussion, the word "angle" is used to represent both a geometric measure and the real argument of a circular function.)

As can be seen from Table C-4, the values of the trigonometric functions for angles between 0 and $\pi/4$ (45°) determine the values for all angles. To show this, consider a circle of radius $r > 0$, as shown in Figure 5-22. Right triangle OPS contains the acute angle θ, which is also a central angle; the terminal line of θ intersects the circle at the point $P = (x, y)$. The angle ψ is the remaining acute angle of triangle OPS. Now construct a right triangle OQT having a central angle ψ, and let the terminal side of central angle ψ intersect the circle at the point $Q = (a, b)$. Then the remaining acute angle of triangle OQT is equal to θ, since θ and ψ are complementary angles.

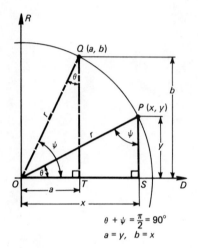

$\theta + \psi = \dfrac{\pi}{2} = 90°$

$a = y, \quad b = x$

FIGURE 5-22

> **DEFINITION** Two acute angles are complementary angles if their sum equals $\pi/2$ radians, or 90°.

But triangles OPS and OQT are congruent, because two angles and the included side in one triangle are equal to two angles and the included side in the other. Hence, the lengths of corresponding sides of these triangles are equal. Therefore,

$$a = y \quad \text{and} \quad b = x$$

But by definition,

$$\cos \theta = \frac{x}{r} \quad \text{and} \quad \sin \psi = \frac{b}{r}$$

Since $b = x$,

$$\sin \psi = \frac{x}{r}$$

and hence,

▶ $\cos \theta = \sin \psi$

Similar arguments will show that

$$\sin \theta = \cos \psi$$
$$\tan \theta = \cot \psi$$
$$\cot \theta = \tan \psi$$
$$\sec \theta = \csc \psi$$
$$\csc \theta = \sec \psi$$

where θ and ψ are complementary angles, that is, $\theta = (\pi/2) - \psi$ (or $\theta = 90° - \psi$) and $\psi = (\pi/2) - \theta$ (or $\psi = 90° - \theta$). The equations above state that *cofunctions* of complementary angles are equal; that is, the sine and *co*sine, when applied to complementary angles, have the same value, and similarly for the tangent and *co*tangent, and for the secant and ·*co*secant. This justifies the following theorem.

THEOREM 5-1 For the set of circular functions, cofunctions of complementary angles are equal.

Thus, the trigonometric functions for angles from 0 through $\pi/4$ (45°) determine the trigonometric functions for all angles from 0 through 2π (360°).

EXAMPLE 5-12 If $\tan \pi/3 = \sqrt{3}$, find $\cot \pi/6$.
  We have

$$\cot \pi/6 = \cot(\pi/2 - \pi/3)$$
$$= \tan \pi/3 = \sqrt{3}$$

EXAMPLE 5-13 If $\sec \pi/3 = 2$, for which angle t does $\csc t = 2$?
  We have $\csc t = 2 = \sec \pi/3$. But we also know that $\csc t = \sec(\pi/2 - t)$, so $\sec(\pi/2 - t) = \sec \pi/3$. Therefore, $\pi/2 - t = \pi/3$ and $t = \pi/2 - \pi/3 = \pi/6$.

Angles not in the First Quadrant

  Since standard trigonometric tables list only those angles θ such that $0 \leqslant \theta \leqslant \pi/2$ (90°), how can we find the value of a trigonometric function for an angle θ outside this region? To do this, it is again necessary to consider the four quadrants of the circle. Figure 5-23 shows the four quadrants and the trigonometric functions that are positive in each.

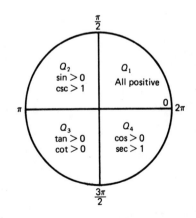

FIGURE 5-23

(Note that the quadrantal angles, 0, $\pi/2$, π, etc., are not within any quadrant but rather separate the different quadrants.) In the first quadrant, all the trigonometric functions are positive. To evaluate a trigonometric function at any angle not in the first quadrant, we must relate the angle to the corresponding one in the first quadrant. Let T represent any trigonometric function. Then for any real number u in the domain of T, the value $T(u)$ can be related to a value $T(u_1)$ such that $0 \leqslant u_1 \leqslant \pi/2$, by the following rules:

1. If the angle is in the first quadrant, $0 < u < \pi/2$ (90°), evaluate $T(u)$ directly from the table; hence, $T(u) = T(u_1)$.
2. If the angle is in the second quadrant, $\pi/2 < u < \pi$ (180°), then $T(u) = \pm T(\pi - u) = \pm T(180° - u) = \pm T(u_1)$.
3. If the angle is the third quadrant, $\pi < u < 3\pi/2$ (270°), then $T(u) = \pm T(\pi + u) = \pm T(180° + u) = \pm T(u_1)$.
4. If the angle is in the fourth quadrant, $3\pi/2 < u < 2\pi$ (360°), then $T(u) = \pm T(2\pi - u) = \pm T(360° - u) = \pm T(u_1)$.
5. If the angle is not in the interval $0 \leqslant u \leqslant 2\pi$, use the periodic property of T to convert the angle to one in the interval $0 \leqslant u < 2\pi$.

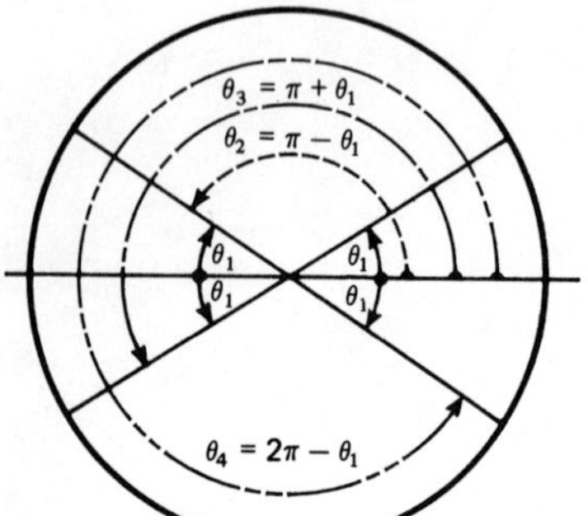

These rules are justified by the geometric properties illustrated in Figure 5-24. The proper sign for $T(u)$ depends on whether the function T is positive or negative in the quadrant that contains u.

For the following examples, use Table C-3 of Appendix C if the angle is in radians and Table C-4 if the angle is in degrees.

FIGURE 5-24

EXAMPLE 5-14 Find sin 0.66.

Since $0 < 0.66 < \pi/2 = 1.57\cdots$, the angle is in the first quadrant. Hence, from Table C-3, sin 0.66 = 0.6131.

EXAMPLE 5-15 Find tan 2.43.

Since $\pi/2 = 1.57\cdots < 2.43 < \pi = 3.14\cdots$, the angle is in the second quadrant. Since the tangent function is negative in the second quadrant, $\tan 2.43 = -\tan(\pi - 2.43) = -\tan 0.71159\cdots \approx -\tan 0.71 = -0.8595$. Therefore,

$$\tan 2.43 \approx -0.8595$$

EXAMPLE 5-16 Find sec 223°.

Since $180° < 223° < 270°$, the angle is in the third quadrant. Since the secant is negative in this quadrant, $\sec 223° = -\sec(223° - 180°) = -\sec 43° = -1.367$, as found from Table C-4. Therefore, $\sec 223° \approx -1.367$.

EXAMPLE 5-17 Find cos 24.79.

The angle 24.79 is in radians (why?) and represents an angle generated by several counterclockwise revolutions. Since one revolution is $2\pi = 6.28$ radians, four revolutions is 8π. So

$$\cos 24.79 = \cos(8\pi - 24.79) = \cos(25.1327\cdots - 24.79)$$
$$= \cos 0.3427\cdots \approx \cos 0.34 = 0.9428$$

Therefore, $\cos 24.79 \approx 0.9428$.

EXAMPLE 5-18 Find $\tan -9.28$.

Since -9.28 is a negative radian value, we successively add 2π (approximately 6.28) to it until we obtain a positive value between 0 and 2π.

$$-9.28 + 6.28 = -3$$
$$-3 + 6.28 = 3.28$$

Therefore, after two successive additions of 2π, an angle value of approximately 3.28 is obtained. Since this angle is in the third quadrant,

$$\tan -9.28 = \tan(4\pi - 9.28) = \tan 3.2864\cdots$$
$$= \tan(3.2864\cdots - \pi)$$
$$= \tan 0.1447\cdots \approx \tan 0.14 = 0.1409$$

Therefore, $\tan -9.28 \approx 0.1409$. We choose the positive sign because the tangent is positive in the third quadrant.

EXAMPLE 5-19 Evaluate
$$y = 5 \sin u(\cos u)^2$$
for $u = 1726$ radians.

The first step is to find the basic reference angle corresponding to 1726 radians. This is done by dividing 1726 by 2π:

$$\frac{1726}{2\pi} = 274.7014 \text{ periods}$$

The integer part, 274, can be dropped, since it simply represents the whole number of rotations about the unit circle. The decimal represents the portion of 2π that determines the reference angle. Thus,

$$0.7014 \text{ periods} = 0.7014 (2\pi) = 4.4070 \text{ radians} = 252.504°$$

a third quadrant angle. The basic reference angle is obtained by subtracting 180° from this value, which yields 72.504°. Then

$$(5 \sin 1726)(\cos 1726)^2 = (-5 \sin 72.504\cdots°)(-\cos 72.504\cdots°)^2$$

Using either a table or a calculator, we get

$$\sin 72.504\cdots° = 0.95374, \qquad \cos 72.504\cdots° = 0.30064$$

and the final value is

$$y \approx -0.4310$$

EXERCISES 5-3

Set A

1. Using the trigonometric tables in Appendix C, find the following. (All angles are in radians unless otherwise indicated.)
   (a) sin 27.5°   (b) cos 63°40′
   (c) cos 16°20′   (d) sin 71°50′
   (e) tan 0.73   (f) cos 1.2
   (g) sin 0.03   (h) tan 1.34
   (i) cos 18°   (j) sin 43°10′
   (k) tan 34°50′   (l) tan 0.92

2. Evaluate the following using the trigonometric tables in Appendix C.
   (a) sin 2.1   (b) cos 4.3
   (c) tan 6   (d) sin 5.1
   (e) cos 342°30′   (f) tan 152°
   (g) tan 243°   (h) sin 304°
   (i) cos 5.2   (j) cos 6.1
   (k) sin 202°40′   (l) tan 692°10′

Set B

● 3. Evaluate the following.
   (a) cos 742°   (b) sin 72.3
   (c) tan − 2.4   (d) sec − 27°
   (e) csc − 31   (f) cos − 543°
   (g) cot 2431   (h) sin 2431°
   (i) cos − 78.31   (j) tan 34128°

4. Using Table C-4 of Appendix C, evaluate the following products:
   (a) (tan 62°)(tan 46°)   (b) (sin 18°)(cos 26°)
   (c) (cos 53°)(tan 82°)   (d) (sin 2.6°)(cos 42°)
   (e) (tan 36°)(sin 36°)(cos 36°)

● 5. Evaluate the following expressions for the given angles to four decimal places:
   (a) $y = 6 \sin u \cos u$, $u = 483$
   (b) $y = (-3 \cos u)(\sin u)^3$, $u = 972.43°$
   (c) $y = (8 \tan u)^2(\sec u)$, $u = 329$
   (d) $y = 4 \sin u + 12 \cos u$, $u = 527.22°$

Set C

6. Show that the following equations are true. (These are examples of more general trigonometric identities that will be proven in Chapter 6.)

   (a) $\tan 120° = \dfrac{2 \tan 60°}{1 - (\tan 60°)^2}$

   (b) $\sin 110° = 2(\sin 55°)(\cos 55°)$
   (c) $\cos 130° = (\cos 65°)^2 - (\sin 65°)^2$

5-4 SIMPLE APPLICATIONS USING TRIGONOMETRIC FUNCTIONS

Right Angle Trigonometry

Many problems can be solved with right triangles and an appropriate trigonometric function of one of the acute angles of the triangle. For this reason, it is useful to redefine the circular functions in terms of the sides of a right triangle. Figure 5-25 shows a right triangle in a circle of radius r; the acute angles of this triangle are θ and its complementary angle $\psi = \pi/2 - \theta$. If the coordinates of P are (x, y), then the legs of the triangle have lengths x and y. Note that r is the hypotenuse of the triangle, x the side adjacent to θ and opposite ψ, and y the side opposite θ and adjacent to ψ. Therefore, the trigonometric functions for θ and ψ are given by the following equations:

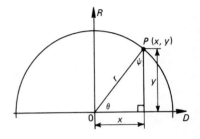

FIGURE 5-25

$$\sin \theta = \frac{y}{r}, \qquad \sin \psi = \frac{x}{r}$$

$$\cos \theta = \frac{x}{r}, \qquad \cos \psi = \frac{y}{r}$$

$$\tan \theta = \frac{y}{x}, \qquad \tan \psi = \frac{x}{y}$$

$$\sec \theta = \frac{r}{x}, \qquad \sec \psi = \frac{r}{y}$$

$$\csc \theta = \frac{r}{y}, \qquad \csc \psi = \frac{r}{x}$$

$$\cot \theta = \frac{x}{y}, \qquad \cot \psi = \frac{y}{x}$$

These equations reflect the cofunction properties described in Section 5-3. The following examples illustrate some simple applications of the trigonometric functions.

EXAMPLE 5-20 Figure 5-26 shows a ladder of length 15 feet placed against a wall. If the acute angle between the ladder and the wall is 20°, find the distance, S, between the bottom of the ladder and the wall.

Assuming that the ground and the wall meet at a right angle, we know that this is a right triangle with a hypotenuse of length $r = 15$ feet and one angle, ψ, of measure 20°. The unknown value, S, is the length of the side opposite the 20° angle. Hence, the sine function can be used to solve for S. The equation becomes

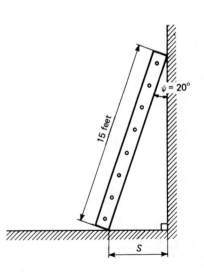

$$\sin 20° = \frac{S}{15} \quad \text{or} \quad S = 15 \sin 20°$$

FIGURE 5-26

Using Table C-4 or a calculator, we obtain

$$S = 15(0.3420)$$

or, to two decimal places, $S = 5.13$ feet.

Many interesting problems can be designed to illustrate the use of right angle trigonometry. Most common are those problems that involve *angles of elevation* or *depression*.

DEFINITION   An **angle of elevation** is an angle formed by rotating a horizontal ray upward. An **angle of depression** is an angle formed by rotating a horizontal ray downward.

EXAMPLE 5-21   A man is standing on a cliff which is 1000 feet above a valley below him. As the man looks at a town in the valley, the angle of depression formed is 25°. (See Figure 5-27.) How far is the town from the base of the cliff?

For this problem, the angle of depression (the angle looking downward from the horizontal line of sight into the valley) is given as 25°. We assume that the valley and the cliff meet in a right angle. Although we are not given either of the acute angles of the right triangle, the angle of depression can be used in either of two ways. Since the line of sight is horizontal, the angle formed by the cliff and the line of sight is a right angle; moreover, since the angle of depression is 25°, the complementary angle, which is an acute angle of the right triangle, must be 65°.

Alternatively, we may realize that the line of sight and the line representing the valley are parallel; then the line connecting the top of the cliff to the town in the valley forms a transversal. Since alternate interior angles of parallel lines are equal, the angle at the bottom of the valley must also be 25°. This is the approach we will use. Hence, the right triangle under consideration has an acute angle of 25°, with an opposite side of length 1000 feet and an adjacent side of length s feet. The function that associates the angle with the legs opposite and adjacent to it is the tangent function (or the cotangent). By definition,

$$\tan 25° = \frac{1000}{s}$$

Solving for s, we get

$$s = \frac{1000}{\tan 25°}$$

Since $\tan 25°$ is 0.4663,

$$s = \frac{1000}{0.4663}$$

$$= 2145 \text{ feet}$$

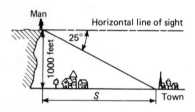

FIGURE 5-27

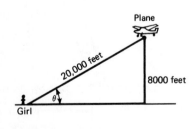

FIGURE 5-28

EXAMPLE 5-22 Suppose a girl is standing on the ground looking at an airplane in flight. The plane is 20,000 feet in a direct line from the girl and is flying at an altitude of 8000 feet. What is the angle at which the girl is looking upward?

We assume that the height of the girl is negligible compared to the height of the plane. The problem is to determine the angle of elevation of the girl's line of sight. We call this angle θ. The distance of the plane from the girl (20,000 feet) is the hypotenuse of the right triangle, and the altitude (8000 feet) is the side opposite θ. (See Figure 5-28.)

A trigonometric function of θ that involves the hypotenuse and the side opposite θ is the cosecant function (or the sine). By definition,

$$\csc \theta = \frac{20,000}{8000}$$

$$= \tfrac{5}{2} = 2.5$$

Looking in the tables for the angle whose cosecant is 2.5, we find that the angle whose cosecant is closest to 2.5 is 20°30′. Therefore, the angle of inclination is approximately 23°30′.

● **EXAMPLE 5-23** A man is observing a rocket on its launching pad. He knows that the height of the rocket and the launching pad is 450 feet, and the angle of elevation from his observation post to the rocket's tip is 18°. Exactly 50 seconds after the launch, he measures the angle of elevation to the rocket's tip as 68°. (See Figure 5-29.)

(a) How far is the observation post from the rocket?
(b) What is the average speed, in feet per second, of the rocket during the first 50 seconds after the launch?
(c) If 88 feet per second = 60 miles per hour, what is the rocket's speed in miles per hour?

The right triangle that describes problem (a) is shown in Figure 5-30. The trigonometric functions that involve θ, L, and the rocket's height are the tangent or cotangent. If we use the cotangent, we have

$$\cot 18° = \frac{L}{450}$$

From a table or a calculator, we find that cot 18° = 3.0778. Solving for L yields

$$L = 450 \cot 18° = (450)(3.0778)$$
$$= 1385.01$$

Thus, $L \approx 1385$ feet.

To solve (b), we need the height to which the rocket's tip has risen. The right triangle for this problem is shown in Figure 5-31. We use the tangent function. So,

$$\tan 68° = \frac{H}{1385}$$

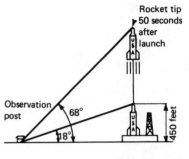

FIGURE 5-29

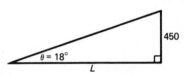

FIGURE 5-30

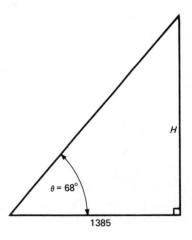

FIGURE 5-31

Solving for H yields

$$H = (1385) \tan 68°$$
$$= 3427.89 \text{ feet}$$

Thus, $H \approx 3428$ feet. Now, in 50 seconds, the rocket has moved a distance of

$$3428 \text{ feet} - 450 \text{ feet} = 2978 \text{ feet}$$

The average speed is given as

$$V_{av} = \frac{\text{Distance}}{\text{Time}} = \frac{2978 \text{ feet}}{50 \text{ seconds}} = 59.56 \text{ feet per second}$$

To solve (c), we form the following proportion:

$$\frac{V_{mph}}{60} = \frac{V_{fps}}{88}$$

Solving for V_{mph} yields

$$V_{mph} = \tfrac{60}{88} V_{fps}$$
$$= \tfrac{60}{88}(59.56)$$
$$= 40.609$$

Therefore,

$$V_{mph} \approx 40.61 \text{ miles per hour}$$

The Law of Cosines and the Law of Sines

When the triangle that best describes a problem does not contain a right angle, it may still be possible to use trigonometry to obtain a solution. Two important rules that can be applied to such problems are the Law of Cosines and the Law of Sines, which we derive using the trigonometry of right triangles.

THEOREM 5-2 (Law of Cosines) Let a, b, and c be the lengths of the sides of a triangle with opposite angles A, B, and C, respectively.

▶ $a^2 = b^2 + c^2 - 2bc \cos A$
▶ $b^2 = a^2 + c^2 - 2ac \cos B$
▶ $c^2 = a^2 + b^2 - 2ab \cos C$

PROOF Position the triangle on the DR plane so that A is at the origin and side AB extends along the positive D axis, as shown in Figure 5-32. Let θ = angle A. If a line from vertex C is dropped perpendicular to line AB, then the coordinates of C are ($b \cos \theta$, $b \sin \theta$), because the legs of the right triangle formed are the sides adjacent and opposite to angle θ. The coordinates of point B are (c, 0), since the length of side AB is c. Therefore, the length of the side opposite the angle θ is the distance between points B and C. By the distance formula,

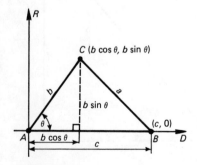

FIGURE 5-32

$$a^2 = (c - b \cos \theta)^2 + (0 - b \sin \theta)^2$$
$$= (c - b \cos \theta)^2 + (-b \sin \theta)^2$$
$$= c^2 - 2 bc \cos \theta + (b \cos \theta)^2 + (b \sin \theta)^2$$

But $b \cos \theta$ and $b \sin \theta$ are the lengths of the legs of a right triangle, so by the Pythagorean Theorem, $(b \cos \theta)^2 + (b \sin \theta)^2 = b^2$. Hence,

$$a^2 = b^2 + c^2 - 2bc \cos \theta$$

or

$$a^2 = b^2 + c^2 - 2bc \cos A$$

Similar arguments, with $\theta = B$ and then $\theta = C$, prove the remaining two relations. ∎

In any triangle for which we know the measure of one angle and the lengths of the two sides adjacent to that angle, the Law of Cosines can be used to find the length of the third side.

EXAMPLE 5-24 Two ships sail out to sea, one traveling at 10 knots and the other at 20 knots. The first ship travels east, while the second ship leaves at the same time and travels northwest. After two hours, how far apart are the two ships?

The angle between the courses of the two ships (east and northwest) is 135°, as shown in Figure 5-33. After two hours, the first ship has traveled 20 nautical miles, and the second ship has traveled 40 nautical miles. The distance between the two ships, s, is the side opposite the angle of 135°. By the Law of Cosines,

$$s^2 = 40^2 + 20^2 - 2(40)(20) \cos 135°$$
$$= 1600 + 400 - 1600 \cos 135°$$

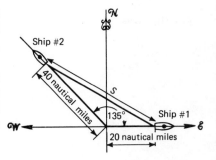

FIGURE 5-33

Since 135° is a second quadrant angle, we subtract 135° from 180° to obtain 45°. The cosine in the second quadrant is negative, so $\cos 135° = -\cos 45° = -\sqrt{2}/2$. Substituting this value in the equation above, we have

$$s^2 = 2000 - 1600\left(-\frac{\sqrt{2}}{2}\right)$$

$$= 2000 + 800\sqrt{2}$$
$$= 2000 + 800(1.4142135)$$
$$= 2000 + 1131.37$$
$$= 3131.37$$

or $s = 56.0$ nautical miles, accurate to one decimal place.

● **EXAMPLE 5-25** A surveyor is measuring a triangular plot of land, which includes a portion of a lake. The measurements are shown in Figure 5-34. What is the distance, E, that forms the third side of the property?

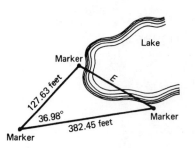

FIGURE 5-34

From the Law of Cosines,

$$E^2 = (127.63)^2 + (382.45)^2 - 2(127.63)(382.45) \cos 36.98°$$
$$= 16,289.42 + 146,268 - 77,986.65$$
$$= 84,570.77$$

Thus, $E = 290.81$ feet.

THEOREM 5-3 (Law of Sines) Let a, b, and c be the lengths of the sides of a triangle with opposite angles A, B, and C, respectively. Then

$$\blacktriangleright \quad \frac{\sin A}{a} = \frac{\sin B}{b} = \frac{\sin C}{c}$$

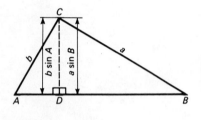

FIGURE 5-35

PROOF From angle C drop a line perpendicular to line AB at D, as shown in Figure 5-35. Then the side opposite angle A in right triangle ACD is CD. Since b is the hypotenuse of this right triangle, the length of CD is $b \sin A$.

On the other hand, if we consider the other right triangle, BCD, then CD is the side opposite angle B. In this right triangle, the hypotenuse is a, so the length of CD is $a \sin B$. Therefore,

$$b \sin A = a \sin B$$

or

$$\frac{\sin A}{a} = \frac{\sin B}{b}$$

By similar reasoning, we can show that $\sin(C)/c = \sin(A)/a$. Hence,

$$\frac{\sin A}{a} = \frac{\sin B}{b} = \frac{\sin C}{c} \quad \blacksquare$$

There are two cases where the Law of Sines fails to give a unique solution. In one case, no physical answer is possible, and in the other, an ambiguity occurs. These possibilities are the subject of Exercise 12 at the end of this section.

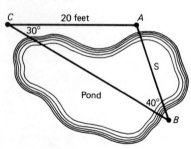

FIGURE 5-36

EXAMPLE 5-26 A surveyor wishes to measure the distance between two points, A and B, on opposite sides of a pond, as shown in Figure 5-36. Standing at point C, 200 feet away from point A, she measures an angle of 30° between the lines of sight to A and to B. After marking this point, she measures the angle at B between the lines of sight to A and to C as 40°. Find the distance between A and B.

Let s be the distance between A and B. Then by the Law of Sines,

$$\frac{s}{\sin 30°} = \frac{200}{\sin 40°}$$

Solving for s,

$$s = \frac{200}{\sin 40°} (\sin 30°)$$

Since sin 30° = $\frac{1}{2}$ = 0.5 and sin 40° = 0.6428, we have

$$s = \frac{200}{0.6428}(0.5)$$

$$= \frac{100}{0.6428}$$

or s = 156 feet, correct to three significant digits.

● **EXAMPLE 5-27** A resident of an island wishes to visit a friend who has just moved to Town A (see Figure 5-37), which he has never visited. From a previous survey, he knows that the distance from his town to a third town, Town B, is 11.7243 miles and that $\alpha = 93.665°$ and $\beta = 58.711°$. How far is Town A from his town?

In order to use the Law of Sines, we must compute the angle γ. This is easily done, since the sum of the angles of any plane triangle is 180°. So

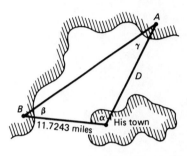

FIGURE 5-37

$$\gamma = 180° - (\beta + \alpha)$$
$$= 180° - 152.376°$$
$$= 27.624°$$

Now, by the Law of Sines,

$$\frac{\sin 27.624°}{11.7243 \text{ miles}} = \frac{\sin 58.711°}{D}$$

Solving for D yields

$$D = (11.7243)\frac{\sin 58.711°}{\sin 27.624°}$$

Substitution of the sine values yields

$$D = (11.7243)\frac{(0.854559)}{(0.463667)}$$

Therefore, D = 21.608 miles, or $D \approx$ 21.61 miles.

EXERCISES 5-4

Set A

For Exercises 1 through 6 a calculator is recommended. Compute all answers to two decimal places.

1. A boy standing 60 feet away from the base of a tall pine tree measures the angle of elevation to the top of the tree as 58°. How tall is the tree?

2. A burglar wishing to enter a house through a window finds that the window is located in such a way that a ladder must be placed 6 feet from

the house at an angle of 72° with the ground. How long a ladder must the burglar use to reach the window?

3. A lighthouse keeper knows that his lighthouse is located 200 feet from a straight road located on shore. He sees a hiker walking along the road and decides to find out how fast the hiker is walking. He does this by making successive angular measurements to the hiker with respect to a perpendicular line to the road. His first measurement is 76°. Five minutes later, he measures an angle of 42°. How far did the hiker travel in the five minutes? If 60 miles per hour = 5280 feet per minute, what is the speed in miles per hour of the hiker?

4. A pyramid is 130 feet tall and 72 feet wide at the base. What angle does the side make with the ground?

5. A woman ties her boat to a dock at high tide. At this point, the taut rope is horizontal, and the distance from the dock to the boat is 15 feet. Four hours later, the tide has fallen 4 feet. What is the angle of declination that the taut rope makes with the horizontal?

6. Each of the following describes a triangle with sides a, b, and c and corresponding opposite angles A, B, and C. For each description, draw the triangle and compute the remaining sides and angles using either right triangle trigonometry, the Law of Cosines, or the Law of Sines.

    (a) $A = 90°$, $b = 13$, $C = 24°$ (b) $a = 7$, $b = 4$, $C = 90°$
    (c) $a = 4$, $b = 7$, $C = 45°$ (d) $c = 13$, $b = 9$, $A = 64°$
    (e) $a = 15$, $b = 10$, $A = 38°$ (f) $c = 24$, $a = 16$, $C = 78°$
    (g) $a = 15$, $b = 17$, $c = 8$ (h) $a = 15$, $b = 39$, $c = 36$
    (i) $a = 23.2$, $c = 17.4$, $B = 123°$ (j) $a = 14.3$, $b = 18.4$, $A = 16°20'$

Set B

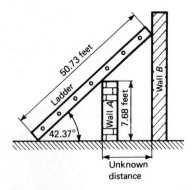

50.73 feet

Ladder

Wall A

7.68 feet

Wall B

42.37°

Unknown distance

FIGURE 5-38

In Exercises 7 and 8, consider East–West the horizontal direction and North–South the vertical direction.

7. Several students find that the entrance of the administration building is located 400 yards southwest of the flagpole and the entrance of the library is 100 yards southeast of the flagpole. How far is it from the entrance of the administration building to the entrance of the library?

8. A plane travels from Town A to Town B in a direction N 15° E at 600 miles per hour for two hours. Then at Town B it turns to a direction S 75° E and travels for an additional $1\frac{1}{2}$ hours. How far from the starting point and in what direction is the plane now located with respect to Town A? (Note that N 15° E means 15° east of due north.)

● 9. In Figure 5-38, a 50.73-foot ladder has been placed in such a way that it touches wall A and wall B as shown and makes an angle of 42.37° with the ground. Wall A is 7.68 feet tall. What distance separates the front of wall A from the front of wall B?

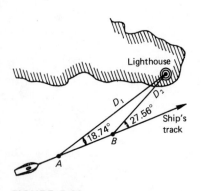

Lighthouse

D_1

D_2

27.56°

Ship's track

18.74°

B

A

FIGURE 5-39

● 10. A ship's navigator is taking sightings using a lighthouse as her reference marking (see Figure 5-39). At point A, she measures the angle between the track of the ship and the lighthouse as 18.74°. Thirty minutes later, at point B, she measures the same angle and obtains a measure of

27.56°. If the ship is traveling at a constant speed of 22.62 miles per hour, calculate the distances from the ship to the lighthouse at points A and B by using the Law of Sines.

11. · A 30-foot flagpole is placed in the exact center of a conical hill (see Figure 5-40). A Boy Scout wishes to find the height of the hill to the nearest foot by using the Law of Sines. He takes the measurements indicated in the diagram. What height does he calculate?

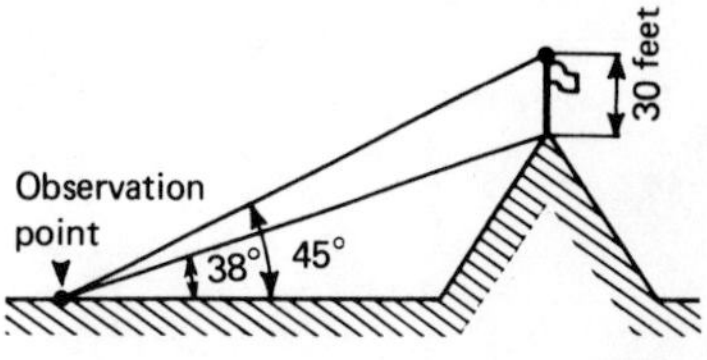

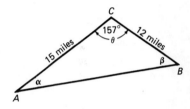

FIGURE 5-40

Set C

12. Consider the ratios involved in the Law of Sines.
    (a) Show that if $a < b \sin A$, then no solution exists.
    (b) Show that if $b \sin A < a < b$, two solutions exist.

13. Two planes leave an airport at the same time. One travels in the direction 48° at 230 miles per hour and the other in the direction 282° at 310 miles per hour. How far apart are they after $1\frac{1}{2}$ hours?

14. In Figure 5-41, Town A is connected to Town B by two roads, which intersect at C. If the distance from A to C is 15 miles and the distance from B to C is 12 miles and angle θ is 157°, what savings in mileage would be obtained by building a road directly from A to B? At what angles, α and β, would this new road intersect the old roads?

FIGURE 5-41

15. A surveyor is standing at point A. He measures the distance to a pump-house at point B as 172 feet. From point B, he measures the distance to a watertower at point C as 120 feet and the angle BAC as 112°. How far is it from point C to point A?

REVIEW EXERCISES FOR CHAPTER 5

1. Convert the following angles from degrees to radians or from radians to degrees:
    (a) 0.573   (b) 2.93
    (c) 327.4°   (d) 0.013°
    (e) 27°36′42″   (f) 0.0086

2. Using the arc length formula, $s = r\theta$, and the linear velocity formula, $v = r\omega$, find the unknown quantity.
    (a) $s = 4$ meters, $r = 2$ centimeters
    (b) $\theta = 3.7$ radians, $r = 2.2$ feet
    (c) $\theta = 1.7$ radians, $s = 36$ inches
    (d) $v = 23$ feet/second, $r = 18$ inches
    (e) $v = 88$ feet/second, $\omega = 2$ radians/minute
    (f) $\omega = 2$ radians/second, $r = 3$ millimeters
    (g) $s = 36$ millimeters, $\theta = 245°$
    (h) $r = 3$ feet, $\theta = 172°$

3. For the data given, calculate the missing side of the right triangle that is used to define the trigonometric functions of angle θ. (See Figure 5-21.) Then calculate $\sin \theta$, $\cos \theta$, and $\tan \theta$. (Answers may be left in radical form.)

(a) $y = -5, x = 3$
(b) $r = 25, y = 2, x < 0$
(c) $r = 16, x = -7, y > 0$
(d) $r = 18, x = -9, y < 0$
(e) $r = 36, y = -10, x > 0$
(f) $y = -15, x = -9$

4. Using the tables of circular functions, evaluate the following expressions to three decimal places:

(a) $\dfrac{\sin 137°}{\cos 49°}$

(b) $(\cos 1.8)(\sin 3.6) + \cos 5.9$

(c) $3 \tan 155° + 2(\cos 40°)^2$

(d) $\dfrac{1 + \tan 115°}{1 - (\tan 115°)^2}$

(e) $\dfrac{\tan 1.76}{\cos 4.26}$ (angles in radians)

5. Evaluate the following functions:

(a) $\cos \dfrac{16\pi}{3}$

(b) $\sin(-33)$

(c) $\tan 792°$

(d) $\cos 23.1$

(e) $\tan \dfrac{17\pi}{4}$

(f) $\cot(-548°)$

6. In constructing a temporary wall, a carpenter must use a beam, running from the top of the wall to the ground, as a brace. If the wall is 20 feet tall and the beam makes an angle of 67° with the ground, how far from the wall is the bottom of the beam located?

7. A farmer wishes to fence in an odd triangular plot. He knows that two of the sides are 126 feet long and 87 feet long. He measures the included angle between these sides as 137°. If fencing costs $2 per foot installed, how much will the farmer have to pay to fence in this area?

8. An electrician must run a wire among three buildings, which form a triangle. Two of the buildings are 160 feet apart, and the angles from these buildings to the remaining building are 71° and 59°. How much wire will be needed?

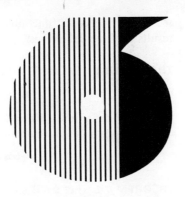

Properties of the Circular Functions

6-1 TRIGONOMETRIC IDENTITIES

The various techniques used to solve algebraic equations involve manipulation of equations to isolate a given variable. However, the nature of transcendental equations makes isolation of the variables difficult or impossible, because the variables are usually contained within the arguments of the functions, as, for example, in the expressions $\sin x$ and $\cos(x^2 - 1)$. For trigonometric functions, the difficulties are lessened by the use of *identities*.

> **DEFINITION** An **identity** is an equation that is true for all permissible values of the variables.

Identities often simplify transcendental equations to a point where the values of the variable can be obtained. The trigonometric identities are derived from the definitions of the functions, the Pythagorean Theorem, and the properties of the unit circle.

Basic Trigonometric Identities

In Chapter 5, we defined the cosine and sine functions in terms of the horizontal and vertical components of points on the unit circle centered at the origin. Using these two functions, we defined the tangent, cotangent, secant, and cosecant functions. Theorems 6-1, 6-2, and 6-3 are immediate results of these definitions.

THEOREM 6-1 Let $u \in \mathbb{R}$ such that $u \neq (n + \frac{1}{2})\pi$ for any $n \in \mathbb{J}$. Then

$$\blacktriangleright \quad \cos u \sec u = 1$$

PROOF By definition, $\sec u = 1/\cos u$, $\cos u \neq 0$. Multiplying both sides of this equation by $\cos u$, we obtain

$$\cos u \sec u = 1 \quad \blacksquare$$

THEOREM 6-2 Let $u \in \mathbb{R}$ such that $u \neq n\pi$ for any $n \in \mathbb{J}$. Then

$$\blacktriangleright \quad \sin u \csc u = 1$$

PROOF By definition, $\csc u = 1/\sin u$, $\sin u \neq 0$. Multiplying both sides of this equation by $\sin u$, we obtain

$$\sin u \csc u = 1 \quad \blacksquare$$

THEOREM 6-3 Let $u \in \mathbb{R}$ such that $u \neq n\pi/2$ for any $n \in \mathbb{J}$. Then

$$\blacktriangleright \quad \tan u \cot u = 1$$

PROOF The proof is left as an exercise. $\blacksquare$

In summary, for properly restricted $u \in \mathbb{R}$,

$$\cos u \sec u = 1$$
$$\sin u \csc u = 1$$
$$\tan u \cot u = 1$$

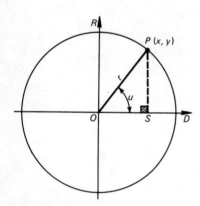

FIGURE 6-1

Now consider any point P on a circle of radius $r > 0$ centered at the origin, as shown in Figure 6-1. The coordinates of P, (x, y), are related to r and u by the equations

$$x = r \cos u \quad \text{and} \quad y = r \sin u$$

where $u \in \mathbb{R}$. This defines a right triangle, OPS, for which (by the Pythagorean Theorem)

$$x^2 + y^2 = r^2$$

This leads to the following identity:

THEOREM 6-4 For any $u \in \mathbb{R}$,

$$\blacktriangleright \quad \cos^2 u + \sin^2 u = 1$$

PROOF Since $x = r \cos u$, $y = r \sin u$, and $x^2 + y^2 = r^2$, then

$$(r \cos u)^2 + (r \sin u)^2 = r^2$$

or

$$r^2(\cos u)^2 + r^2(\sin u)^2 = r^2$$

Dividing by r^2, $r \neq 0$, gives

$$(\cos u)^2 + (\sin u)^2 = 1$$

or

$$\cos^2 u + \sin^2 u = 1 \quad \blacksquare$$

The notation $\cos^2 u$ is an abbreviation for $(\cos u)^2$, that is, the square of the function. In contrast, the expression $\cos u^2$ means that the number u is squared. Hence, $\cos u^2 \neq (\cos u)^2 = \cos^2 u$, for all $u \in \mathbb{R}$.

Since the equation $\cos^2 u + \sin^2 u = 1$ is true for all $u \in \mathbb{R}$, it is an identity, usually known as the Fundamental Trigonometric Identity. The following three identities are proved in a similar way:

THEOREM 6-5   Let $u \in \mathbb{R}$ such that $u \neq (n + \frac{1}{2})\pi$ for any $n \in \mathbb{J}$. Then

▶ $\quad 1 + \tan^2 u = \sec^2 u$

PROOF   Divide the identity $\cos^2 u + \sin^2 u = 1$ by $\cos^2 u$, $\cos u \neq 0$. Then

$$\frac{\cos^2 u}{\cos^2 u} + \frac{\sin^2 u}{\cos^2 u} = \frac{1}{\cos^2 u}$$

that is,

▶ $\quad 1 + \tan^2 u = \sec^2 u \quad \blacksquare$

THEOREM 6-6   Let $u \in \mathbb{R}$ such that $u \neq n\pi$ for any $n \in \mathbb{J}$. Then

$$1 + \cot^2 u = \csc^2 u$$

PROOF   Divide the identity $\cos^2 u + \sin^2 u = 1$ by $\sin^2 u$, $\sin u \neq 0$. Then

$$\frac{\cos^2 u}{\sin^2 u} + \frac{\sin^2 u}{\sin^2 u} = \frac{1}{\sin^2 u}$$

that is,

$$\cot^2 u + 1 = \csc^2 u \quad \blacksquare$$

THEOREM 6-7   Let $u \in \mathbb{R}$ such that $u \neq n\pi/2$ for any $n \in \mathbb{J}$. Then

▶ $\quad \csc^2 u + \sec^2 u = \csc^2 u \sec^2 u$

PROOF   The proof is left as an exercise. $\blacksquare$

In summary, for properly restricted $u \in \mathbb{R}$,

$$\cos^2 u + \sin^2 u = 1$$
$$1 + \tan^2 u = \sec^2 u$$
$$1 + \cot^2 u = \csc^2 u$$
$$\csc^2 u + \sec^2 u = \csc^2 u \sec^2 u$$

EXAMPLE 6-1   Verify the following identities for $t = \pi/4$.

(a) $\cos^2 t + \sin^2 t = 1$

$$\left(\cos\frac{\pi}{4}\right)^2 + \left(\sin\frac{\pi}{4}\right)^2 = 1$$

$$\left(\frac{\sqrt{2}}{2}\right)^2 + \left(\frac{\sqrt{2}}{2}\right)^2 = 1$$

$$\frac{2}{4} + \frac{2}{4} = 1$$

(b) $1 + \tan^2 t = \sec^2 t$

$$1 + \left(\tan\frac{\pi}{4}\right)^2 = \left(\sec\frac{\pi}{4}\right)^2$$

$$1 + (1)^2 = \left(\frac{2}{\sqrt{2}}\right)^2$$

$$2 = \frac{4}{2}$$

(c) $\csc^2 t + \sec^2 t = \csc^2 t \sec^2 t$

$$\left(\csc\frac{\pi}{4}\right)^2 + \left(\sec\frac{\pi}{4}\right)^2 = \left(\csc\frac{\pi}{4}\right)^2\left(\sec\frac{\pi}{4}\right)^2$$

$$\left(\frac{2}{\sqrt{2}}\right)^2 + \left(\frac{2}{\sqrt{2}}\right)^2 = \left(\frac{2}{\sqrt{2}}\right)^2\left(\frac{2}{\sqrt{2}}\right)^2$$

$$\frac{4}{2} + \frac{4}{2} = \left(\frac{4}{2}\right)\left(\frac{4}{2}\right)$$

$$4 = 4$$

Formulas for the Difference and Sum of Angles

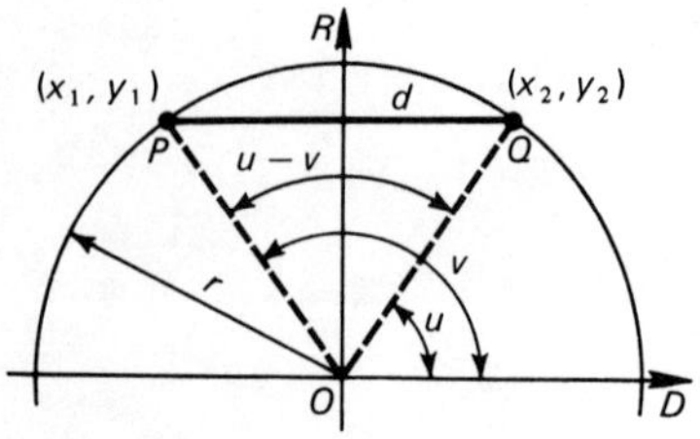

The argument of a trigonometric function may contain two terms; the expression $\tan(3t^2 + 4)$ is one example. We now show that certain trigonometric functions of binomial arguments can be reexpressed using functions of each term of the binomial.

Suppose P and Q are two distinct points on a circle of radius $r > 0$ centered at the origin. Let (x_1, y_1) be the coordinates of P, (x_2, y_2) the coordinates of Q, and u and v the radian measures of the corresponding central angles, as shown in Figure 6-2. Then the minor arc PQ defines the central angle $u - v$ and the corresponding chord of length d. The coordinates of P and Q can also be expressed as $(x_1, y_1) = (r\cos u, r\sin u)$ and $(x_2, y_2) = (r\cos v, r\sin v)$. Thus, by the distance formula,

$$d = \sqrt{(x_1 - x_2)^2 + (y_1 - y_2)^2}$$

$$= \sqrt{(r\cos u - r\cos v)^2 + (r\sin u - r\sin v)^2}$$

$$= r\sqrt{(\cos u - \cos v)^2 + (\sin u - \sin v)^2}$$

Now on the same circle of radius r centered at the origin, consider points $A = (r, 0)$ and B such that the arc AB will have the same measure as the arc PQ. (See Figure 6-3.) Then the central angle corresponding to

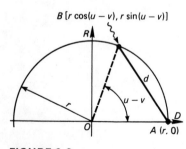

FIGURE 6-2

FIGURE 6-3

arc AB has the same measure as the central angle corresponding to PQ, namely, $u - v$. The coordinates of B are

6-1 Trigonometric **221**
Identities

$$[r \cos(u - v), r \sin(u - v)]$$

The chord between A and B has length d' given by

$$d' = \sqrt{[r \cos(u - v) - r]^2 + [r \sin(u - v) - 0]^2}$$
$$= r\sqrt{[\cos(u - v) - 1]^2 + \sin^2(u - v)}$$

But for the same circle, equal arcs determine equal chords, so

$$d = d'$$

or

$$r\sqrt{(\cos u - \cos v)^2 + (\sin u - \sin v)^2}$$
$$= r\sqrt{[\cos(u - v) - 1]^2 + [\sin(u - v)]^2}$$

Dividing both sides of this equation by r, squaring both sides, and expanding, we obtain

$$\cos^2 u - 2 \cos u \cos v + \cos^2 v + \sin^2 u - 2 \sin u \sin v + \sin^2 v$$
$$= \cos^2(u - v) - 2 \cos(u - v) + 1 + \sin^2(u - v)$$

Regrouping terms gives

$$(\cos^2 u + \sin^2 u) + (\cos^2 v + \sin^2 v) - 2(\cos u \cos v + \sin u \sin v)$$
$$= [\cos^2(u - v) + \sin^2(u - v)] + 1 - 2 \cos(u - v)$$

Since $\cos^2 t + \sin^2 t = 1$ for any $t \in \mathbb{R}$, this becomes

$$1 + 1 - 2(\cos u \cos v + \sin u \sin v) = 1 + 1 - 2 \cos(u - v)$$

or

$$\cos(u - v) = \cos u \cos v + \sin u \sin v$$

This proves the following theorem:

THEOREM 6-8 Let $u, v \in \mathbb{R}$. Then

▶ $\cos(u - v) = \cos u \cos v + \sin u \sin v$

EXAMPLE 6-2 Find $\cos(\pi/12)$ using $\pi/4$ and $\pi/6$.

$$\cos\left(\frac{\pi}{12}\right) = \cos\left(\frac{\pi}{4} - \frac{\pi}{6}\right) = \cos\frac{\pi}{4}\cos\frac{\pi}{6} + \sin\frac{\pi}{4}\sin\frac{\pi}{6}$$
$$= \left(\frac{\sqrt{2}}{2}\right)\left(\frac{\sqrt{3}}{2}\right) + \left(\frac{\sqrt{2}}{2}\right)\left(\frac{1}{2}\right) = \frac{\sqrt{2}}{4}(\sqrt{3} + 1)$$
$$= 0.9659$$

From the graphs of $y = \cos u$ and $y = \sin u$ shown in Figure 6-4, it is clear that the cosine function possesses even symmetry and the sine function possesses odd symmetry. Hence

$$\cos(-u) = \cos u \quad \text{and} \quad \sin(-u) = -\sin u$$

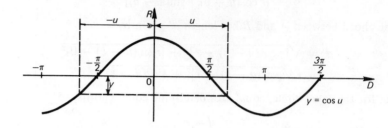

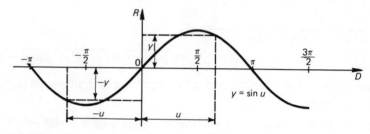

FIGURE 6-4

The following theorem results:

THEOREM 6-9   The cosine is an even function, and the sine is an odd function; that is, for all $u \in \mathbb{R}$,

$$\blacktriangleright \quad \cos(-u) = \cos u$$
$$\blacktriangleright \quad \sin(-u) = -\sin u$$

PROOF   Let $u \in \mathbb{R}$ be such that on the unit circle, the components corresponding to u are $(x, y) = (\cos u, \sin u)$, and let $-u$ be such that the components corresponding to $-u$ are $(x', y') = (\cos(-u), \sin(-u))$. By the formula for the cosine of the difference between two angles,

$$\cos(-u) = \cos(0 - u) = \cos 0 \cos u + \sin 0 \sin u$$

which yields

$$\cos(-u) = \cos u$$

Hence, $x' = x$.
   From Theorem 6-4,

$$\cos^2(-u) + \sin^2(-u) = 1$$

since $\cos(-u) = \cos u$, $\cos^2(-u) = \cos^2 u = 1 - \sin^2 u$. Substituting for $\cos^2(-u)$ in the above yields

$$1 - \sin^2 u + \sin^2(-u) = 1$$

or

$$\sin^2(-u) = \sin^2 u$$

This equation has two possible solutions,

$$\sin(-u) = \sin u \quad \text{or} \quad \sin(-u) = -\sin u$$

Suppose $\sin(-u) = \sin u$; then $y' = y$, which means that $(x', y') = (x, y)$ for *all* $u \in \mathbb{R}$. But this is true *only* for $u = n\pi$, $n \in \mathbb{J}$, which leads to a contradiction. Therefore, $\sin(-u) = -\sin u$. ∎

From these symmetry properties, it is possible to find $\cos(u + v)$.

THEOREM 6-10 Let $u, v \in \mathbb{R}$. Then

▶ $\cos(u + v) = \cos u \cos v - \sin u \sin v$

PROOF

$$\cos(u + v) = \cos[u - (-v)] = \cos u \cos(-v) + \sin u \sin(-v)$$

Since $\cos(-v) = \cos v$ and $\sin(-v) = -\sin v$, this becomes

$$\cos(u + v) = \cos u \cos v - \sin u \sin v \quad ∎$$

EXAMPLE 6-3 Find $\cos 7\pi/12$ using $\pi/4$ and $\pi/3$.

$$\cos \frac{7\pi}{12} = \cos\left(\frac{\pi}{4} + \frac{\pi}{3}\right) = \cos \frac{\pi}{4} \cos \frac{\pi}{3} - \sin \frac{\pi}{4} \sin \frac{\pi}{3}$$

$$= \left(\frac{\sqrt{2}}{2}\right)\left(\frac{1}{2}\right) - \left(\frac{\sqrt{2}}{2}\right)\left(\frac{\sqrt{3}}{2}\right) = \frac{\sqrt{2}}{4}(1 - \sqrt{3})$$

$$= -0.2588$$

For the quadrantal angles $\pi/2$ and π, the following identities result:

THEOREM 6-11 Let $t \in \mathbb{R}$. Then

▶ $\cos\left(\dfrac{\pi}{2} - t\right) = \sin t$

▶ $\cos\left(\dfrac{\pi}{2} + t\right) = -\sin t$

▶ $\cos(\pi - t) = -\cos t$
▶ $\cos(\pi + t) = -\cos t$

PROOF We have

$$\cos\left(\frac{\pi}{2} - t\right) = \cos \frac{\pi}{2} \cos t + \sin \frac{\pi}{2} \sin t$$

$$= 0(\cos t) + 1(\sin t) = \sin t$$

and

$$\cos\left(\frac{\pi}{2} + t\right) = \cos \frac{\pi}{2} \cos t - \sin \frac{\pi}{2} \sin t$$

$$= 0(\cos t) - 1(\sin t) = -\sin t$$

The proofs that $\cos(\pi - t) = -\cos t$ and $\cos(\pi + t) = -\cos t$ are left as exercises. ∎

We know that $\cos(\pi/2 - u) = \sin u$ for all u. Thus, if $u = \pi/2 - t$, then $\cos[\pi/2 - (\pi/2 - t)] = \sin(\pi/2 - t)$. Hence, $\sin(\pi/2 - t) = \cos t$. This results in the following identities:

THEOREM 6-12 For all $u, v \in \mathbb{R}$,

▶ $\sin(u - v) = \sin u \cos v - \cos u \sin v$
▶ $\sin(u + v) = \sin u \cos v + \cos u \sin v$

PROOF

$$\sin(u - v) = \cos\left[\frac{\pi}{2} - (u - v)\right] = \cos\left[\left(\frac{\pi}{2} - u\right) + v\right]$$

$$= \cos\left(\frac{\pi}{2} - u\right)\cos v - \sin\left(\frac{\pi}{2} - u\right)\sin v$$

$$= \sin u \cos v - \cos u \sin v$$

and

$$\sin(u + v) = \sin[u - (-v)] = \sin u \cos(-v) - \cos u \sin(-v)$$
$$= \sin u \cos v + \cos u \sin v \quad \blacksquare$$

● **EXAMPLE 6-4** Verify that $\sin(u + v) = \sin u \cos v + \cos u \sin v$ for $u = 3.75$ and $v = 2.46$.
We have

$$\sin(3.75 + 2.46) = (\sin 3.75)(\cos 2.46) + (\cos 3.75)(\sin 2.46)$$
$$\sin(6.21) = (-0.5715611)(-0.7765702)$$
$$+ (-0.8205598)(0.6300308)$$
$$-0.073120 = 0.44385731 - 0.51697794 = -0.073120$$

As before, by letting $u = \pi/2$ or $u = \pi$, we obtain the following identities:

THEOREM 6-13 For all $t \in \mathbb{R}$,

▶ $\sin\left(\dfrac{\pi}{2} - t\right) = \cos t$

▶ $\sin\left(\dfrac{\pi}{2} + t\right) = \cos t$

▶ $\sin(\pi - t) = \sin t$
▶ $\sin(\pi + t) = -\sin t$

PROOF We have

$$\sin\left(\frac{\pi}{2} + t\right) = \sin\frac{\pi}{2}\cos t + \cos\frac{\pi}{2}\sin t$$

$$= 1(\cos t) + 0(\sin t) = \cos t$$

The other proofs are left as exercises. $\blacksquare$

The following identities result from the definition $\tan t = \sin(t)/\cos(t)$, $\cos t \neq 0$:

THEOREM 6-14   Let $u, v \in \mathbb{R}$. Then

$$\blacktriangleright \quad \tan(u + v) = \frac{\tan u + \tan v}{1 - \tan u \tan v}$$

where $(u + v)$, u, and v are not equal to $(n + \frac{1}{2})\pi$ for $n \in \mathbb{J}$.

$$\blacktriangleright \quad \tan(u - v) = \frac{\tan u - \tan v}{1 + \tan u \tan v}$$

where $(u - v)$, u, and v are not equal to $(n + \frac{1}{2})\pi$ for $n \in \mathbb{J}$.

PROOF   The proof is left as an exercise.   ∎

● **EXAMPLE 6-5**   Verify that

$$\tan(u - v) = \frac{\tan u - \tan v}{1 + \tan u \tan v}$$

for $u = 3.75$ and $v = 2.46$.

$$\tan(3.75 - 2.46) = \frac{\tan 3.75 - \tan 2.46}{1 + \tan 3.75 \tan 2.46}$$

$$\tan(1.29) = \frac{0.6965502 - (-0.8112992)}{1 + (0.6965502)(-0.8112992)}$$

$$3.46720 = \frac{1.5078494}{1 - 0.5651106} = 3.46720$$

   Although it is possible to derive sum and difference identities for other trigonometric functions, the uses of such identities are too rare to justify their development in this text.

Double-Angle and Half-Angle Formulas

   The following theorems and identities result when $v = u$ in the sum formulas. These are the double-angle formulas for the sine, cosine, and tangent.

THEOREM 6-15   For all $u \in \mathbb{R}$,

$$\blacktriangleright \quad \sin 2u = 2 \sin u \cos u.$$

PROOF   We have

$$\sin 2u = \sin(u + u) = \sin u \cos u + \cos u \sin u = 2 \sin u \cos u \quad \blacksquare$$

THEOREM 6-16   For all $t \in \mathbb{R}$,

$$\blacktriangleright \quad \cos 2t = \cos^2 t - \sin^2 t$$
$$= 1 - 2 \sin^2 t$$
$$= 2 \cos^2 t - 1$$

PROOF We have

$$\cos 2t = \cos(t + t) = \cos t \cos t - \sin t \sin t = \cos^2 t - \sin^2 t$$

Since $\cos^2 t + \sin^2 t = 1$, substituting for $\cos^2 t$ gives $\cos^2 t = 1 - 2 \sin^2 t$; then substituting for $\sin^2 t$ gives $\cos 2t = 2 \cos^2 t - 1$. ∎

THEOREM 6-17 Let $t \in \mathbb{R}$ such that $t \neq (2n + 1)\pi/4$ for any $n \in \mathbb{J}$. Then

$$\tan 2t = \frac{2 \tan t}{1 - \tan^2 t}$$

PROOF The proof is left as an exercise. ∎

EXAMPLE 6-6 Find $\sin 3t$ in terms of $\sin t$ and $\cos t$.
We have

$$\begin{aligned}
\sin(3t) &= \sin(t + 2t) = \sin t \cos 2t + \cos t \sin 2t \\
&= \sin t(\cos^2 t - \sin^2 t) + \cos t(2 \sin t \cos t) \\
&= \sin t \cos^2 t - \sin^3 t + 2 \sin t \cos^2 t \\
&= 3 \sin t \cos^2 t - \sin^3 t
\end{aligned}$$

Note that there are alternative forms of the answer depending on which substitution for $\cos 2t$ is selected.

By rewriting the double-angle formulas, we can derive the half-angle formulas. The identity $\cos 2t = 2 \cos^2 t - 1$ can be rewritten as $2 \cos^2 t = 1 + \cos 2t$, and the identity $\cos 2t = 1 - 2 \sin^2 t$ can be rewritten as $2 \sin^2 t = 1 - \cos 2t$. The following theorems, called the half-angle formulas, result:

THEOREM 6-18 For all $t \in \mathbb{R}$,

$$\cos\left(\frac{t}{2}\right) = \pm\sqrt{\frac{1 + \cos t}{2}}$$

$$\sin\left(\frac{t}{2}\right) = \pm\sqrt{\frac{1 - \cos t}{2}}$$

PROOF Since $2 \cos^2 u = 1 + \cos 2u$, let $2u = t$; then $2 \cos^2(t/2) = 1 + \cos t$. Dividing by 2 and taking the square root, we obtain

$$\cos\left(\frac{t}{2}\right) = \pm\sqrt{\frac{1 + \cos t}{2}}$$

The equation for $\sin(t/2)$ can be obtained by similar reasoning. ∎

THEOREM 6-19 Let $t \in \mathbb{R}$ such that $t \neq (2n + 1)\pi$ for any $n \in \mathbb{J}$. Then

$$\tan\left(\frac{t}{2}\right) = \frac{\sin t}{1 + \cos t}$$

PROOF We have

$$\tan\left(\frac{t}{2}\right) = \frac{\sin(t/2)}{\cos(t/2)} = \frac{\sin(t/2)}{\cos(t/2)} \frac{2 \cos(t/2)}{2 \cos(t/2)} = \frac{2 \sin(t/2) \cos(t/2)}{2 \cos^2(t/2)}$$

Using the double-angle formulas in both numerator and denominator, we obtain

$$\tan\left(\frac{t}{2}\right) = \frac{\sin t}{1 + \cos t} \quad \blacksquare$$

Summary

The following is a summary of the identities presented in this section, included here for easy reference. These identities are true for all real numbers except as indicated, and n is any integer.

Identity	*Restriction (if any)*
$\cos u \sec u = 1$	$u \neq (n + \frac{1}{2})\pi$
$\sin u \csc u = 1$	$u \neq \pi n$
$\tan u \cot u = 1$	$u \neq n\pi/2$
$\cos^2 u + \sin^2 u = 1$	
$1 + \tan^2 u = \sec^2 u$	$u \neq (n + \frac{1}{2})\pi$
$1 + \cot^2 u = \csc^2 u$	$u \neq n\pi$
$\csc^2 u + \sec^2 u = \csc^2 u \sec^2 u$	$u \neq n\pi/2$
$\cos(-u) = \cos u$	
$\sin(-u) = -\sin u$	
$\cos(u - v) = \cos u \cos v + \sin u \sin v$	
$\cos(u + v) = \cos u \cos v - \sin u \sin v$	
$\cos(\pi/2 - t) = \sin t$	
$\cos(\pi/2 + t) = -\sin t$	
$\cos(\pi - t) = -\cos t$	
$\cos(\pi + t) = -\cos t$	
$\sin(u - v) = \sin u \cos v - \cos u \sin v$	
$\sin(u + v) = \sin u \cos v + \cos u \sin v$	
$\sin(\pi/2 - t) = \cos t$	
$\sin(\pi/2 + t) = \cos t$	
$\sin(\pi - t) = \sin t$	
$\sin(\pi + t) = -\sin t$	
$\tan(u + v) = \dfrac{\tan u + \tan v}{1 - \tan u \tan v}$	$(u + v)$, and u, and $v \neq (n + \frac{1}{2})\pi$
$\tan(u - v) = \dfrac{\tan u - \tan v}{1 + \tan u \tan v}$	$(u - v)$, and u, and $v \neq (n + \frac{1}{2})\pi$
$\sin 2u = 2 \sin u \cos u$	
$\cos 2u = \cos^2 u - \sin^2 u$	
$\quad = 2 \cos^2 u - 1$	
$\quad = 1 - 2 \sin^2 u$	
$\tan 2u = \dfrac{2 \tan u}{1 - \tan^2 u}$	$u \neq (2n + 1)\pi/4$

$$\cos(u/2) = \pm\sqrt{\frac{1 + \cos u}{2}} \qquad \text{minus sign used when } u/2 \text{ is in second or third quadrant}$$

$$\sin(u/2) = \pm\sqrt{\frac{1 - \cos u}{2}} \qquad \text{minus sign used when } u/2 \text{ is in third or fourth quadrant}$$

$$\tan(u/2) = \frac{\sin u}{1 + \cos u} \qquad u \neq (2n + 1)\pi$$

EXAMPLE 6-7 Show that the following are identities:

(a) $\sin u \sec u \cot u = 1$

$$\sin u \sec u \cot u = (\sin u)\frac{1}{\cos u}\frac{\cos u}{\sin u} = 1$$

(b) $(1 + \cot^2 t)(1 - \cos^2 t) = 1$

$$(1 + \cot^2 t)(1 - \cos^2 t) = \csc^2 t \sin^2 t = \frac{1}{\sin^2 t}\sin^2 t = 1$$

(c) $\dfrac{\sec \theta + \csc \theta}{1 + \tan \theta} = \csc \theta$

$$\frac{\sec \theta + \csc \theta}{1 + \tan \theta} = \csc \theta\left[\frac{(\sec \theta)/(\csc \theta) + 1}{1 + \tan \theta}\right]$$

$$= \csc \theta\left[\frac{\tan \theta + 1}{1 + \tan \theta}\right] = \csc \theta$$

(d) $\dfrac{1 + \cos 2u}{\sin 2u} = \cot u$

$$\frac{1 + \cos 2u}{\sin 2u} = \frac{1 + 2\cos^2 u - 1}{2 \sin u \cos u} = \frac{\cos^2 u}{\sin u \cos u}$$

$$= \frac{\cos u}{\sin u} = \cot u$$

EXERCISES 6-1

Set A

1. Using the sum, difference, and double-angle trigonometric identities, convert the argument of the given function to a first-quadrant angle and evaluate. (Remember that $90° = \pi/2 \approx 1.57$, $180° = \pi \approx 3.14$, $270° = \frac{3}{2}\pi \approx 4.71$, and $360° = 2\pi \approx 6.28$. Use tables in Appendix C.)
    (a) $\sin 236°$ (b) $\cos 5.27$
    (c) $\tan 2.43$ (d) $\sec 206°$
    (e) $\cos 3.28$ (f) $\cot -127°$
    (g) $\csc 4.92$ (h) $\sin 2.76$
    (i) $\cos 320°$ (j) $\sin 3.21$
    (k) $\tan 2.05$ (l) $\sec 280°$

2. Prove that $\tan t \cot t = 1$ for $t \neq n\pi/2$, $n \in \mathbb{J}$.

3. Prove that for all $t \in \mathbb{R}$,
   (a) $\cos(\pi - t) = -\cos t$
   (b) $\cos(\pi + t) = -\cos t$
   (c) $\sin(\pi/2 - t) = \cos t$
   (d) $\sin(\pi - t) = \sin t$
   (e) $\sin(\pi + t) = -\sin t$

4. Prove that the tangent is an odd function.

Set B

5. Prove Theorem 6-14.

6. Prove that
$$\tan 2t = \frac{2\tan t}{1 - \tan^2 t}$$
   for $t \neq (2n + 1)\pi/4$.

7. Prove that $\sec^2 t \csc^2 t = \sec^2 t + \csc^2 t$. What restrictions, if any, must be made on t for this to be true?

8. Express $\cos 3t$ in terms of functions having argument t.

9. Show that the following are identities and indicate any restrictions on $u \in \mathbb{R}$.
   (a) $\sin 2u - \tan u \cos 2u = \tan u$
   (b) $\sin 4u + 2\sin 2u = 4\sin 2u \cos^2 u$
   (c) $\dfrac{2\sin u - \sin 2u}{1 - \cos u} = 2\sin u$
   (d) $\dfrac{1 + \sec u}{\csc u} = \sin u + \tan u$
   (e) $\tan^2 \theta - \sin^2 \theta = \sin^2 \theta \tan^2 \theta$
   (f) $\dfrac{1 - \sin x}{\cos x} = \dfrac{1}{\sec x + \tan x}$
   (g) $(\sin t - \cos t)^2 = 1 - 2\sin t \cos t$
   (h) $\cos u \cot u = \csc u - \sin u$
   (i) $\dfrac{\sec^4 y - 1}{\tan^2 y} = \tan^2 y + 2$

Set C

10. Prove that for all $u, v \in \mathbb{R}$,
    (a) $\cos u \cos v = \frac{1}{2}\cos(u - v) + \frac{1}{2}\cos(u + v)$
    (b) $\sin u \sin v = \frac{1}{2}\cos(u - v) - \frac{1}{2}\cos(u + v)$
    (c) $\sin u \cos v = \frac{1}{2}\sin(u + v) + \frac{1}{2}\sin(u - v)$
    (d) $\cos u \sin v = \frac{1}{2}\sin(u + v) - \frac{1}{2}\sin(u - v)$

11. Prove that for $u, v \in \mathbb{R}$ with proper restrictions on u and v, the following is an identity:
$$\tan v + \tan u \tan v \tan(u - v) = \tan u - \tan(u - v)$$

6-2 INVERSE TRIGONOMETRIC RELATIONS

Introduction

We discussed the general concept of an inverse relation in Chapter 2. To review, if ρ is a relation, then ρ^{-1} is the relation obtained by interchanging the domain and range elements of the ordered pairs of ρ. If the relation is a function, f, then the inverse relation, f^{-1}, is a function if and only if f is one to one *and* onto.

Consider the problem of finding the inverse function for $y = f(x) = x^2 - 6$, $x \geqslant 0$. Since $x \geqslant 0$, f is a strictly monotonic function and thus is one to one. Moreover, for $A = \{x \mid x \geqslant 0\}$ and $B = \{y \mid y \geqslant -6\}$, we have

$$f: A \twoheadrightarrow B$$

Thus, f is an onto mapping and has an inverse *function*.

In order to find f^{-1}, we use the method developed in Chapter 2. This yields the inverse relation

$$z = \pm \sqrt{x + 6} = f^{-1}(x)$$

which is not a function. The inverse function is obtained by selecting the principal branch of f^{-1}. Figure 6-5 shows the graphs of f and of f^{-1} (with its two branches). Clearly, the principal branch is

$$f^{-1}(x) = +\sqrt{x + 6}$$

so this is the equation of the inverse function.

To see what happens when the wrong branch is chosen, suppose we had chosen

$$f^{-1}(x) = -\sqrt{x + 6}$$

as the inverse function. Then since $f^{-1}[f(x)]$ must equal $f[f^{-1}(x)] = x$, we would have

$$f^{-1}[f(x)] = -\sqrt{f(x) + 6} = -\sqrt{(x^2 - 6) + 6} = -\sqrt{x^2} = -|x|$$

Thus, $-|x| = x$ or $|x| = -x$. But this is true only if $x \leqslant 0$, which contradicts the original assumption that $x \geqslant 0$.

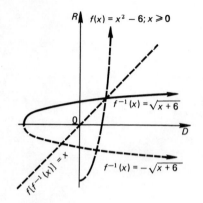

FIGURE 6-5

The Inverse Tangent Function

It is clear from the graphs of the circular functions that these are *not* strictly monotonic functions; therefore, there is no guarantee that their inverse relations will be functions. Figure 6-6 shows the graph of the tangent as a function of the real variable t; the range is the set of all real numbers. If we select an element from the range, say, $+1$, then there exists at least one element of the domain, t, such that $\tan t = 1$. In fact, there are an infinite number of such values of t, such as $t = \pi/4$, $5\pi/4$, and $-3\pi/4$.

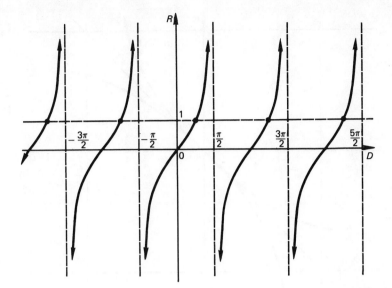

FIGURE 6-6

Specifically,

$$\tan t = 1 \quad \text{when} \quad t = \frac{4k+1}{4}\pi$$

where $k \in J$. Clearly, the inverse relation of the tangent is *not* a function.

In Chapter 2, we saw that when the inverse relation is not a function, it is often possible to restrict the domain of the function so that its inverse is also a function. We can find a suitable restriction by asking in which portions of its domain is the function strictly monotonic. For the case $f(t)$ = tan t, it can be seen from Figure 6-6 that there are an infinite number of such regions. It is usual to choose the region where the graph of f passes through the origin, that is, the interval $-\pi/2 < t < \pi/2$. Thus, the restriction

$$f(t) = \tan t \quad \text{for } -\pi/2 < t < \pi/2$$

is the *principal branch* of the tangent function. Furthermore, for $A = \{t \mid -\pi/2 < t < \pi/2\}$ and $B = \mathbb{R}$,

$$f: A \twoheadrightarrow B$$

that is, f maps A *onto* B. Thus, f has an inverse *function*, f^{-1}, which maps B onto A:

$$f^{-1}: B \twoheadrightarrow A$$

To distinguish the principal branch of the tangent function from the tangent defined for the largest possible domain, we capitalize the name of the principal branch. Thus, Tan t is the principal branch of tan t. The inverse function is symbolized

$$\text{Tan}^{-1} \quad \text{or} \quad \text{Arctan}$$

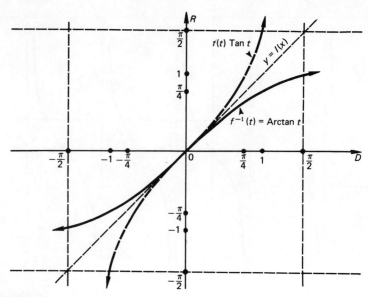

FIGURE 6-7

Figure 6-7 shows the principal branch of $f(t) = \text{Tan } t$ with its inverse function, $f^{-1}(t) = \text{Tan}^{-1} t = \text{Arctan } t$. Note that

$$f[f^{-1}(t)] = f^{-1}[f(t)] = I(t) = t$$

where I is the Identity Function, so the graphs of $f(t) = \text{Tan } t$ and $f^{-1}(t) = \text{Tan}^{-1} t = \text{Arctan } t$ are symmetric about the line $y = I(t) = t$.

DEFINITION Let $t \in \mathbb{R}$. Then the **inverse tangent** of t, denoted $\text{Tan}^{-1} t$ or $\text{Arctan } t$, is the real number u, $-\pi/2 \leqslant u \leqslant \pi/2$, such that $t = \tan u$; that is,

▶ $\text{Tan}^{-1} = \{(t, u) \mid t = \tan u \text{ for } -\pi/2 < u < \pi/2\}$

Note that if no restriction is made on the domain to define the principal branch, then the inverse is not a function. The inverse relation is denoted

▶ $\tan^{-1} = \arctan = \{(t, u) \mid t = \tan u \text{ for } u \in \mathbb{R}, u \neq (n + \tfrac{1}{2})\pi\}$

EXAMPLE 6-8 Find s such that $s = \text{Tan}^{-1}\sqrt{3}$.
By definition, $\tan s = \sqrt{3}$. Since $-\pi/2 < s < \pi/2$, $s = \pi/3$.

EXAMPLE 6-9 Find v such that $v = \text{Arctan}(-1)$.
By definition, $\tan v = -1$. For v in the principal branch, $v = -\pi/4$.

The Inverse Sine Function

Now consider the graph of the sine function, shown in Figure 6-8. Clearly, this function is *not* strictly monotonic and therefore does not have an inverse function. By restricting the domain, we can define a principal branch of $y = \sin u$ that is strictly monotonic. If we choose the domain $A = \{u \mid -\pi/2 \leqslant u \leqslant \pi/2\}$, then the restricted function, which we call Sin, is one to one and onto the set $B = \{y \mid -1 \leqslant y \leqslant 1\}$. Thus,

$$\text{Sin}: A \twoheadrightarrow B$$

and there exists an inverse function,

$$\text{Sin}^{-1}: B \twoheadrightarrow A$$

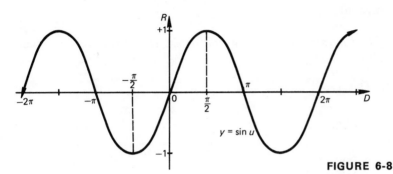

FIGURE 6-8

which is also one to one and onto. Figure 6-9 shows the graph of the inverse sine function, Sin^{-1}, and the principal branch of the sine function, which are symmetric about the graph of the identity function.

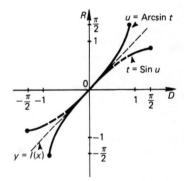

FIGURE 6-9

DEFINITION   Let $t \in \mathbb{R}$, $-1 \leqslant t \leqslant 1$. Then the **inverse sine** of t, denoted $\text{Sin}^{-1} t$ or Arcsin t, is the real number u, $-\pi/2 \leqslant u \leqslant \pi/2$, such that $t = \sin u$; that is,

▶ $\text{Sin}^{-1} = \{(t, u) \mid t = \sin u \text{ for } -\pi/2 \leqslant u \leqslant \pi/2\}$

As with the inverse tangent, if no restriction is made to a principal branch, then the inverse sine is not a function but is a relation denoted

▶ $\sin^{-1} = \text{arcsin} = \{(t, u) \mid t = \sin u \text{ for all } u \in \mathbb{R}\}$

EXAMPLE 6-10   Find v such that $v = \text{Sin}^{-1}(-\frac{1}{2})$.
By definition, $\sin v = -\frac{1}{2}$. For v in the principal branch, $v = -\pi/6$.

The Inverse Cosine Function

In a similar way, we can define the inverse cosine function. Figure 6-10 shows the graph of the inverse cosine function, Cos^{-1}, with the principal branch of the cosine function. Note that in this case, the restricted domain is $\{u \mid 0 \leqslant u \leqslant \pi\}$.

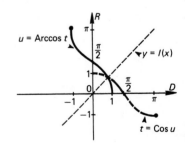

FIGURE 6-10

DEFINITION   Let $t \in \mathbb{R}$, $-1 \leqslant t \leqslant 1$. Then the **inverse cosine** of t, denoted $\text{Cos}^{-1} t$ or Arccos t, is the real number u, $0 \leqslant u \leqslant \pi$, such that $t = \cos u$; that is,

▶ $\text{Cos}^{-1} = \{(t, u) \mid t = \cos u \text{ for } 0 \leqslant u \leqslant \pi\}$

As before, if no restriction is made to the principal branch, then the inverse is not a function. The inverse relation is denoted

▶ $\cos^{-1} = \arccos = \{(t, u) \mid t = \cos u \text{ for all } u \in \mathbb{R}\}$

EXAMPLE 6-11 Find $y = \text{Cos}^{-1}[\sin(\pi/6)]$.

Since $\sin \pi/6 = \frac{1}{2}$, $y = \text{Cos}^{-1}(\frac{1}{2})$. Then $\text{Cos } y = \frac{1}{2}$ and $y = \pi/3$.

Summary

The following is a summary of the six inverse trigonometric functions with their regions of definition:

TABLE 6-1

Inverse function	Domain of inverse	Range of inverse
$u = \text{Tan}^{-1} t$ $\quad = \text{Arctan } t$	$t \in \mathbb{R}$	$-\pi/2 < u < \pi/2$
$u = \text{Sin}^{-1} t$ $\quad = \text{Arcsin } t$	$-1 \leqslant t \leqslant 1$	$-\pi/2 \leqslant u \leqslant \pi/2$
$u = \text{Cos}^{-1} t$ $\quad = \text{Arccos } t$	$-1 \leqslant t \leqslant 1$	$0 \leqslant u \leqslant \pi$
$u = \text{Cot}^{-1} t$ $\quad = \text{Arccot } t$	$t \in \mathbb{R}$	$0 < u < \pi$
$u = \text{Csc}^{-1} t$ $\quad = \text{Arccsc } t$	$t \in \mathbb{R}, t \geqslant 1, t \leqslant -1$	$-\pi/2 \leqslant u \leqslant \pi/2, u \neq 0$
$u = \text{Sec}^{-1} t$ $\quad = \text{Arcsec } t$	$t \in \mathbb{R}, t \geqslant 1, t \leqslant -1$	$0 \leqslant u \leqslant \pi, u \neq \pi/2$

EXAMPLE 6-12 Find $s = \text{Arccot}[\cos(-\pi/6)]$.

Since $\cos(-\pi/6) = \sqrt{3}/2$, $s = \text{Arccot } \sqrt{3}/2$. Then $\text{Cot } s = \sqrt{3}/2$. Then s is the number whose cotangent is $\sqrt{3}/2$. But $\text{Cot } s = 1/\text{Tan } s$, so since $\text{Cot } s = \sqrt{3}/2$, we have $\text{Tan } s = 2/\sqrt{3}$. Therefore, $s = 0.85707$.

EXAMPLE 6-13 Find $h = \tan(\text{Arcsin } 2/5)$.

Let $v = \text{Arcsin } 2/5$; then $\text{Sin } v = 2/5$, so $v = 0.4115$. Then $h = \tan 0.4115 = 0.4364$.

EXERCISES 6-2

Set A

1. Evaluate the following expressions, to two decimal places, if possible:
    (a) Arcsin 0.7
    (b) Arcsin 5
    (c) Arccos −2.4
    (d) Arccos −0.3

(e)   Arctan 0.75   (f)   Arcsin -0.56

(g)   Arctan -0.42 (h)   Arccos 0.82

(i)   Arcsec 0.4   (j)   Arccsc 0.8

2.   Evaluate the following expressions, to two decimal places, if possible:

(a) $u = \sin(\text{Tan}^{-1}\frac{4}{3})$ (b) $v = \cos(\text{Arcsin }\frac{1}{5})$

(c) $\theta = \text{Tan}^{-1}(\cos 4)$ (d) $\phi = \text{Cos}^{-1}(\tan \pi/3)$

(e) $s = \text{Sin}^{-1}(\cot \pi/6)$ (f) $t = \text{Arccos}(\tan 2)$

(g) $y = \cos(\text{Cot}^{-1} 0)$ (h) $x = \sec(\text{Tan}^{-1} \pi/3)$

Set B

3.   Graph the following functions for their proper domain:

(a) $u = \text{Cot}^{-1} t$ (b) $u = \text{Csc}^{-1} t$

(c) $u = \text{Sec}^{-1} t$

4.   Prove that the Arctan is an odd function.

5.   Prove that the arcsec is neither an odd nor even relation.

6.   Prove that for $-1 \leqslant t \leqslant 1$, $\text{Cos}^{-1} t + \text{Sin}^{-1} t = \pi/2$.

Set C

In Exercises 7, 8, and 9, prove that the given relationships are true. (*Hint:* Construct a right triangle with hypotenuse of length 1 or $\sqrt{1 + u^2}$. The expressions containing u can be related to trigonometric functions of the angles.)

7. $\text{Arcsin } u = \dfrac{\pi}{2} - \text{Arccos } u, u^2 \leqslant 1$

8. $\text{Arctan } u = \text{Arcsin } \dfrac{u}{\sqrt{1 + u^2}}, u \in \mathbb{R}$

9. $\text{Arctan } u + \text{Arcsec } \dfrac{\sqrt{1 + u^2}}{u} = \dfrac{\pi}{2}, u \in \mathbb{R}$

6-3   TRIGONOMETRIC EQUATIONS

Trigonometric identities and the inverse trigonometric relations have useful applications in the solution of equations that contain circular relations. Such equations are called *trigonometric equations*. There is no standard technique to be used in solving these equations, but the basic idea is to perform any legitimate substitution or operation that will isolate the variable for which we wish to solve.

The following examples serve as a guide for solving trigonometric equations. Note that principal branch restrictions are usually not specified; in such cases, since the trigonometric functions are periodic, there are an infinite number of solutions. When the solutions are restricted to the principal branch of the function, they are called *basic solutions*.

EXAMPLE 6-14   Find the basic solution to the equation $\sin 2t = \cos t$.
Since the arguments of the functions are not the same, an

appropriate identity is needed. Since $\sin 2t = 2 \sin t \cos t$, the original equation becomes

$$2 \sin t \cos t = \cos t$$

Bringing $\cos t$ to the left and factoring, we obtain

$$\cos t (2 \sin t - 1) = 0$$

which has the solutions $\cos t = 0$ and $2 \sin t - 1 = 0$. In the first case,

$$\cos t = 0$$

so $t = \arccos 0$. For the basic solution,

$$t = \text{Arccos } 0$$

The angle in the principal branch whose cosine is 0 is $\pi/2$. In the second case,

$$2 \sin t - 1 = 0$$
$$\sin t = \tfrac{1}{2}$$

so $t = \arcsin \tfrac{1}{2}$. For the basic solution,

$$t = \text{Arcsin } \tfrac{1}{2}$$

The angle in the principal branch whose sine is $\tfrac{1}{2}$ is $\pi/6$. Hence, the basic solution set, S, of the equation $\sin 2t = \cos t$ is $S = \{\pi/2, \pi/6\}$.

In solving the equation of the previous example, one might be tempted to proceed as follows:

$$\sin 2\theta = \cos \theta$$
$$2 \sin \theta \cos \theta = \cos \theta$$

Canceling $\cos \theta$ from both sides of the equation gives

$$2 \sin \theta = 1$$
$$\sin \theta = \tfrac{1}{2}$$
$$\theta = \text{Arcsin } \tfrac{1}{2} = \pi/6$$

This is a serious error. Why??

EXAMPLE 6-15 Solve the equation $\cos 2x + \sin x = 0$ for all values x.
If we convert the double angle to a single value by a trigonometric identity, the equation becomes

$$1 - 2 \sin^2 x + \sin x = 0$$

or

$$-2 \sin^2 x + \sin x + 1 = 0$$

or

$$2(\sin x)^2 - \sin x - 1 = 0$$

This is a quadratic equation in $\sin x$, which can be solved either by the quadratic formula or by factoring. The equation is factorable into the form

$$(2 \sin x + 1)(\sin x - 1) = 0$$

So the solutions are $2 \sin x + 1 = 0$ and $\sin x - 1 = 0$, which yield $\sin x = -\frac{1}{2}$ and $\sin x = 1$, respectively. In the first case,

$$x = \arcsin(-\tfrac{1}{2}) = \ldots, -\frac{5\pi}{6}, -\frac{\pi}{6}, \frac{7\pi}{6}, \frac{11\pi}{6}, \ldots$$

so there are two solution sets,

$$S_1 = \left\{ x \mid x = (12k - 1)\frac{\pi}{6} \text{ for } k \in \mathbb{J} \right\}$$

and

$$S_2 = \left\{ x \mid x = (12k - 5)\frac{\pi}{6} \text{ for } k \in \mathbb{J} \right\}$$

In the second case,

$$x = \arcsin 1 = \ldots, -\frac{3\pi}{2}, \frac{\pi}{2}, \frac{5\pi}{2}, \ldots$$

so the solution set, S_3, is

$$S_3 = \left\{ x \mid x = (4k + 1)\frac{\pi}{2} \text{ for } k \in \mathbb{J} \right\}$$

The complete solution set, S, is the union of these sets.

$$S = S_1 \cup S_2 \cup S_3$$
$$= \Big\{ x \mid x = (12k - 1)\frac{\pi}{6}, \text{ or } x = (12k - 5)\frac{\pi}{6},$$
$$\text{or } x = (4k + 1)\frac{\pi}{2} \text{ for } k \in \mathbb{J} \Big\}$$

We leave it to the student to find the basic solution set (see Exercise 4 at the end of this section).

EXAMPLE 6-16 Find all values of t that satisfy the equation

$$\sin t \cos t = \sqrt{2}$$

If we multiply both sides of the equation by 2, the left side becomes the form of the double-angle formula for the sine:

$$2 \cos t \sin t = 2\sqrt{2}$$
$$\sin 2t = 2\sqrt{2}$$

Then

$$2t = \arcsin 2\sqrt{2}$$
$$t = \tfrac{1}{2} \arcsin 2\sqrt{2}$$

But this solution is impossible, because the domain of arcsin x is $-1 \leqslant x \leqslant 1$. Hence, there is no solution, so the solution set is $S = \varnothing$.

EXAMPLE 6-17   A biologist studying an ecological system discovers that the birth and death rates for the dominant animal species are given by

$$B = \cos^2 t + 2 \cos t \quad \text{and} \quad D = -\cos 2t$$

respectively, where t is the time in months measured from some fixed reference. What is the smallest positive t value for which the birth and death rates are equal? (Assume that time, t, is not negative, i.e., $t \geqslant 0$.)

Setting $B = D$ results in

$$\cos^2 t + 2 \cos t = -\cos 2t$$

By the double-angle cosine formula, this becomes

$$\cos^2 t + 2 \cos t = 1 - 2 \cos^2 t$$

which simplifies to

$$3 \cos^2 t + 2 \cos t - 1 = 0$$

When factored, this equation becomes

$$(3 \cos t - 1)(\cos t + 1) = 0$$

which yields

$$\cos t = \tfrac{1}{3}, \qquad \cos t = -1$$

When $\cos t = \tfrac{1}{3}$, the smallest nonnegative value of t is

$$t = \text{Arccos}(\tfrac{1}{3}) = 1.2310$$

in months. When $\cos t = -1$, the smallest nonnegative value of t is

$$t = \text{Arccos}(-1) = \pi = 3.1416$$

in months. Therefore, the smallest t value for which the birth and death rates are equal is

$$t = 1.2310 \text{ months}$$

EXERCISES 6-3

Set A

1.   For each of the following equations, find the solution set in the principal branch of the function (where possible, leave answers in terms of π):
   (a) $\sin x = 1$
   (b) $\cos u = -\tfrac{1}{2}$
   (c) $\tan 2t = 1$
   (d) $\cot 4x = 0$
   (e) $\sin^2 \theta = \tfrac{1}{4}$
   (f) $\sec^2 v = 4$
   (g) $\tan^3 4s = 1$
   (h) $\sqrt{2} \sin^{1/2} 2n = 1$

2. For equations (a) and (b) in Exercise 1, find the complete solution set.

3. Find the basic solution set for each of the following equations:
   (a) $\sin^2 u + \cos^2 u - 1 = 0$
   (b) $\tan^2 v - \sec^2 v + 1 = 0$
   (c) $\sin 2\theta - 3 = 0$
   (d) $\sec^2 t - \frac{1}{4} = 0$
   (e) $2 \csc u - 1 = 0$

4. Find the basic solution set for the result of Example 6-15.

Set B

5. Find the solution set for each of the following equations for $-\pi < t \leqslant \pi$:
   (a) $\sin t + \cos t = -6$
   (b) $\sin^3 2t = 1$
   (c) $\cos t = \cos 2t$
   (d) $\sin t = \sin 2t$
   (e) $\sin t = \cos 2t$
   (f) $\cos t = \sin 2t$
   (g) $\cos^2 t + 4 \cos t = 5$
   (h) $\sin t - \sin^2 t = 2$
   (i) $\sin 2t - \sin 4t = 0$
   (j) $\tan t - 2 \sin t = 0$
   (k) $\sec^2 t - 4 \tan t = 1$
   (l) $3 \cot t + \tan t = 6$

6. Solve for t.
   (a) $\text{Sin}^{-1} 2t = \text{Cos}^{-1}(t)$
   (b) $\text{Sin}^{-1}(\tan t) = \pi/2$
   (c) $2 \text{Cos}^{-1}\sqrt{2}/2 + t = 5\pi/4$
   (d) $\sqrt{3} \text{Cos } t - \text{Sin } t + 1 = 0$
   (e) $3 \text{Cos}^2 t + 2 \text{Sin } t + 2 = 0$
   (f) $\text{Tan } t - \text{Sec } t + 1 = 0$

Set C

7. Solve for u.
   (a) $\cos u = \pi/4$
   (b) $\tan u = \pi/2$
   (c) $\cos(\sin u) = 0$
   (d) $\sec(\cos u) = 1$
   (e) $\text{Cos}^{-1}(\text{Sin}^{-1} u) = \pi$
   (f) $\text{Tan}^{-1}(\text{Cos}^{-1} u) = 1$

8. A government agency has determined that the rate of welfare cost, u, and the rate of economic growth, G, were trigonometric functions of time, t. For $t \geqslant 0$ and initial time $t = 2$, find when u and G will next have the same value if

$$u = 27 - 20 \sin^2 t \quad \text{and} \quad G = 10 - 17 \cos t$$

9. Solve for x.
   (a) $\text{Sin}^2 x = 6 \text{Sin } x + 7$
   (b) $\text{Sin } x = \text{Sin } 4x$
   (c) $\text{Sin } 4x = \text{Cos } x$

REVIEW EXERCISES FOR CHAPTER 6

1. Find the values of the following expressions by using the trigonometric identities to convert the arguments to first-quadrant angles:
   (a) $\sin 7.24$
   (b) $\cos 8.31$
   (c) $\cos -4.1$
   (d) $\sin -2.8$
   (e) $\tan 14.2$
   (f) $\sec 16.9$

2. Prove the following identities:
   (a) $\csc \theta \sec \theta = \tan \theta + \cot \theta$
   (b) $\cot \theta = \csc 2\theta + \cot 2\theta$

3. Find the values of the following functions to three decimal places:
   (a) Arctan 23
   (b) Arcsin 0.34
   (c) Arccos -0.23
   (d) Arcsec -7.1

4. Solve for x.
   (a) $\text{Csc}^2 x = 9$
   (b) $\text{Cot } 2x = 1$
   (c) $\text{Sec } 4x = 0$
   (d) $\text{Cos}^2 x = 0.81$

5. Solve for u.

   (a) $\frac{1}{2} = \text{Sin}(\text{Cos}^{-1} u)$
   (b) $u = \text{Tan}^{-1}\left(\sin\frac{2\pi}{3}\right)$

   (c) $\text{Sec } u = \text{Tan}^{-1} \sqrt{3}$

The Exponential and Logarithmic Functions

7-1 THE EXPONENTIAL FUNCTION

Introduction

Suppose a bacterial culture has the property of doubling its population every hour. How can this property be formulated mathematically? If A_0 is the size of the initial population, then hourly observations will yield the population sizes listed in Table 7-1. For each hour after the initial observa-

TABLE 7-1

Hour n	Population size
Initial observation	A_0
1	$2A_0$
2	$4A_0$
3	$8A_0$
4	$16A_0$

tion, the coefficient of A_0 is an integral power of 2; that is, $A_1 = 2^1 A_0$, $A_2 = 2^2 A_0$, $A_3 = 2^3 A_0$, $A_4 = 2^4 A_0$, etc. Hence, after n hours have passed, the population size is given by the equation

$$A_n = A_0 2^n, \qquad n = 1, 2, 3, \ldots$$

Base Conditions and the Exponential Function

Is it possible to give meaning to observation times that are not integers? And since the observation time appears as the exponent of 2, is it permissible to use any real exponent in this equation? These questions lead us to consider equations of the form

$$A(x) = A_0 2^x, \qquad x \in \mathbb{R}$$

and, more generally, equations in which the base is an arbitrary fixed real number, b:

$$A(x) = A_0 b^x, \qquad x \in \mathbb{R}$$

Such an equation always describes a relation, but not always a real-valued relation or a function. What values of b will make this relation real? Certainly, b must be real. However, since $x \in \mathbb{R}$, the expression $A_0 b^x$ will take on such values as $(-3)^{1/2}$. This is not a real number, because by the laws of exponents,

$$(-3)^{1/2} = \sqrt{-3} = i\sqrt{3}$$

a pure imaginary number. In general, if b is negative, then certain values of the exponent, x, will result in an even root of b, which is an imaginary number. Thus, we exclude negative values of b.

In the case $b = 0$, the expression $A_0 b^x$ has no meaning when x is negative, because

$$b^{-n} = \frac{1}{b^n} = \frac{1}{0^n} = \frac{1}{0}$$

and division by 0 is an undefined operation. Thus, we restrict b to the set

$$\{b \in \mathbb{R} \mid b > 0\}$$

We can also exclude $b = 1$ from consideration, since

$$1^x = 1 \quad \text{for all } x \in \mathbb{R}$$

Thus, although the relation is real for $b = 1$, it is a constant relation, belonging to a class of functions already discussed. So we wish to consider the real-valued relation

$$A(x) = A_0 b^x, \qquad x \in \mathbb{R}, \, b > 0, \, b \neq 1$$

When is this relation a function?

In the case of the relation

$$y = 2^x, \qquad x \in \mathbb{R}$$

which has $b = 2$, we know how to evaluate y for any rational value of x. For rational x, this relation satisfies the definition of a function, because for each value of x, there is only one corresponding value of y. Furthermore, expressions such as $2^{\sqrt{1.7}}$, $2^{-\pi}$, and $2^{\sqrt{5}}$, which involve irrational exponents, can be given unique numerical values with the techniques of the calculus, so the equation $y = 2^x$ $(x \in \mathbb{R})$ describes a real-valued function. In general, the equation

$$A(x) = A_0 b^x, \qquad x \in \mathbb{R}, b > 0, b \neq 1$$

describes a real-valued function with domain $\mathbb{R}$. However, because defining the unique value of b^x for irrational x requires the methods of the calculus, we will simply assume that b^x has a unique value for any $b > 0$, $x \in \mathbb{R}$. In particular, the function given by

$$\blacktriangleright \quad y = b^x, \qquad x \in \mathbb{R}, b > 0, b \neq 1$$

is called an *exponential function*.

DEFINITION   Let $x, b \in \mathbb{R}$, where $b > 0$, $b \neq 1$. Then the function E_b defined by

$$\blacktriangleright \quad E_b: x \rightarrow b^x$$

is called the **exponential function** with base b.

EXAMPLE 7-1   The functions

$$\begin{array}{ll} A(x) = 3^x, & x \in \mathbb{R} \\ G(x) = \pi^{-x}, & x \in \mathbb{R} \\ H(x) = (\sqrt{2})^{3x}, & x \in \mathbb{R} \end{array}$$

are all exponential functions, because in each case, the base is a positive real number not equal to 1 and the exponent takes on all real values. In contrast, the functions

$$\begin{array}{ll} P(x) = 4x^2 - 3x, & x \in \mathbb{R} \\ Q(x) = (x^2 + 1)^{-4}, & x \in \mathbb{R} \end{array}$$

are algebraic, because the base values are the variables and the exponents are fixed rational numbers.

Graphing Exponential Functions

Consider the exponential function

$$E_2(x) = 2^x$$

for integer domain values from $x = -4$ to $x = +4$. Using these domain values, we can determine the corresponding range values, plot these ordered pairs in the DR plane, and thus obtain a graphical representation for this function. We have

$$\begin{array}{ll} E_2(-4) = 2^{-4} = \frac{1}{16} & E_2(1) = 2^1 = 2 \\ E_2(-3) = 2^{-3} = \frac{1}{8} & E_2(2) = 2^2 = 4 \\ E_2(-2) = 2^{-2} = \frac{1}{4} & E_2(3) = 2^3 = 8 \\ E_2(-1) = 2^{-1} = \frac{1}{2} & E_2(4) = 2^4 = 16 \\ E_2(0) = 2^0 = 1 & \end{array}$$

These domain values and their corresponding range values are listed in Table 7-2.

TABLE 7-2

x	$E_2(x) = 2^x$
-4	$\frac{1}{16}$
-3	$\frac{1}{8}$
-2	$\frac{1}{4}$
-1	$\frac{1}{2}$
0	1
1	2
2	4
3	8
4	16

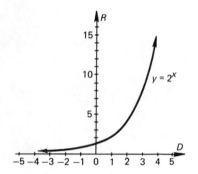

FIGURE 7-1

By plotting these points and connecting them with a smooth curve, we obtain the graph for the exponential function 2^x. As we mentioned earlier, drawing this smooth curve assumes that raising 2 to nonintegral powers (and, in particular, to irrational powers) yields a unique value that falls on the curve. The graph is shown in Figure 7-1.

Note that as x becomes larger and larger, the function value, $E_2(x)$, also becomes increasingly larger. For example, if $x = 10$, then $E_2(10) = 2^{10} = 1024$. On the other hand, when x is negative, the function value, $E_2(x)$, is positive and less than 1; for extremely large negative values of x, the function approaches 0 through positive values. For example, if $x = -10$, then $E_2(-10) = 2^{-10} = 1/1024$, which is a small positive number. Therefore, the function $E_2(x) = 2^x$ is positive for all $x \in \mathbb{R}$. In fact, any exponential function, E_b, maps $\mathbb{R}$ onto the set of positive real numbers. Hence, if set B is defined as

$$B = \{y \mid y > 0\}$$

then we can write

$$\blacktriangleright \quad E_b \colon \mathbb{R} \twoheadrightarrow B$$

There are an infinite number of exponential functions, because b can be any positive real number not equal to 1. The functions 3^x, 10^x, 27^x, π^x, 6^x, and 7.654^x are other examples of exponential functions.

An interesting special case of an exponential function is $E_{10}(x) = 10^x$, which has the property that when the values of x are integers, the values of $E_{10}(x)$ form the basis of the decimal system. The values of this function for some integral values of x are listed in Table 7-3. If we plot the corresponding points and connect them with a smooth curve, we obtain the graph shown in Figure 7-2. For comparison, the graph of the function $E_2(x) = 2^x$ is also shown.

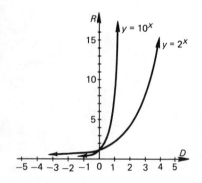

FIGURE 7-2

TABLE 7-3

7-1 *The Exponential* **245**
Function

x	$E_{10}(x) = 10^x$
-4	0.0001
-3	0.001
-2	0.01
-1	0.1
0	1
1	10
2	100
3	1000
4	10,000

Simple Exponential Equations

The basic laws of exponents can be used to evaluate simple exponential forms, especially if the base value is an integer. The following example illustrates the process.

● **EXAMPLE 7-2** Using the laws of exponents, evaluate and graph $y = 10(1 - 2^{-x})^2$ for $0 \leqslant x \leqslant 6$, for x in increments of 1.

First, put the equation in the form

$$y = 10\left(1 - \frac{1}{2^x}\right)^2$$

Table 7-4 lists the calculated values of y, and the graph is shown in

TABLE 7-4

$y = 10(1 - 2^{-x})^2$

x	y
0	0
1	2.5
2	5.625
3	7.65625
4	8.78906
5	9.38477
6	9.68994

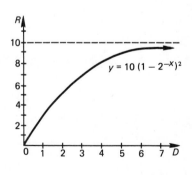

FIGURE 7-3

Figure 7-3. Note that the curve asymptotically approaches the line $y = 10$. The student should verify this by evaluating y for $x = 7, 8, 9,$ and 10.

Although the base may be any positive number except 1, certain values of the base have particular importance in various branches of mathematics.

Base 2 is the foundation of Boolean algebra, which is intimately connected with digital computer science. Base 10 is the foundation of the decimal number system and also, as will be shown later, the base used in performing computations with logarithms. Another very important value of the base is e, the irrational number $2.718\ldots$, which occurs in the study of calculus. The exponential function with base e has many uses, of which we mention only a few. The form $y = e^x$ is the solution to many linear differential equations that arise in physics, biology, chemistry, social science, and engineering. It is possible to express many of the elementary functions in terms of the exponential function with base e. This function also appears in many time-related problems involving decay and growth. The number e is called the *natural base number* and, along with π, is one of the basic constants of mathematics.

Simple exponential equations may be solved by employing the fact that when the base values of an exponential equation are all equal, the exponents must also be equal. (See Exercise 8.)

EXAMPLE 7-3 Solve for x: $3^{2x} = 243$.

To solve this equation, we must express 243 in exponential form with base 3. Since $243 = 3^5$, we have

$$3^{2x} = 3^5$$

Since the base values are equal, the exponents must be equal. Therefore,

$$2x = 5 \quad \text{and} \quad x = \tfrac{5}{2} = 2.5$$

EXAMPLE 7-4 Solve for x: $8^{(2/3)x} = 16$.

In this instance, 8 and 16 can both be expressed as powers of 2, as follows:

$$8 = 2^3 \quad \text{and} \quad 16 = 2^4$$

Substituting these expressions in the equation yields

$$(2^3)^{(2/3)x} = 2^4$$

By the laws for exponents,

$$(2^3)^{(2/3)x} = 2^{3(2/3)x} = 2^{2x}$$

and thus,

$$2^{2x} = 2^4$$

Now both sides are expressed with the same base, so the exponents may be equated. This yields

$$2x = 4$$
$$x = 2$$

EXAMPLE 7-5   Solve $6^{2x+3} = 216$.

Try to express both sides with the same base. For this example, 216 can be written as

$$216 = 6^3$$

Substituting into the right side yields

$$6^{2x+3} = 6^3$$

Now both sides are expressed with the same base, and the exponents can be equated. This yields

$$2x + 3 = 3$$
$$x = 0$$

EXERCISES 7-1

Set A

1. Solve the following exponential equations for x.
    (a) $2^x = 8$
    (b) $2^{3x} = 16$
    (c) $(\frac{1}{2})^x = 4$
    (d) $9^x = 27$
    (e) $25^x = 625$
    (f) $25^x = 125$
    (g) $16^x = 32$
    (h) $5^{2x-1} = 125$
    (i) $4^{2x+3} = 64$
    (j) $2^{3-4x} = 32$
    (k) $2^{2x/3} = 32$
    (l) $6^{(4x/5)-1} = 1296$
    (m) $5^{1-3x} = 625$
    (n) $7^{1-(1/2)x} = 343$
    (o) $3^{x-7} = 243$
    (p) $9^{5x/4} = 243$
    (q) $25^{x+1} = 625$
    (r) $16^{(x/3)+2} = 256$
    (s) $15^{x-6} = 225$
    (t) $13^{1-2x} = 169$

2. Sketch the graphs of the following exponential functions for integer values of x in the interval $-4 \leqslant x \leqslant 4$.
    (a) $y = 3^x$
    (b) $y = 2^{2x}$
    (c) $y = (\frac{1}{3})^x$
    (d) $y = (\frac{1}{2})^{-x}$
    (e) $y = 2^{-x}$
    (f) $y = (\frac{1}{2})^x$

Set B

3. Why does a negative base have no meaning in the function $y = b^x$? Give a graphical example to illustrate your answer.

4. Consider an investment function given by

    $$y = 5400x + 5000, \quad x \geqslant 0$$

    and a sales function given by

    $$y = 1000(2^x), \quad x \geqslant 0$$

    At what value of x (to one decimal place) will the sales equal the investment? Solve graphically.

5. Suppose that a piece of equipment depreciates according to the relation

$$y = \$15{,}000(3^{-x}), \qquad x \geq 0$$

If x represents years, solve graphically for the number of years (to one decimal place) necessary for the equipment to depreciate to values of
   (a) $10,000   (b) $5000
   (c) $1500

6. Let $f(x) = b^{2x}$ and $g(x) = x^2$. Find
   (a) $(f \circ g)(t)$ (b) $(g \circ f)(t)$
   (c) $(f \cdot g)(x^2)$ (d) $(f/g)(t)$

7. Show that for $b > 0$ and $b \neq 1$, $f(t) = b^t$ is neither odd nor even.

8. Prove that if $b^x = b^y$ (where $b > 0$, $b \neq 1$), then $x = y$.

Set C

9. In the study of probability, the equation for a normal distribution is $\phi(x) = ae^{-bx^2}$ where a and b are constants and $e = 2.71828\ldots$. Let $a = b = 1$, and use $e \approx 3$; graph $\phi(x)$. Classify $\phi(x)$ as to its symmetry.

10. Let $F(x) = \operatorname{Sin} x$ and $G(x) = 2^x$. Form the composite functions $F \circ G$ and $G \circ F$. Find the domains and ranges of the valid composites. (Refer to Section 2-3 for a review of the conditions.) A calculator would be helpful in finding the domain of $F \circ G$.

⬤ 11. Use the tables of values of e^x and e^{-x} in Appendix C and the laws of exponents to graph the function given by

$$y = \frac{10}{1 + 4e^{-2x}}, \qquad x \geq 0$$

This is a form of the logistic curve, which is very important in the study of population problems with inhibiting factors. Find the value of x for which $y = 5$. This is called the *inflection point* of the curve, where the rate of population growth is maximum.

⬤ 12. Use the tables of values of e^x and e^{-x} and the laws of exponents to graph the curves

$$y = \frac{e^x + e^{-x}}{2} \quad \text{and} \quad y = \frac{e^x - e^{-x}}{2}$$

for $-4 \leq x \leq 4$, x in increments of 0.2. These are the hyperbolic cosine and hyperbolic sine functions, respectively.

7-2 THE LOGARITHMIC FUNCTION

Development

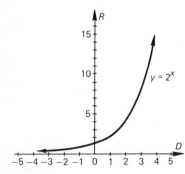

FIGURE 7-1

In Section 7-1, we discussed the exponential function $E_2(x) = 2^x$ $(x \in \mathbb{R})$; its graph, shown in Figure 7-1, is reproduced here. Clearly, this is the graph of a *strictly monotonic increasing function.* As we saw in Section 2-3, any strictly monotonic onto function has an inverse function. In fact, any exponential function of the form

$$y = b^x, \qquad x \in \mathbb{R}, b > 0, b \neq 1$$

is a strictly monotonic onto function for $\mathcal{D} = \mathbb{R}$ and $\mathcal{R} = \{y \mid y > 0\}$ and, hence, possesses an inverse function.

Using the reflection technique illustrated in Section 2-3, we can obtain the graph of $E_2^{-1}(x)$, which is shown in Figure 7-4. The interchange of domain and range values can be seen by comparing Tables 7-2 and 7-5; Table 7-2 is repeated here.

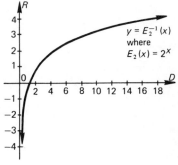

FIGURE 7-4

TABLE 7-2	
$y = E_2(x) = 2^x$	
x	y
-4	$\frac{1}{16}$
-3	$\frac{1}{8}$
-2	$\frac{1}{4}$
-1	$\frac{1}{2}$
0	1
1	2
2	4
3	8
4	16

TABLE 7-5	
$y = E_2^{-1}(x)$	
x	y
$\frac{1}{16}$	-4
$\frac{1}{8}$	-3
$\frac{1}{4}$	-2
$\frac{1}{2}$	-1
1	0
2	1
4	2
8	3
16	4

The exponential function, like the circular functions, is transcendental; therefore, algebraic methods cannot be used to obtain a mathematical expression for its inverse function. However, note that for the exponential function $y = b^x$ ($x \in \mathbb{R}, b > 0, b \neq 1$), b is the base, x the exponent, and y is a power of b. The domain consists of exponent values and the range of the powers of b. For the inverse function, then, the domain values will be the powers of b, and the range values will be the exponents. If

$$E_b: x \rightarrow b^x, \qquad x \in \mathbb{R}, b > 0, b \neq 1$$

then

$$E_b^{-1}: z \rightarrow g(b, z), \qquad z > 0, b > 0, b \neq 1$$

where g is the functional form of the inverse. So for

$$y = E_b(x) = b^x, \qquad x \in \mathbb{R}, b > 0, b \neq 1$$

we define the inverse function as

$$y = g(b, z) = E_b^{-1}(z) = \log_b z, \qquad z > 0, b > 0, b \neq 1$$

This is read "the logarithm of z to the base b"; "log" is the abbreviated form for "logarithm." Thus,

$$y = E_2^{-1}(z) = \log_2 z$$

is the inverse function of $E_2(x) = 2^x$. In general, if $y = b^x$, then

$$x = \log_b y$$

for $x \in \mathbb{R}$, $b > 0$, $b \neq 1$, and $y > 0$.

> **DEFINITION** Let $x, b \in \mathbb{R}$ with $x > 0$, $b > 0$, and $b \neq 1$. Then the *logarithm* of x to the base b, denoted $\log_b x$, is the real number y such that $x = b^y$. In functional notation,
>
> ▶ $\log_b = \{(x, y) \mid x = b^y \text{ for } y, b \in \mathbb{R}; b > 0, b \neq 1\}$
>
> Hence, if $A = \{x \mid x > 0\}$ and $b > 0$, $b \neq 1$, then
>
> ▶ $\log_b: A \twoheadrightarrow \mathbb{R}$
>
> That is, the function $\log_b$ is an onto mapping from the positive real numbers to the real numbers. Since this function is also one to one, the equation
>
> $$\log_b x = \log_b y$$
>
> implies $x = y$, for $x > 0, y > 0$.

EXAMPLE 7-6 Let $y = 2^x$. Give the logarithmic form for the case $x = 3$.

For $x = 3$, $y = 2^3 = 8$. Thus, in logarithmic form, $3 = \log_2 8$.

Simple Logarithmic Equations

Simple logarithmic equations can be easily solved by using the definition of the logarithm as an inverse function.

EXAMPLE 7-7 Solve $x = \log_5 25$ for x.

In exponential form, the equation becomes

$$5^x = 25$$

Using the techniques developed in the last section, we rewrite this as

$$5^x = 5^2$$

Therefore,

$$x = 2$$

EXAMPLE 7-8 Solve $\log_2 x = 3$ for x.

Again, put the equation into the exponential form. This yields

$$2^3 = x$$

so

$$8 = x$$

EXAMPLE 7-9   Solve $\log_x 49 = 2$ for x.

In exponential form, the equation becomes

$$x^2 = 49$$

Solving this equation for x yields

$$x = \pm 7$$

Since the base value cannot be negative, the value $x = 7$ is the solution.

EXERCISES 7-2

Set A

Solve for x in the following logarithmic equations:

1. $\log_3 9 = x$
2. $\log_5 x = 2$
3. $\log_x 16 = 2$
4. $\log_x 5 = 2$
5. $\log_4 64 = 3x$
6. $\log_x 27 = \frac{3}{2}$
7. $\log_2 x = \frac{5}{3}$
8. $\log_3 (2x/3) = 4$
9. $\log_{2x} 1000 = 3$
10. $\log_6 216 = 2x - 1$

11. $\log_5 x = 4$
12. $\log_{25} 625 = x$
13. $\log_x 243 = \frac{5}{2}$
14. $\log_5 625 = x$
15. $\log_7 343 = x$
16. $\log_4 64 = x$
17. $\log_x 1296 = 4$
18. $\log_x 64 = 6$
19. $\log_x 1296 = 2$
20. $\log_{15} 225 = x - 3$

Set B

21. (a) Why are the logarithms of negative numbers not defined?
    (b) If $F(x) = \log_b (x^2 - 9)$, what is the domain of $F(x)$?
    (c) What is the range of $F(x)$?

22. Solve the following for x, $x \in J$:
    (a) $\log_x 32 = 2x + 1$ (b) $\log_3 9x = x$

23. For $x \in R$, find the domain of the following functions:
    (a) $F(x) = \log_b (x^2 + 7x)$ (b) $H(x) = \log_b |x - 6|$
    (c) $G(x) = \log_b (3/(x - 4))$ (d) $W(x) = \log_b (\text{Sin } x)$

24. Let $F(x) = \log_b x$ and $G(x) = x^2 - 4$. Form the following composites and indicate the domains that make them valid.
    (a) $F \circ G$ (b) $G \circ F$

25. For the functions of Exercise 24, find the following functions and indicate their domains.
    (a) $F \cdot G$ (b) F/G
    (c) $F \cdot G^2$ (d) $F^2 \cdot G$

Set C

26. Let $w = F(x) = \log_b \sqrt{4 - x}$ and $z = G(y) = \sqrt{y + 4}$. Form the composite $(F \circ G)(y)$ and find the restrictions necessary for the composite to be valid. (Refer to Section 2-3 for a review of the conditions.)

7-3 PROPERTIES OF THE LOGARITHMIC FUNCTION

Introduction

Certain properties of the logarithmic function are very useful in evaluating complicated mathematical expressions. We develop these properties using the fact that the composite of any function on its inverse is the identity function. The exponential function $y = E_b(x) = b^x$ ($x \in \mathbb{R}$, $b > 0$, $b \neq 1$) has the inverse function E_b^{-1} defined as

$$y = E_b^{-1}(x) = \log_b x, \qquad x > 0, b > 0, b \neq 1$$

Therefore, the composite $E_b \circ E_b^{-1}$ is the identity function. Hence,

$$x = E_b[E_b^{-1}(x)]$$

or

$$x = b^{E_b^{-1}(x)}$$

or

▶ $x = b^{\log_b x}, \qquad x > 0, b > 0, b \neq 1$

Since the variable can be represented by any symbol, we can also write

$$m = b^{\log_b m}, \qquad m > 0, b > 0, b \neq 1$$

This equation is called the *exponential identity*. Similarly, forming the composite $E_b^{-1} \circ E_b$ yields

$$x = E_b^{-1}[E_b(x)]$$

or

$$x = \log_b[E_b(x)]$$

or

▶ $x = \log_b (b^x), \qquad x \in \mathbb{R}, b > 0, b \neq 1$

As before, the letter used to represent the variable is of no consequence, so we can write

$$n = \log_b (b^n), \qquad n \in \mathbb{R}, b > 0, b \neq 1$$

This equation is called the *logarithmic identity*. We use these two identities to derive some important properties of logarithmic functions.

Properties of Logarithms

Let X and Y be positive numbers expressed as powers of b; that is, $X = b^u$ and $Y = b^v$ $(u, v \in \mathbb{R})$. Then

$$XY = b^u b^v, \qquad u, v \in \mathbb{R}$$

By the laws for exponents,

$$XY = b^{u+v}$$

Taking the logarithm of both sides to base b yields

$$\log_b (XY) = \log_b (b^{u+v})$$

Then, by the logarithmic identity,

$$\log_b (XY) = u + v$$

However, note that if

$$X = b^u, \quad \text{then} \quad u = \log_b X$$

and if

$$Y = b^v, \quad \text{then} \quad v = \log_b Y$$

Thus, we can write

$$\log_b (XY) = u + v = \log_b X + \log_b Y$$

That is, the logarithm of the product of two numbers is the sum of the logarithms of these numbers to the same base. This is the first important property of logarithmic functions.

For the same representation of X and Y as b^u and b^v, we can consider the quotient

$$\frac{X}{Y} = \frac{b^u}{b^v}$$

By the laws for exponents,

$$\frac{X}{Y} = b^{u-v}$$

As in the derivation of the first logarithmic property, we take the logarithm of both sides and then use the logarithmic identity.

$$\log_b \left(\frac{X}{Y} \right) = \log_b (b^{u-v})$$

$$= u - v$$
$$= \log_b X - \log_b Y$$

This is the second important property of logarithmic functions. The logarithm of the quotient of two numbers is the difference of the logarithms of those numbers to the same base.

Now suppose that

$$X = (b^u), \qquad u \in \mathbb{R}$$

Then

$$X^n = (b^u)^n, \qquad n, u \in \mathbb{R}$$

or

$$X^n = b^{nu}$$

Again, use of the logarithmic identity yields

$$\log_b (X^n) = \log_b (b^{nu})$$

so

$$\log_b (X^n) = nu$$

Since $u = \log_b x$, this becomes

$$\log_b (X^n) = n \log_b X, \qquad n \in \mathbb{R}$$

This is the third property of logarithmic functions: The logarithm of a number raised to a power is the power times the logarithm of the number to the same base.

Summary and Examples

We summarize the three major properties of logarithmic functions. For $X, Y, n \in \mathbb{R}$ and $X, Y > 0$,

▶ 1. $\log_b (XY) = \log_b X + \log_b Y$

▶ 2. $\log_b \left(\dfrac{X}{Y} \right) = \log_b X - \log_b Y$

▶ 3. $\log_b (X^n) = n \log_b X$

EXAMPLE 7-10 Using the logarithmic properties, reexpress the following equation in logarithmic form:

$$P = \frac{x^{1.4} y^3}{z^{4.8}}$$

Taking the logarithm to base b of both sides yields

$$\log_b P = \log_b \left(\frac{x^{1.4} y^3}{z^{4.8}} \right)$$

By the quotient property, this becomes

$$\log_b P = \log_b (x^{1.4} y^3) - \log_b (z^{4.8})$$

Using the product rule on the first term of the right side, we obtain

$$\log_b P = \log_b x^{1.4} + \log_b y^3 - \log_b z^{4.8}$$

Finally, the exponent rule applied to all three terms on the right side yields

$$\log_b P = 1.4 \log_b x + 3 \log_b y - 4.8 \log_b z$$

This is the desired form.

EXAMPLE 7-11 Use logarithms to reexpress P in logarithmic form, where

$$P = \frac{(3.7)^{0.5}(0.098)^{5.4}}{2.7^{3.6}}$$

Taking the logarithm to base b of both sides, we have

$$\log_b P = \log_b \left(\frac{(3.7)^{0.5}(0.098)^{5.4}}{(2.7)^{3.6}} \right)$$

By the quotient rule, this becomes

$$\log_b P = \log_b [(3.7)^{0.5}(0.098)^{5.4}] - \log_b [(2.7)^{3.6}]$$

Using the product rule on the first term of the right side, we obtain

$$\log_b P = \log_b (3.7)^{0.5} + \log_b (0.098)^{5.4} - \log_b (2.7)^{3.6}$$

Finally, by the exponent rule, this becomes

$$\log_b P = 0.5 \log_b 3.7 + 5.4 \log_b 0.098 - 3.6 \log_b 2.7$$

which is the desired form.

EXAMPLE 7-12 Use the logarithmic properties in reverse to find the original equation from which the following logarithmic equation was obtained:

$$2 \log_b P = 0.5 \log_b x + 4 \log_b y - \log_b z - 3 \log_b w$$

First, we use the exponential rule in reverse. The equation becomes

$$\log_b P^2 = \log_b x^{0.5} + \log_b y^4 - (\log_b z + \log_b w^3)$$

Now we use the product rule, in reverse, on the sums. The equation becomes

$$\log_b P^2 = \log_b (x^{0.5} y^4) - \log_b (zw^3)$$

Finally, we use the quotient rule on the log difference. The equation becomes

$$\log_b P^2 = \log_b \left(\frac{x^{0.5} y^4}{zw^3} \right)$$

Since both sides of this equation are logarithms to the same base, the quantities within the logarithmic expressions must be equal. So we have

$$P^2 = \frac{x^{0.5}y^4}{zw^3}$$

which is the desired solution.

EXERCISES 7-3

Set A

Using the logarithmic properties developed in this section, rewrite the following as logarithmic equations in the indicated base. Do *not* evaluate any of the logarithmic expressions.

1. $P = A^3B$ in base 10

2. $W = \dfrac{x}{y^3}$ in base π

3. $N = \dfrac{\sqrt{x}\, y^3}{v}$ in base 3

4. $N = \dfrac{(6.4)^{1.3}(7.2)^{3.4}}{(5.3)^2}$ in base 2

5. $N = \sqrt[3]{\dfrac{\sqrt{72.4}\,\sqrt[3]{27.2}}{(0.0043)^{-7.1}}}$ in base 10

6. $N = \dfrac{(0.039)^{5.4}(0.007)^{2.8}}{(6.1)^{-2.1}}$ in base 10

Set B

Find the algebraic equations from which the following logarithmic equations were derived by using the logarithmic properties in reverse. Do *not* evaluate any of the logarithmic expressions.

7. $\log_2 N = 3\log_2 x + 4\log_2 y - \frac{1}{2}\log_2 Z$

8. $\log_\pi N = \frac{3}{2}\log_\pi V - 1.7\log_\pi W - 3.2\log_\pi V$

9. $\log_{10} N = \frac{1}{2}(\log_{10} 6.4 - \log_{10} 12 - 3\log_{10} 8)$

10. $\log_3 N = -\frac{6}{5}\log_3 17.6 - \frac{3}{5}\log_3 22.7$

11. $\log_{10} 17.4 = \frac{4}{3}\log_{10} 243 + 3\log_{10} x - 2\log_{10} 1.03$

12. $\log_{10} N = -2.3\log_{10} 4.73 + 6.1\log_{10} x$

Set C

13. Research the meaning of
    (a)   the logarithm of a negative number
    (b)   the logarithm of a complex number
    What set is used to express the images of such arguments?

14. Research the work done by the mathematicians Joost Bürgi, John Napier, and Henry Briggs. Discuss how they developed the logarithmic tables.

7-4 USE OF LOGARITHMIC TABLES

Common Logarithms of Numbers

A very interesting utilization of the properties of logarithms can be illustrated in the use of the decimal system for representation of quantities. In Section 1-4, we discussed the representation of numbers in scientific notation. For example, the number 256 can be represented as

$$2.56 \cdot 10^2$$

In general, any number N can be represented in scientific notation as

$$N = P \cdot 10^k$$

where P is a number between 1 and 10, and k is an integer. If we take the logarithms to base b of both sides of this equation, we get

$$\log_b N = \log_b (P \cdot 10^k), \qquad b > 0, b \neq 1$$

Since the logarithm of a product can be written as a sum of logarithms, this becomes

$$\log_b N = \log_b P + \log_b 10^k$$

We know that $\log_b 10^k = k \log_b 10$, so

$$\log_b N = \log_b P + k \log_b 10$$

Although this form of the equation seems more complicated than the original, it has the advantage that the second term, $k \log_b 10$, would be an integer (namely, the integer k) if $\log_b 10$ were always equal to 1. The value of b such that $\log_b 10 = 1$ can be found from the logarithmic identity, $\log_b(b^n) = n$. Letting $b^n = 10$ (so that $n = 1$), we obtain

$$1 = \log_{10} (10^1)$$

This reduces to $1 = \log_{10} 10$. Thus, for $N = P \cdot 10^k$,

▶ $$\log_{10} N = \log_{10} P + k \log_{10} 10 = \log_{10} P + k$$

In fact, the logarithm of any admissible number taken to the same base is always 1. Since base 10 is used frequently because of its relationship to the decimal system, logarithms to the base 10 are often called *common logarithms*. It is standard practice to write the base 10 logarithms as simply "log" with no base value.

In the equation for the common logarithm of N, $\log_{10} N = \log_{10} P + k$ (where $N = P \cdot 10^k$), the integer k is called the *characteristic* of N, and $\log_{10} P$ is called the *mantissa*. For common logarithms, the mantissa is always a number greater than or equal to 0 but less than 1. This representation of a number is often used in logarithmic computations. The values of log P are listed in Table C-5 of Appendix C.

Evaluations of the Common Logarithm

The use of Table C-5 is illustrated in the following examples. The table can be used directly for any number that has three significant digits; for numbers with more significant digits, either a process called interpolation (to be discussed later) or a more comprehensive table must be used.

EXAMPLE 7-13   Use Table C-5 to find log 6.92.

In the left-hand column, locate the first two digits, 69. Since the last digit is 2, move horizontally to the column marked 2 across the top of the table. The number in this position is the mantissa of the logarithm. Since the number 6.92 is already between 1 and 10, the characteristic is 0. Thus, the logarithm is

$$\log 6.92 = 0.8401$$

EXAMPLE 7-14   Use Table C-5 to calculate log 7430.

Write the number in scientific notation as

$$7430 = 7.43 \cdot 10^3$$

Then, by the product rule for logarithms,

$$\log 7430 = \log(7.43 \cdot 10^3)$$
$$= \log 7.43 + \log 10^3$$

Using the exponent rule on the last term and recalling that the logarithm of a number taken to the same base equals 1, we write

$$\log 7430 = \log 7.43 + 3 \log 10$$
$$= \log 7.43 + 3(1)$$
$$= \log 7.43 + 3$$

To evaluate log 7.43, find the mantissa at the intersection, in Table C-5, of the horizontal row for 74 and the vertical column for 3:

$$\log 7430 = 0.8710 + 3$$
$$= 3.8710$$

EXAMPLE 7-15   Use Table C-5 to find log 0.00521.

Write the number in scientific notation as

$$0.00521 = 5.21 \cdot 10^{-3}$$

Then

$$\log 0.00521 = \log 5.21 + \log 10^{-3}$$
$$= 0.7168 + (-3) \cdot 1$$
$$= 0.7168 - 3$$

Note that the logarithm is negative. It can either be left in this form or be reexpressed using the fact that -3 can be written as the difference between two numbers. For example,

$$-3 = 7 - 10$$
$$-3 = 3 - 6$$
$$-3 = 5 - 8$$

The choice of the numbers used depends on the operations involved in the problem. Later examples will illustrate the process. When only the value of the logarithm is needed, the form most often used is $7 - 10$. Hence,

$$\log 0.00521 = 0.7168 + 7 - 10$$
$$= 7.7168 - 10$$

Antilogarithms of Numbers

Consider the equation

$$\log N = 4.1176$$

Here, the logarithm of N is known to be 4.1176, but N is unknown. We say that N is the *antilogarithm* of 4.1176 (abbreviated antilog 4.1176). The following examples illustrate the process used to find the antilog of a number from the tables. The technique generally used is to write $\log N$ in the form

$$\log N = m + k$$

where $m = \log P$ and k is the exponent of 10 in the scientific notation for N. This means that m must be a positive number between 0 and 1, and it ensures that the final expression for N is in scientific notation.

EXAMPLE 7-16   Find antilog $(8.4871 - 10)$.
   This is the logarithm of a number with a negative characteristic. We rewrite the expression as

$$\log N = 8.4871 - 10 = 0.4871 - 2$$

Then 0.4871 is the mantissa of N. From Table C-5, we find that

$$0.4871 = \log 3.07$$

Since $-2 = \log 10^{-2}$, we have

$$\log N = \log 3.07 + \log 10^{-2}$$
$$= \log(3.07 \cdot 10^{-2})$$

Therefore,

$$N = 3.07 \cdot 10^{-2}$$

EXAMPLE 7-17   Find antilog 6.483.
   We wish to find N such that

$$\log N = 6.483$$

where 6 is the characteristic and 0.483 the mantissa of N. We rewrite this as

$$\log N = 0.483 + 6$$

Thus, N is a number between 1 and 10 times a power of 10, namely, 10^6. From Table C-5, we find the corresponding antilog, which is 3.04. Hence,

$$N = 3.04 \cdot 10^6 = 3{,}040{,}000$$

EXAMPLE 7-18   Find antilog -3.762.

We wish to find N such that $\log N = -3.762$. The value -3.762 came from subtracting a whole number, the characteristic of N, from a positive number between 0 and 1, which is the mantissa of N. Finding the quantity that was subtracted is simple: it must be the next highest integer above 3. Thus $\log N = -3.762 = m - 4$, where m is the mantissa. Solving this simple algebraic problem yields

$$\log N = 0.238 - 4$$

which is a logarithm having a positive mantissa, 0.238, and a characteristic of -4. From Table C-5, we find that the antilogarithm of 0.238 has the digits 173. Hence, N is a number between 1 and 10 times a power of 10, namely,

$$1.73 \cdot 10^{-4}$$

EXAMPLE 7-19   If $\log N = -4.4921$, find N.

We write this logarithm as

$$\log N = -4.4921 = m - 5$$

and solve for m. This yields

$$\log N = 0.5079 - 5$$

Then the mantissa is 0.5079, and characteristic is -5. Using Table C-5, we obtain

$$N = 3.22 \cdot 10^{-5}$$

The values of logarithms can be obtained from an electronic calculator as well as from Table C-5. A calculator usually provides more accurate values.

Linear Interpolation

Quite often, a problem yields a logarithm that is between two numbers given in the table, so that the antilogarithm is not readily available. This means that the answer requires an additional significant digit in the third decimal place. To obtain this next significant digit, we use a method called *interpolation.* It is evident from the graph of the logarithmic function in Figure 7-4 that the function is not linear. However, for any two points on the curve that are close together, the curve joining these points can be considered, for all practical purposes, a straight line. Using this fact, we can determine the distance between the two points by using the simple ratio concept. A few examples will serve to illustrate the principle involved.

EXAMPLE 7-20 If $\log N = 2.7280$, find N.

The characteristic is 2, and the mantissa is 0.7280. However, the mantissa value of 0.7280 is not listed in Table C-5. The closest values listed in the table are 0.7275, corresponding to the digits 5.34, and 0.7284, corresponding to 5.35. So the answer sought must lie between these two values. Table 7-6 shows the values. In the left column, the

TABLE 7-6

$\log(P)$	P
0.7284	5.350
d_1 d_2 → 0.7280	X d_4 d_3
0.7275	5.340

outer difference, d_1, equals 9 in the last decimal places, and the inner difference, d_2, equals 5 in the last decimal places. In the right column, the outer difference, d_3, is 10 in the last decimal places, and the inner difference, d_4, is unknown. Assuming that the logarithmic curve connecting the two outer points is linear, the simple proportion

$$\frac{d_2}{d_1} = \frac{d_4}{d_3}$$

must be true. Substituting in the values and solving for d_4, we obtain

$$\frac{5}{9} = \frac{d_4}{10}$$

$$d_4 = \frac{50}{9} = 5.5\overline{5}, \quad \text{or} \quad d_4 \approx 6$$

This means that the value of x must be 6 higher than 5.340 in the last decimal place, so $x = 5.346$. Therefore,

$$N = 5.346 \cdot 10^2 = 534.6$$

EXAMPLE 7-21 Use interpolation to calculate $\log 0.02793$.

We form Table 7-7 and substitute the values of d_1, d_3, and d_4 into the ratio

$$\frac{d_2}{d_1} = \frac{d_4}{d_3}$$

TABLE 7-7

$\log(P)$	P
$0.4456 - 2$	0.02790
x	0.02793
$0.4472 - 2$	0.02800

The values are $d_1 = 16$, $d_3 = 10$, and $d_4 = 3$, so

$$\frac{d_2}{16} = \frac{3}{10} \quad \text{and} \quad d_2 = 4.8$$

This value is rounded off to 5 for use as an answer; thus,

$$\log 0.02793 = 0.4461 - 2 = 8.4461 - 10$$

EXAMPLE 7-22 Compute the value of

$$\frac{(0.0031)^{1/4}(334)^{-3}}{(0.763)^{2.4}}$$

Let

$$N = \frac{(0.0032)^{1/4}(334)^{-3}}{(0.763)^{2.4}}$$

Then

$$\log N = \log\left(\frac{(0.0031)^{1/4}(334)^{-3}}{(0.763)^{2.4}}\right)$$

$$
\begin{aligned}
\log N &= \log[(0.0031)^{1/4}] + \log[(334)^{-3}] - \log[(0.763)^{2.4}] \\
&= \tfrac{1}{4}\log 0.0031 + (-3)\log 334 - 2.4\log 0.763 \\
&= \tfrac{1}{4}\log(3.1\cdot 10^{-3}) - 3\log(3.34\cdot 10^2) - 2.4\log(7.63\cdot 10^{-1}) \\
&= \tfrac{1}{4}(7.4914 - 10) - 3(2.3692) - 2.4(9.8825 - 10)
\end{aligned}
$$

This leaves only the arithmetic to carry out.

$$
\begin{aligned}
\log N &= 1.8728 - 2.5 - 7.1076 - (23.780 - 24) \\
&= 24 + 1.8728 - 2.5 - 7.1076 - 23.7180 \\
&= 25.8728 - 33.3256
\end{aligned}
$$

If we subtract these two numbers, the result will be a negative quantity and we will have a negative mantissa. We can avoid this by adding and subtracting a sufficiently large value from 25.8728 to make the mantissa positive. In this case, we can use any number greater than or equal to 8. Hence,

$$
\begin{aligned}
\log N &= 35.8728 - 33.3256 - 10 \\
&= 2.5472 - 10
\end{aligned}
$$

This is the logarithm of a number having a characteristic of $2 - 10 =$

$$N = 3.525 \cdot 10^{-8}$$

EXERCISES 7-4

Set A

1. Find the common logarithms of the following numbers by using Table C-5:
   - (a) 17.4
   - (b) 231
   - (c) 17400
   - (d) 3.72
   - (e) 982,000
   - (f) 77,400,000
   - (g) 0.892
   - (h) 0.000713
   - (i) 0.531
   - (j) 0.00613
   - (k) 0.0000000000106
   - (l) 0.00000119

2. Find the antilogarithms of the following numbers using Table C-5.
   (Approximate without interpolation.)
   - (a) 2.6542
   - (b) 1.0492
   - (c) 0.4065
   - (d) 3.9542
   - (e) 13.5465
   - (f) −3.8153
   - (g) −1.7423
   - (h) −9.8729
   - (i) −0.5969
   - (j) −13.1273

Set B

3. Use interpolation to find the antilogarithms of the following numbers.
   (Use Table C-5.)
   - (a) 3.6471
   - (b) 2.9780
   - (c) −1.2366
   - (d) 17.0090
   - (e) −8.4182
   - (f) 4.8334

4. Use interpolation to find the logarithms of the following numbers. (Use
   Table C-5.)
   - (a) 1.061
   - (b) 382.5
   - (c) 7261
   - (d) 9,283,000
   - (e) 0.0004718
   - (f) 0.006128
   - (g) 0.5036
   - (h) 0.00000008322

5. In a book of mathematical tables, look up the logarithms of the following
   numbers to six decimal places in the mantissa:
   - (a) 236.42
   - (b) 1.0439
   - (c) 0.81924
   - (d) 0.0061723
   - (e) 0.00007614
   - (f) 7,283,900

6. Use common logarithms to evaluate the following expressions to four
   significant digits:
   - (a) $(276.4)^8$
   - (b) $(0.000728)^9$
   - (c) $(0.043)^2(17.9)^4$
   - (d) $\sqrt[3]{936}$
   - (e) $\sqrt[5]{27.4}$
   - (f) $\sqrt[9]{0.000372}$

(g) $\sqrt[8]{54}\ \sqrt[9]{83}$

(h) $\dfrac{(63.7)^5}{(29.2)^4}$

(i) $\dfrac{(16.2)^{1.9}}{(0.0063)^{4.2}}$

(j) $\dfrac{(0.00107)^{-3}}{(0.004)^3}$

Set C

● 7. Use an electronic calculator to evaluate the expression

$$y = \frac{\pi}{g}\sqrt[3]{\frac{(1+x)^{5.9}}{x^{7.1}}}$$

with logarithms, where $g = 32.2$ and x has the values

(a) 0.01
(b) 0.10
(c) 1.00
(d) 10.00
(e) 100

Then investigate the use of logarithmic graph paper and plot the results. What are some advantages of using logarithmic graph paper?

7-5 CHANGE OF BASE IN LOGARITHMS

As we saw in Section 7-2, logarithms can use any base, b, provided that $b > 0$ and $b \neq 1$. Although logarithms to the base 10 are convenient for working with decimal numbers, they are not the most widely used logarithms in all disciplines. Scientists and engineers often use the natural base, $e = 2.71828\ldots$. It may seem strange that one would even consider such a base, since we are accustomed to bases being integers. However, the number e often arises in the solution of differential equations, which are used to describe the dynamics of systems such as populations, chemical reactions, business cycles, and electronic circuits.

It is often necessary to convert logarithms in one base to logarithms in another base. Suppose we wish to know the logarithm of a certain number, N, to the base a but have only logarithmic tables to the base b. Can we find the $\log_a N$ with the table of logarithms to the base b?

We wish to find x such that $x = \log_a N$, or equivalently, such that $N = a^x$. With the table of logarithms to the base b, we can find the logarithm to the base b of each side of this equation. Hence,

$$\log_b N = \log_b a^x = x \log_b a$$

and since $x = \log_a N$, this becomes

$$\log_b N = (\log_a N)(\log_b a)$$

We solve this for $\log_a N$, obtaining

▶ $$\log_a N = \frac{\log_b N}{\log_b a}$$

This expression is the change of base formula for logarithms: To find the logarithm of a number to a base that is not available, take the logarithm of the number to the base that is available and divide it by the logarithm of the desired base to the base that is available.

EXAMPLE 7-23   Find $\log_2 5$.

Since a table in base 2 is not available and one in base 10 is available, we find $\log_{10} 5$ and divide it by $\log_{10} 2$. Hence,

$$\log_2 5 = \frac{\log_{10} 5}{\log_{10} 2}$$

$$= \frac{0.6990}{0.3010} = 2.3219$$

This process can be used for any number and any base, even seemingly difficult cases such as base π, base 13, base 23.2, and, of course, base e.

EXAMPLE 7-24   Find $\log_\pi 73.2$.

$$\log_\pi 73.2 = \frac{\log_{10} 73.2}{\log_{10} \pi}$$

$$= \frac{1.8645}{0.4971} = 3.7508$$

EXAMPLE 7-25   Find $\log_{44} 22$.

$$\log_{44} 22 = \frac{\log_{10} 22}{\log_{10} 44}$$

$$= \frac{1.3424}{1.6435} = 0.8168$$

EXAMPLE 7-26   Find $\log_e \pi$.

Of course, the symbols π and e represent irrational numbers approximated by 3.14 and 2.718, respectively. Thus,

$$\log_e \pi = \frac{\log_{10} \pi}{\log_{10} e}$$

$$= \frac{0.4971}{0.4343} = 1.1446$$

EXERCISES 7-5

Set A

Use the change of base formula to calculate the logarithms to four decimal places of the following numbers to the given bases. Use the base 10 table as the reference table. An electronic calculator would be helpful and should be used if available.

1. $\log_\pi 27$ 2. $\log_e 726$

3. $\log_5 529$

4. $\log_{98} 6.927$

5. $\log_{17} 0.00143$

6. $\log_{100} 832$

7. $\log_e 0.0413$

8. $\log_e 329.2$

9. $\log_\pi 0.0000386$

10. $\log_2 938$

11. $\log_\pi 46{,}720$

12. $\log_e 804$

13. $\log_{12} 0.1640$

14. $\log_7 0.777$

15. $\log_2 0.05142$

16. $\log_{22} 2222$

Set B

Solve the following logarithmic equations for the unknown variable by using the change of base formula. Compute answers to four significant digits.

17. $\log_\pi y = \log_\pi 37.2 + \log_\pi 0.043 - 2\log_\pi 7.6$

18. $\log_2 17.6 + 3\log_{10} x - 2\log_2 0.076 = 6\log_2 104$

19. $\log_e 38.4 - 3.1\log_e 8.19 = \log_{10} Z + 1.41\log_e 6.19$

20. $2\log_{10} x - 3\log_5 0.0043 - 2.1\log_5 61.3 = 0$

21. $4.6\log_e 9.19 + \log_{10} x^2 = 4 - 2\log_e 3.17$

Set C

● 22. The following equations are the solutions to differential equations of real systems:

(a) $\quad i = \dfrac{E}{R}(1 - e^{-\alpha t}), \quad t \geqslant 0$ (b) $\quad y = \dfrac{k}{1 + Ce^{\alpha t}}, \quad t \geqslant 0$

The first comes from electronic circuit theory, and the second is the logistics equation that results from population studies. Use the change of base formula and an electronic calculator to evaluate the equations for the following conditions. Then graph the results gaainst t. In equation (a), use

$$E = 100, \quad R = 20, \quad \alpha = 0.5$$

In equation (b), use

$$k = 10{,}000, \quad C = 4, \quad \alpha = 0.1$$

Evaluate each equation for integer values of t in the range $0 \leqslant t \leqslant 8$. Then graph i and y as a function of t.

REVIEW EXERCISES FOR CHAPTER 7

1. Solve the following exponential equations:
   (a) $16^{x-1} = 64$
   (b) $3^{2x+1} = 243$
   (c) $4^{2-x} = 32$
   (d) $6^{x+2} = 216$
   (e) $25^{3x} = 125$
   (f) $36^{2x-1} = 1296$

2. Use the laws of exponents to graph the following functions for integer values of x, $0 \leqslant x \leqslant 8$:

(a) $y = \dfrac{6}{1 + 3^x}$, $x \geqslant 0$

(b) $y = 5(1 - 2^{-x})^2$, $x \geqslant 0$

3. Write, but do not evaluate, the following equations in logarithmic form to the base 10:

(a) $T = 2\pi\sqrt{\dfrac{L}{g}}$

(b) $V = e^{-at} \sin \omega t$

(c) $y = \dfrac{\sqrt{x + 1}}{(x - 1)^2}$

4. Use common logarithms to evaluate the following expressions to four significant digits:

(a) $(136.4)^{8.5}$

(b) $\sqrt[16]{2172}$

(c) $\dfrac{\sqrt[3]{72.3}\,(0.172)^{4.3}}{(0.062)^{5.1}}$

(d) $\dfrac{(973)^{4.2}}{(127)^{7.1}}$

(e) $(6.17)^{10}(2.13)^8$

(f) $\sqrt[3]{172}\,\sqrt[4]{29.3}$

● 5. Use common logarithms to as many places as available (use U.S. Bureau of Standards tables if possible) to evaluate the expression

$$y = (1 + h)^{1/h}$$

for $h = -0.5, -0.1, -0.01, -0.001, -0.0001, 0.0001, 0.001, 0.01, 0.1,$ and 1.

In calculus, the base value e is defined as

$$e = \lim_{\text{as } h \to 0} [(1 + h)^{1/h}]$$

Compare the value you obtained for e in your calculations to the true value of e.

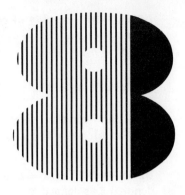

Complex Numbers

8-1 INTRODUCTION TO COMPLEX NUMBERS

Basic Definitions

The set of complex numbers was the largest set of numbers discussed in Section 1-2. We defined the set of complex numbers, $\mathbb{C}$, as the direct sum of the set of real numbers, $\mathbb{R}$, and the set of pure imaginary numbers, $\mathbb{I}$; that is, $\mathbb{C} = \mathbb{R} \oplus \mathbb{I}$.

> **DEFINITION** A **complex number**, z, is a number of the form
> $$z = a + bi$$
> where $a, b \in \mathbb{R}$ and $i = \sqrt{-1}$.

For the complex number $z = a + bi$, the number a is the *real part* of z, and the number b is the *imaginary part* of z.

> **EXAMPLE 8-1** The complex number $z = 3 + 4i$ has real part 3 and imaginary part 4.

The real numbers are those complex numbers with imaginary part 0, and the pure imaginary numbers are those complex numbers with real part 0.

> **EXAMPLE 8-2** The complex number $z = 5 + 0i = 5$ is real. The complex number $z = 0 + 7i = 7i$ is pure imaginary.

269

DEFINITION **Equality of complex numbers** is defined as follows: If $z_1 = a_1 + b_1 i$ and $z_2 = a_2 + b_2 i$, then $z_1 = z_2$ if and only if $a_1 = a_2$ and $b_1 = b_2$.

EXAMPLE 8-3 Let $z_1 = 4p + 3i$ and $z_2 = 7 - qi$. Find p and q if $z_1 = z_2$.

By the definition of equality of complex numbers, $4p = 7$ and $3 = -q$. Hence, $p = \frac{7}{4}$ and $q = -3$.

DEFINITION Let $z = a + bi$. Then the **complex conjugate** of z, denoted $\bar{z}$, is defined as

$$\bar{z} = a - bi$$

For example, if $z = 3 + 4i$, then $\bar{z} = 3 - 4i$.

Arithmetic Operations

The basic operations of addition, subtraction, multiplication, and division of complex numbers follow the same principles as those used for algebraic binomial expressions, with slight differences due to the presence of the i factor.

DEFINITION Let $z_1 = a_1 + b_1 i$ and $z_2 = a_2 + b_2 i$. Then the **sum** $z_1 + z_2$ is given by

$$\blacktriangleright \quad z_1 + z_2 = (a_1 + a_2) + (b_1 + b_2)i$$

and the **difference** $z_1 - z_2$ is given by

$$\blacktriangleright \quad z_1 - z_2 = (a_1 - a_2) + (b_1 - b_2)i$$

EXAMPLE 8-4 If $z_1 = 2 + 3i$ and $z_2 = 7 - 6i$, find $z_1 + z_2$ and $z_1 - z_2$.

We have

$$
\begin{aligned}
z_1 + z_2 &= (2 + 3i) + (7 - 6i) \\
&= (2 + 7) + (3 - 6)i \\
&= 9 + (-3)i \\
&= 9 - 3i
\end{aligned}
$$

$$
\begin{aligned}
z_1 - z_2 &= (2 + 3i) - (7 - 6i) \\
&= (2 - 7) + (3 + 6)i \\
&= -5 + 9i
\end{aligned}
$$

Multiplication of complex numbers is similar to multiplication of binomials.

DEFINITION Let $z_1 = a_1 + b_1 i$ and $z_2 = a_2 + b_2 i$. Then the **product** $z_1 z_2$ is given by

▶ $z_1 z_2 = (a_1 a_2 - b_1 b_2) + (a_1 b_2 + a_2 b_1)i$

We can justify this definition by multiplying the two complex numbers as a product of two binomials:

$z_1 z_2 = (a_1 + b_1 i)(a_2 + b_2 i) = a_1 a_2 + b_1 b_2 i^2 + a_1 b_2 i + a_2 b_1 i$

Since $i^2 = -1$, we have

$z_1 z_2 = (a_1 a_2 - b_1 b_2) + (a_1 b_2 + a_2 b_1)i$

EXAMPLE 8-5 If $z_1 = 2 + 3i$ and $z_2 = 7 - 6i$, find $z_1 z_2$.

$$\begin{aligned} z_1 z_2 &= [2 \cdot 7 - 3(-6)] + [2(-6) + 7 \cdot 3]i \\ &= (14 + 18) + (-12 + 21)i \\ &= 32 + 9i \end{aligned}$$

Division of two complex numbers proceeds in a manner similar to that of rationalizing a denominator. That is, we multiply the expression by a ratio equal to 1 (namely, the ratio of the complex conjugate of the denominator with itself) and simplify the result.

DEFINITION Let $z_1 = a_1 + b_1 i$ and $z_2 = a_2 + b_2 i$. Then the **quotient** z_1/z_2 is given by

▶ $\dfrac{z_1}{z_2} = \dfrac{(a_1 a_2 + b_1 b_2) + (b_1 a_2 - a_1 b_2)i}{a_2^2 + b_2^2}$

We can justify this definition as follows:

$$\begin{aligned} \frac{z_1}{z_2} &= \left(\frac{a_1 + b_1 i}{a_2 + b_2 i}\right)\left(\frac{a_2 - b_2 i}{a_2 - b_2 i}\right) = \frac{a_1 a_2 - b_1 b_2 i^2 + a_2 b_1 i - a_1 b_2 i}{a_2^2 + a_2 b_2 i - b_2 a_2 i - b_2^2 i^2} \\ &= \frac{a_1 a_2 + b_1 b_2 + (b_1 a_2 - a_1 b_2)i}{a_2^2 + b_2^2} \end{aligned}$$

EXAMPLE 8-6 If $z = 1 - 4i$, find $\bar{z}/z$.
  Since $\bar{z} = 1 + 4i$, the quotient is

$$\begin{aligned} \frac{\bar{z}}{z} &= \frac{1 + 4i}{1 + (-4)i} = \frac{1(1) + 4(-4) + [4(1) - 1(-4)]i}{1^2 + (-4)^2} \\ &= \frac{1 - 16 + (4 + 4)i}{1 + 16} = \frac{-15 + 8i}{17} = \frac{-15}{17} + \frac{8i}{17} \end{aligned}$$

The definitions of multiplication and division presented here are somewhat cumbersome. In Section 8-2, we develop an alternative method, which does not involve lengthy algebraic manipulation.

EXERCISES 8-1

Set A

1. Perform the indicated operations on the following complex numbers:
   (a) Add $5 + 6i$, $-9 - 14i$, and $17 - 22i$.
   (b) Subtract $16 - 12i$ from $-20 - 6i$.
   (c) Multiply $6 + 3i$ by $-7 - 4i$.
   (d) Divide $5 + 12i$ by $4 + 3i$.
   (e) Simplify $(-5 - 3i) + (6 - 4i) - (-9 - 30i)$.

2. For what values of x and y are the following equations true?
   (a) $(x) + (2x - y + 1)i = 6 - 5i$
   (b) $(x + y) - (y - 4)i = 8 - 2yi$
   (c) $(3x - 2) + (y - 6)i = y + 4i$

Set B

3. Find the complex conjugates of the following complex numbers. Then multiply each of the original complex numbers by its complex conjugate. What general conclusion can be made about the product of a complex number and its complex conjugate?
   (a) $-5 - 12i$ (b) $8 + 15i$
   (c) $x + yi$ (d) $(x + 2) - (y + 3)i$
   (e) $(x - y) - (x + y)i$

Set C

4. The algebraic expression $A^2 + B^2$ is real and nonfactorable over the real numbers. Yet the fact that $(A + Bi)(A - Bi) = A^2 + B^2$ seems to refute this. Can you give a brief reason that will clear up this seeming contradiction?

5. Table 8-1 lists equivalent expressions in different sets of variables, set S and set T, where $s \in S$, $t \in T$, $i = \sqrt{-1}$, and k, $\omega \in \mathbb{R}$ (k and ω constants). Show, by substituting the equivalent expressions in set S for the expressions in set T, that the following complex number operations are equivalent:
   (a) $3e^{-i4t} + 3e^{i4t}$ and $\dfrac{6s}{s^2 + 16}$
   (b) $3t + 2e^{-i6t}$ and $\dfrac{2s^2 + 3s + 18i}{s^2(s + 6i)}$
   (c) $2t + 4e^{-i3t} - 4e^{i3t}$ and $\dfrac{2s^2 + 18 - 24s^2i}{s^4 + 9s^2}$

6. The complex numbers obey the closure laws for addition and multiplication. Let the operation $\langle A, B \rangle$ be defined by $\langle A, B \rangle = A \cdot \bar{B}$, where A and B are complex numbers. If $Z = a + bi$, $X = c + di$, and $Y = p + qi$, give expressions for the following in terms of a, b, c, d, p, and q:
   (a) $\langle X, X \rangle$ (b) $\langle Z, X + Y \rangle$
   (c) $\langle X + Y, Z \rangle$ (d) $\langle X, Z \rangle - \langle Z, X \rangle$
   Do the expressions in parts (b) and (c) stand for the same number? Explain.

7. Is the expression in Exercise 6(d) equal to 0? If not, what condition on X and Z will make it equal to 0?

TABLE 8-1

Set T	Set S
kt	$\dfrac{k}{s^2}$
ke^{-iwt}	$\dfrac{k}{s + iw}$
ke^{+iwt}	$\dfrac{k}{s - iw}$

● 8. Find the product of each of the following complex numbers with its complex conjugate:
(a) $z = 18.7781 + 27.2493i$ (b) $z = -761.82 - 44.810i$
(c) $z = 128.443 - 18.201i$

● 9. Using the techniques developed in this section, perform the following operations:
(a) Multiply $6.774 + 3.992i$ by $-7.878 - 3.698i$.
(b) Divide $5.031 + 11.873i$ by $4.111 + 3.217i$.

8-2 TRANSCENDENTAL REPRESENTATION OF COMPLEX NUMBERS

Complex Points

Since a complex number $a + bi$ is composed of two distinct parts, a real part and a pure imaginary part, it can also be represented as an ordered pair, (a, b).

> **DEFINITION** Let $a, b \in \mathbb{R}$. An alternative representation of the complex number $z = a + bi$ is the ordered pair (a, b), where $(a, b) \in \mathbb{C}$.

> **EXAMPLE 8-7** The order pair $(3, 4) \in \mathbb{C}$ is an alternative representation of the complex number $z = 3 + 4i$.

When represented as an ordered pair, the complex number (a, b) can define a point in a two-dimensional *complex plane*. If we let one reference axis represent the real part of z and the other reference axis the imaginary part of z, then any complex number can be represented by a unique point in this complex plane. Figure 8-1 illustrates a cartesian complex plane, in which the horizontal axis represents the real part of z and the vertical axis the imaginary part of z. The complex number (a, b) is a point in this plane, which is usually called the z plane.

The length of the line from the origin to the point (a, b) in the z plane is one characteristic of the complex number (a, b). This length is called the *modulus, magnitude,* or *absolute value* of (a, b).

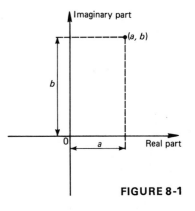

FIGURE 8-1

DEFINITION   Let $z = a + bi$. Then the **modulus** of z, denoted $|z|$, is

$$\blacktriangleright \quad |z| = \sqrt{a^2 + b^2}$$

This definition is justified by virtue of the fact that the real and imaginary parts form the legs of a right triangle whose hypotenuse has length equal to the modulus. Figure 8-2 shows point (a, b) and its modulus.

EXAMPLE 8-8   If $z = 5 - 12i$, find $|z|$.
  By definition,

$$|z| = \sqrt{5^2 + (-12)^2} = \sqrt{25 + 144} = \sqrt{169}$$

so $|z| = 13$.

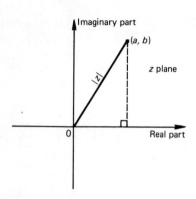

FIGURE 8-2

If $z = a + bi$, then the complex conjugate of z is $\bar{z} = a - bi$. The ordered pair representations of these two numbers are (a, b) and $(a, -b)$, respectively. Figure 8-3 shows the location of these two points. Theorem 8-1 follows immediately.

THEOREM 8-1   Let $z = a + bi$ be a complex number and $\bar{z} = a - bi$ its complex conjugate. Then the modulus of z equals the modulus of $\bar{z}$; that is,

$$|z| = |\bar{z}|$$

PROOF   For $\bar{z} = a - bi$,

$$|\bar{z}| = \sqrt{a^2 + (-b)^2} = \sqrt{a^2 + b^2} = |z| \qquad \blacksquare$$

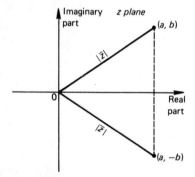

FIGURE 8-3

EXAMPLE 8-9   For $z = -3 - 4i$, $\bar{z} = -3 + 4i$. Then

$$|z| = \sqrt{(-3)^2 + (-4)^2} = \sqrt{9 + 16} = \sqrt{25} = 5$$
$$|\bar{z}| = \sqrt{(-3)^2 + (4)^2} = \sqrt{9 + 16} = \sqrt{25} = 5$$

A useful property of complex numbers involves the product of a complex number and its complex conjugate.

THEOREM 8-2   Let $z = a + bi$ with $\bar{z} = a - bi$. Then $z\bar{z} = a^2 + b^2 = |z|^2$, which is a real number.

PROOF

$$z\bar{z} = (a + bi)(a - bi) = a^2 + abi - abi - b^2i^2 = a^2 + b^2$$

Since $|z| = \sqrt{a^2 + b^2}$, then $|z|^2 = a^2 + b^2 = z\bar{z}$. Since $a, b \in \mathbb{R}$, then $a^2 + b^2 = z\bar{z} \in \mathbb{R}$. $\blacksquare$

EXAMPLE 8-10   If $z = 8 - 15i$, find $z\bar{z}$ and $|z|$.
  In this case, $a = 8$ and $b = -15$, so $z\bar{z} = 8^2 + (-15)^2 = 64 + 225 = 289$. Then $|z|^2 = 289$, so $|z| = 17$.

Trigonometric Representation of Complex Numbers

Consider any point, (x, y), in the z plane. The magnitude of the line from the origin to (x, y) is the modulus of $z = x + yi$. Since the line segment representing the modulus forms an angle, θ, with the real axis, as shown in Figure 8-4, the values of x and y can be calculated from the trigonometric functions of θ. (The diagram shown in Figure 8-4 is called an *Argand diagram*.) Thus, we have

$$x = |z| \cos \theta$$
$$y = |z| \sin \theta$$

If x and y are known, then the angle θ can be determined by the expression

$$\tan \theta = \frac{y}{x}, \quad x \neq 0$$

or

$$\theta = \arctan \frac{y}{x}, \quad x \neq 0, \theta \in [0, 2\pi) - \left\{ \frac{\pi}{2}, \frac{3\pi}{2} \right\}$$

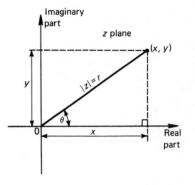

FIGURE 8-4

$\theta = \frac{\pi}{2}$ for $x = 0, y > 0$, $\qquad \theta = \frac{3\pi}{2}$ for $x = 0, y < 0$.

Hence, $z = x + yi = x + iy$ can be written in the form

$$z = |z| \cos \theta + i|z| \sin \theta$$

If we factor out $|z|$ and let $|z| = r$ ($r \in \mathbb{R}, r \geqslant 0$), we obtain

$$z = r(\cos \theta + i \sin \theta)$$

The form $z = x + yi$ is commonly called the *rectangular form* of z, and the form $z = r(\cos \theta + i \sin \theta)$ the *trigonometric form* of z.

THEOREM 8-3 Let $z = r(\cos \theta + i \sin \theta)$ for $r, \theta \in \mathbb{R}$. Then

$$\bar{z} = r(\cos \theta - i \sin \theta)$$

PROOF The proof is left as an exercise. ∎

The trigonometric form of the complex number z is sometimes abbreviated as

▶ $z = r(\underline{c}os \theta + \underline{i} \underline{s}in \theta) = r \text{ cis } \theta$

The word "cis" is composed of the underscored letters of the formal expression. In this form, the modulus and angle of the complex number are prominently displayed.

EXAMPLE 8-11 Write the number $z = \sqrt{3} + i$ in trigonometric and abbreviated form.

In this case, the real part is $\sqrt{3}$ and the imaginary part is 1. The modulus of the number is

$$
\begin{aligned}
r &= \sqrt{(\sqrt{3})^2 + (1)^2} \\
&= \sqrt{3 + 1} \\
&= \sqrt{4} \\
&= 2
\end{aligned}
$$

The angle θ is obtained from $\tan \theta$, which is the ratio of the imaginary part to the real part. Hence, $\tan \theta = 1/\sqrt{3}$, so $\theta = \pi/6$ or $30°$. (Since the real and imaginary parts are positive, θ must be located in the first quadrant.) Therefore, z expressed in trigonometric form is

$$
r(\cos \theta + i \sin \theta) = 2\left(\cos \frac{\pi}{6} + i \sin \frac{\pi}{6}\right)
$$

In abbreviated form, this is written as $2 \operatorname{cis} \pi/6$.

Changing a complex number from trigonometric form to rectangular form is simple: Evaluate the cosine and sine of the angle and multiply each by the modulus. This will give the real and imaginary parts, respectively.

EXAMPLE 8-12 Express the following complex numbers in rectangular form:
(a) $z_1 = 65 \operatorname{cis} 2.10$
(b) $z_2 = \frac{5}{13} \operatorname{cis} -14°20'$
For z_1, we have

$$
\begin{aligned}
z_1 &= 65(\cos 2.10 + i \sin 2.10) \\
&= 65(-0.5048 + 0.8632i) = -32.81 + 56.11i
\end{aligned}
$$

For z_2, we have

$$
\begin{aligned}
z_2 &= \tfrac{5}{13}(\cos -14°20' + i \sin -14°20') \\
&= \tfrac{5}{13}(0.9689 - 0.2476i) = 0.3727 - 0.0952i
\end{aligned}
$$

Exponential Representation of Complex Numbers

The trigonometric form of a complex number can be transformed into an exponential form. It can be shown, using techniques of the calculus, that

$$
\blacktriangleright \quad \cos \theta + i \sin \theta = e^{i\theta}
$$

THEOREM 8-4 (Euler's Identity) Let $\theta \in \mathbb{R}$. Then $e^{i\theta} = \cos \theta + i \sin \theta$.

PROOF   A formal proof requires use of the calculus. A heuristic justification of Euler's identity is presented in Appendix B. ∎

Hence, since

$$
z = r(\cos \theta + i \sin \theta)
$$

then by Euler's Identity,

$$\blacktriangleright \quad z = re^{i\theta}$$

This is called the *exponential form* of a complex number. (Note that θ must be in radians.)

THEOREM 8-5 Let $z = re^{i\theta}$ for $r, \theta \in \mathbb{R}$. Then

$$\blacktriangleright \quad \bar{z} = re^{-i\theta}$$

PROOF   The proof is left as an exercise.   ∎

EXAMPLE 8-13 Express the complex number $z = 3 - 3i$ in exponential form.
   The modulus is

$$r = |z| = \sqrt{3^2 + (-3)^2} = \sqrt{18} = 3\sqrt{2}$$

The angle is $\theta = \arctan[(-3)/3]$, a fourth quadrant angle, so $\theta = \arctan -1 = -\pi/4$. Thus,

$$z = re^{i\theta} = 3\sqrt{2}\, e^{i(-\pi/4)}$$
$$= 3\sqrt{2}\, e^{-i\pi/4}$$

EXAMPLE 8-14 Express $z = 5e^{i\pi/2}$ in rectangular form.
   We have $r = 5$ and $\theta = \pi/2$, so

$$z = r(\cos \theta + i \sin \theta)$$
$$= 5(\cos \pi/2) + 5i(\sin \pi/2) = 5(0) + 5i(1) = 5i$$

Products and Quotients

We now use the exponential representation of complex numbers to develop alternative methods for multiplying and dividing them, in both exponential and trigonometric form. The next two theorems show how multiplication is performed.

THEOREM 8-6 Let $z_1 = r_1 e^{i\theta_1}$ and $z_2 = r_2 e^{i\theta_2}$, where $\theta_1, \theta_2 \in \mathbb{R}$. Then the product $z_1 z_2$ is given by

$$\blacktriangleright \quad z_1 z_2 = r_1 r_2 e^{i(\theta_1 + \theta_2)}$$

PROOF

$$z_1 z_2 = (r_1 e^{i\theta_1})(r_2 e^{i\theta_2})$$
$$= r_1 r_2 e^{i\theta_1} e^{i\theta_2}$$
$$= r_1 r_2 e^{i(\theta_1 + \theta_2)} \qquad\qquad ∎$$

THEOREM 8-7 Let $z_1 = r_1(\cos \theta_1 + i \sin \theta_1)$ and $z_2 = r_2(\cos \theta_2 + i \sin \theta_2)$, where $\theta_1, \theta_2 \in \mathbb{R}$. Then the product $z_1 z_2$ is given by

$$\blacktriangleright \quad z_1 z_2 = r_1 r_2 [\cos(\theta_1 + \theta_2) + i \sin(\theta_1 + \theta_2)]$$

PROOF

$$
\begin{aligned}
z_1 z_2 &= r_1(\cos \theta_1 + i \sin \theta_1) r_2(\cos \theta_2 + i \sin \theta_2) \\
&= r_1 e^{i\theta_1} r_2 e^{i\theta_2} = r_1 r_2 e^{i(\theta_1 + \theta_2)} \\
&= r_1 r_2 [\cos(\theta_1 + \theta_2) + i \sin(\theta_1 + \theta_2)]
\end{aligned}
$$
∎

EXAMPLE 8-15 Let $z_1 = 3 + 4i$ and $z_2 = 5 + 12i$. Find the product $z_1 z_2$ in trigonometric and exponential forms.

Since $z_1 = 3 + 4i$, then $r_1 = \sqrt{3^2 + 4^2} = \sqrt{25} = 5$ and $\theta_1 = \arctan \frac{4}{3} = 0.927$. Since $z_2 = 5 + 12i$, then $r_2 = \sqrt{5^2 + 12^2} = \sqrt{169} = 13$ and $\theta_2 = \arctan 12/5 = 1.176$. Hence, in trigonometric form, the product is

$$
\begin{aligned}
z_1 z_2 &= r_1 r_2 [\cos(\theta_1 + \theta_2) + i \sin(\theta_1 + \theta_2)] \\
&= 5(13)[\cos(1.176 + 0.927) + i \sin(1.176 + 0.927)] \\
&= 65[\cos 2.103 + i \sin 2.103]
\end{aligned}
$$

In abbreviated form, the product $z_1 z_2$ can be represented as 65 cis 2.103. In exponential form,

$$z_1 = 5e^{i(0.927)} \quad \text{and} \quad z_2 = 13e^{i(1.176)}$$

Hence,

$$
\begin{aligned}
z_1 z_2 &= 5(13)(e^{i(0.927 + 1.176)}) \\
&= 65e^{i(2.103)}
\end{aligned}
$$

The following two theorems show how division is performed:

THEOREM 8-8 Let $z_1 = r_1 e^{i\theta_1}$ and $z_2 = r_2 e^{i\theta_2}$, where $\theta_1, \theta_2 \in \mathbb{R}$. Then the quotient z_1/z_2 is given by

$$\blacktriangleright \quad \frac{z_1}{z_2} = \frac{r_1}{r_2} e^{i(\theta_1 - \theta_2)}$$

PROOF

$$\frac{z_1}{z_2} = \frac{r_1 e^{i\theta_1}}{r_2 e^{i\theta_2}} = \frac{r_1}{r_2} e^{i\theta_1} e^{-i\theta_2} = \frac{r_1}{r_2} e^{i\theta_1 + i(-\theta_2)} = \frac{r_1}{r_2} e^{i(\theta_1 - \theta_2)}$$
∎

THEOREM 8-9 Let $z_1 = r_1(\cos \theta_1 + i \sin \theta_1)$ and $z_2 = r_2(\cos \theta_2 + i \sin \theta_2)$, for $\theta_1, \theta_2 \in \mathbb{R}$. Then the quotient z_1/z_2 is given by

$$\blacktriangleright \quad \frac{z_1}{z_2} = \frac{r_1}{r_2} [\cos(\theta_1 - \theta_2) + i \sin(\theta_1 - \theta_2)]$$

PROOF

$$\frac{z_1}{z_2} = \frac{r_1(\cos \theta_1 + i \sin \theta_1)}{r_2(\cos \theta_2 + i \sin \theta_2)} = \frac{r_1 e^{i\theta_1}}{r_2 e^{i\theta_2}}$$

$$= \frac{r_1}{r_2} e^{i\theta_1} e^{-i\theta_2} = \frac{r_1}{r_2} e^{i(\theta_1 - \theta_2)}$$

$$= \frac{r_1}{r_2} [\cos(\theta_1 - \theta_2) + i \sin(\theta_1 - \theta_2)] \qquad \blacksquare$$

EXAMPLE 8-16   For $z_1 = 3 + 4i$ and $z_2 = 5 + 12i$, find the quotient z_1/z_2 in trigonometric and exponential forms.

By the results of the previous example, $r_1 = 5$, $\theta_1 = 0.927$, $r_2 = 13$, and $\theta_2 = 1.176$. Hence, in trigonometric form,

$$\frac{z_1}{z_2} = \frac{r_1}{r_2} [\cos(\theta_1 - \theta_2) + i \sin(\theta_1 - \theta_2)]$$

Substituting, we obtain

$$\frac{z_1}{z_2} = \tfrac{5}{13}[\cos(0.927 - 1.176) + i \sin(0.927 - 1.176)]$$

$$= \tfrac{5}{13}[\cos(-0.249) + i \sin(-0.249)]$$
$$= \tfrac{5}{13}[\cos(0.249) - i \sin(0.249)]$$

In abbreviated form, the result is written as

$$\frac{z_1}{z_2} = \tfrac{5}{13} \operatorname{cis}(-0.249)$$

In exponential form, we have

$$\frac{z_1}{z_2} = \tfrac{5}{13} e^{i(0.927 - 1.176)} = \tfrac{5}{13} e^{-i(0.249)}$$

De Moivre's Theorem

We now use Theorems 8-4 and 8-5 to formulate a method of raising any complex number to any positive integral exponent. This is shown by the following theorem, called DeMoivre's Theorem.

THEOREM 8-10   Let $z \in \mathbb{C}$ and $n \in \mathbb{N}$. Then the nth power of z, denoted z^n, is given in exponential form by

$$\blacktriangleright \quad z^n = r^n e^{in\theta}$$

in trigonometric form by

$$\blacktriangleright \quad z^n = r^n(\cos n\theta + i \sin n\theta)$$

and in abbreviated form by

$$\blacktriangleright \quad z^n = r^n \operatorname{cis} n\theta$$

PROOF   Any $z \in \mathbb{C}$ can be represented in the form $z = re^{i\theta}$. Then $z^n = [re^{i\theta}]^n = r^n e^{in\theta}$. By Euler's Identity, this becomes

$$z^n = r^n[\cos n\theta + i \sin n\theta]$$

or, in abbreviated form,

$$z^n = r^n \text{ cis } n\theta$$

∎

EXAMPLE 8-17 For $z = \sqrt{3} + i$, evaluate z^4 in exponential, trigonometric, and rectangular forms.

From previous examples, z can be written as $z = 2e^{i\pi/6}$. Therefore,

$$z^4 = 2^4 e^{i4(\pi/6)}$$
$$= 16 e^{i2\pi/3}$$

So in trigonometric form,

$$z^4 = 16\left(\cos\frac{2\pi}{3} + i\sin\frac{2\pi}{3}\right)$$

To obtain the rectangular form of z^4, we evaluate $\cos(2\pi/3)$ and $\sin(2\pi/3)$.

$$\cos\frac{2\pi}{3} = -\frac{1}{2} \quad \text{and} \quad \sin\frac{2\pi}{3} = \frac{\sqrt{3}}{2}$$

Substitution of these values into the trigonometric form yields

$$z^4 = 16\left(-\frac{1}{2} + \frac{\sqrt{3}}{2}i\right)$$
$$= -8 + 8\sqrt{3}\,i$$

which is the desired rectangular form.

EXERCISES 8-2

Set A

1. Let $z_1 = 3 + 4i$, $z_2 = 15 - 8i$, and $z_3 = -5 + 12i$. Using the methods developed in this section, calculate the following complex quantities with the trigonometric form. Give the answers in rectangular form.

   (a) $z_1 z_2$ (b) $z_1 \bar{z}_3$ (c) $z_1 z_2 z_3$

   (d) $\dfrac{z_1 z_2}{z_3}$ (e) $\dfrac{\bar{z}_1 \bar{z}_2}{z_3}$ (f) $z_3(z_2 + \bar{z}_1)$

   (g) $z_1^2 z_2$ (h) z_3^3 (i) $\dfrac{z_3^2}{z_1^3}$

   (j) $\dfrac{z_3(z_2)^3}{z_1}$ (k) $\dfrac{z_3 z_2}{z_1}$ (l) $\dfrac{\bar{z}_3}{z_2}$

   (m) $\overline{z_1^2 z_2}$ (n) $\bar{z}_1^2 \bar{z}_2^2$ (o) $z_3 \bar{z}_2$

Set B

2. Use the methods developed in this section to show that if $z = x + yi$, then

$$z\bar{z} = r^2$$

and that the angle, θ, of the product $z\bar{z}$ is 0.

3. Prove the following basic properties for any $z_1 = x_1 + y_1 i$ and $z_2 = x_2 + y_2 i$:

(a) $|z_1 z_2| = |z_1| |z_2|$

(b) $\left| \dfrac{z_1}{z_2} \right| = \dfrac{|z_1|}{|z_2|}$

(c) $\overline{z_1 z_2} = \bar{z}_1 \bar{z}_2$

● 4. Repeat Exercises 1(c), 1(e), and 1(h) for

$z_1 = 6.9972 - (2.4131)i$ $\qquad$ $z_2 = 11.8955 + (27.6142)i$

$z_3 = -9.2466 - (10.5334)i$

Set C

5. Show that the transformation $w = z + 1/z$ maps the boundary of the unit semicircle in the z plane ($z = x + yi$) into the real axis, $v = 0$, of the w plane ($w = u + vi$). (See Figure 8-5.) Is the interior of the unit semicircle in the z plane mapped into the region below or above the u axis in the w plane? (*Hint:* Equate the real and imaginary parts of both sides of the transformation and use the fact that the semicircle is the *unit* semicircle.)

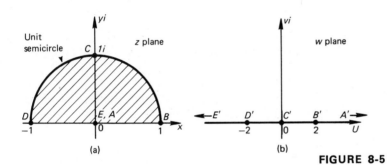

FIGURE 8-5

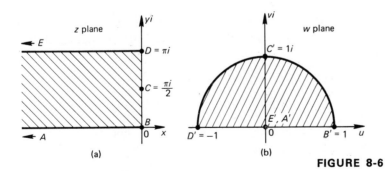

FIGURE 8-6

6. Show that the transformation

$$w = e^z$$

maps the semiinfinite strip shown in Figure 8-6(a) in the z plane into the unit semicircle in the w plane, as shown in Figure 8-6(b).

8-3 NEGATIVE ARGUMENTS OF LOGARITHMS

In Chapter 7, we defined the logarithmic function, $y = \log_b x$, as the inverse of the exponential function with base b, $b > 0$ and $b \neq 1$. As we saw earlier, the logarithmic function has domain $\mathcal{D} = \{x \mid x > 0\}$ and range $\mathcal{R} = \mathbb{R}$. In certain physical situations, however, it is natural to consider negative arguments of the logarithmic function. For example, if $F(x) = \log_3 x$ and $G(t) = \sin t$, then the composite $F \circ G$ is

$$F[G(t)] = \log_3[\sin t]$$

Since the values of $\sin t$, for $t \in \mathbb{R}$, range from -1 to 1, it would be useful if the argument of the logarithmic function could be negative. We can give meaning to the logarithm of a negative real number as follows.

Any complex number, z, can be written as

$$z = r(\cos \theta + i \sin \theta) \quad \text{where} \quad r = |z|$$

Then using Euler's Identity, we can write z as

$$z = re^{i\theta}$$

Now, any negative real number can be written as a complex number with a negative real part and zero imaginary part. For example,

$$-6 = -6 + 0i$$

Since $\cos \pi = -1$ and $\sin \pi = 0$, this complex number has a magnitude of 6 and angle of π. So, in exponential form, we have

$$-6 = 6e^{i\pi}$$

In fact, for $k \in \mathbb{R}$, $k > 0$, any negative number, $-k$, can be written as

$$-k = |-k|e^{i\pi}$$

This equation enables us to give meaning to the logarithm of a negative number. Taking the logarithm to the base b of both sides of the equation, we obtain

$$\log_b(-k) = \log_b(|-k|e^{i\pi})$$
$$= \log_b|-k| + \log_b e^{i\pi}$$
$$\blacktriangleright \quad \log_b(-k) = \log_b|-k| + (\pi \log_b e)i$$

In other words, the logarithm of a negative number is complex rather than real. For the example used earlier, if $-6 = 6e^{i\pi}$, then

$$\log_b(-6) = \log_b 6 + (\pi \log_b e)i$$

In the expression

$$\log_b(-k) = \log_b|-k| + (\pi \log_b e)i$$

the logarithm of a negative real number has real part

$$\log_b|-k|$$

and imaginary part

$$\pi \log_b e$$

Thus, if a real-valued answer is required for $\log_b(-k)$, we select only the real part.

EXAMPLE 8-18   Find the real value of $\log_b(-3)$.
From the discussion above,

$$\log_b(-3) = \log_b|-3|$$
$$= \log_b 3$$

Note that the imaginary part of the logarithm of a negative real number is *always* $\pi \log_b e$.

We can obtain a more elegant form of the logarithm of a negative number by taking the *natural* logarithm (to the base e) on both sides of the equation. For $b = e$,

$$\log_e(-k) = \log_e|-k| + (\pi \log_e e)i$$

And since $\log_e e = 1$,

▶ $\log_e(-k) = \log_e|-k| + \pi i$

EXAMPLE 8-19   Find the real and imaginary parts of the $\log_e(-12)$.
Since $\log_e(-12) = \log_e|-12| + \pi i$, the real part is $\log_e 12$ and the imaginary part is π.

EXERCISES 8-3

Set A

In Exercises 1 through 8, solve for the unknown value using the logarithmic and exponential identities.

1. $4 = 2^{\log_2 x}$

2. $9 = 8^{\log_b 9}$

3. $6 = 6 \log_b 3$

4. $x = 4 \log_\pi \pi$

5. $-2 = \log_{10} y$

6. $-3 = \log_2 x$

7. $x = \log_3(-1)$

8. $x = \log_\pi(-4)$

In Exercises 9 and 10, solve for the unknown value x.

9. $\log_6 x = \log_6 7 + (\pi \log_6 e)i$

10. $\log_e x = \log_e 2 + \pi i$

Set B

Solve for x in the following problems:

11. $\log_b\left(\dfrac{x}{4}\right) = (\pi \log_b e)i$

12. $\log_b\left(\dfrac{x}{29}\right) = (\pi \log_b e)i$

13. $\log_x(-1) = \pi i$

14. $\pi + \log_e\left(\dfrac{x}{5}\right)i = 0$

15. $\pi + (\log_e x)i = 0$

Set C

16. Plot the graphs of the following logarithmic equations in the complex z plane, where $z = x + yi$ and $t \in \mathbb{R}$:
    (a) $z = \log_e(t^2 - 4t + 3)$, $-6 \leqslant t \leqslant 6$, with t in increments of 1
    (b) $z = \log_e(t^3 - 9t)$, $-6 \leqslant t \leqslant 6$, with t in increments of 1
    (c) $z = \log_e(5 \sin t)$, $0 \leqslant t \leqslant 2\pi$, with t in increments of $\pi/6$
    In these equations, t is called a *parameter*. What characteristics does the graph have for those values of t where the argument of the logarithm approaches 0? How is this situation graphically treated?

17. In Exercise 16(c), the argument of the logarithmic function is a real periodic function. Extend the graph of this function to the interval $-2\pi \leqslant t \leqslant 6\pi$, using the same t increments. Based on this graph, can you make any general statement about the logarithm of a real periodic function?

18. Using the concepts developed in this chapter and Euler's Identity, derive the equation of the logarithm of any complex number $z = x + yi$. What is the result if z is pure imaginary?

REVIEW EXERCISES FOR CHAPTER 8

1. For $z_1 = 3 + 4i$, $z_2 = -5 - 12i$, and $z_3 = -8 + 15i$, evaluate the following expressions:
   (a) $\dfrac{z_1 \bar{z}_2}{z_2 \bar{z}_1}$
   (b) $(\bar{z}_1 - z_1)z_2$
   (c) $(z_3 z_1)z_2$
   (d) $(\bar{z}_3)^2(z_1)/z_2$
   (e) $z_1 \bar{z}_3 z_2$
   (f) $\dfrac{3z_1 + z_2}{z_3}$

2. Find the values of x and y that satisfy the following equations:
   (a) $(2x + y) + (x - y)i = 3$
   (b) $(3x + y) + (y - 4x)i = 7i$

3. Let $|z| = r$ (where $r \in \mathbb{R}$, $r > 0$) and $x, y \in \mathbb{R}$. Describe what DR plane curves result from the operation $z\bar{z} = r^2$, if
   (a) $z = x - (y + 3)i$
   (b) $z = \dfrac{(x + 3)}{2} + \dfrac{(y - 1)i}{3}$
   (c) $z = \sqrt{x - 1} + yi$

4. Solve for x in the following equations:
   (a) $\log_e 3x = \log_e 21 + \pi i$
   (b) $x = 3^{\log_3 9}$
   (c) $7 = 4^{\log_b 7}$
   (d) $5 = 2^{\log_2 x}$

Polynomial and Rational Functions

9-1 ZEROS OF POLYNOMIAL EQUATIONS

Introduction

Most of the algebraic functions encountered in this book are linear or second-degree functions. However, there are two additional classes of algebraic functions that are important in more advanced algebraic problems. They are the class of *polynomial functions* and the class of *rational functions*. Polynomial functions are the subject of Sections 9-1 and 9-2.

> **DEFINITION** A **polynomial** is an algebraic expression in which the exponents of all variables are nonnegative integers.

> **EXAMPLE 9-1** The expressions
>
> $$x^2y^3 + 4xy^2 + 7y - 8 \quad \text{and} \quad 16x^2 - 9(y + 3)^3 + 144$$
>
> are polynomials, whereas
>
> $$4x^{-2} + 3y^{1.4} - 4x - 5$$
>
> is not a polynomial.

Polynomials in one variable are of special interest. A useful application of polynomials is in forming nth-degree polynomial functions in one variable, which are defined as follows.

DEFINITION   The function

$$\blacktriangleright \quad y = P(x) = a_0 x^n + a_1 x^{n-1} + a_2 x^{n-2} + \cdots + a_n$$

for constants $a_i \in \mathbb{R}$ $(i = 0, 1, 2, 3, \ldots, n)$, $a_0 \neq 0$, and n a non-negative integer, is a **polynomial function of nth degree** in variable x over $\mathbb{R}$.

EXAMPLE 9-2   The function

$$f(x) = -5x^4 + 8x + 4$$

is a polynomial function of the fourth degree over $\mathbb{R}$, because all coefficients are real, all exponents are positive integers, and the highest exponent is 4.

EXAMPLE 9-3   The function

$$f(x) = 3x^5 + (2i)x^3 - 4x + (8 - 2i)$$

is a polynomial function, but *not over* $\mathbb{R}$, because some of the coefficients are complex.

In this section, we restrict the discussion to polynomial functions over $\mathbb{R}$. By the definition of $P(x)$, for $x \in \mathbb{R}$, any polynomial function P maps $\mathbb{R}$ *into* $\mathbb{R}$; symbolically, we write

$$\blacktriangleright \quad P: \mathbb{R} \to \mathbb{R}$$

Although certain polynomials are mappings *onto* $\mathbb{R}$ [e.g., $P(x) = x^3$], this is not true of all polynomials. In addition, the graphs of polynomial functions over $\mathbb{R}$ are smooth, graphically continuous curves.

Some Theorems on Polynomial Functions

One problem that arises in studying polynomial functions is to determine the real values of x that are the zeros of $P(x)$, that is, the solution set S given by

$$S = \{x \mid P(x) = 0, \, x \in \mathbb{R}\}$$

The existence of such values is guaranteed by the following theorem, called the Fundamental Theorem of Algebra. We present this theorem without proof, because the proof depends on the theory of complex variables, which is beyond the scope of this book.

THEOREM 9-1 (Fundamental Theorem of Algebra)   Every polynomial function, P, of degree $n \geqslant 1$ possesses *at least one* zero, which is not necessarily real.

We also present, without proof, the following generalized version of the Remainder Theorem:

THEOREM 9-2 Let $P(x)$ and $D(x)$ be polynomials over $\mathbb{R}$, $D(x) \neq 0$, such that the degree of $D(x)$ is less than or equal to the degree of $P(x)$. Then there exist unique polynomials $Q(x)$ and $R(x)$ over $\mathbb{R}$ such that

$$\blacktriangleright \quad P(x) = D(x)Q(x) + R(x)$$

and the degree of $R(x)$ is less than the degree of $D(x)$.

The following is an example of the application of this theorem:

EXAMPLE 9-4 Show that the polynomials $D(x) = x^2 + 3$, $Q(x) = x^2 + 4x - 3$, and $R(x) = x + 5$ uniquely determine the real polynomial function

$$P(x) = x^4 + 4x^3 + 13x - 4$$

Subsutution into the form given in Theorem 9-2 yields

$$\begin{aligned} P(x) &= (x^2 + 3)(x^2 + 4x - 3) + (x + 5) \\ &= x^4 + 4x^3 + 12x - 9 + x + 5 \\ &= x^4 + 4x^3 + 13x - 4 \end{aligned}$$

We use Theorem 9-2 to prove the Remainder Theorem.

THEOREM 9-3 (Remainder Theorem) Let $P(x)$ be a polynomial function over $\mathbb{R}$, and let $D(x)$ be the polynomial $x - a$, $a \in \mathbb{R}$. Then there exist a unique polynomial, $Q(x)$, and a unique real number, r, such that

$$\blacktriangleright \quad P(x) = (x - a)Q(x) + r$$

Furthermore,

$$\blacktriangleright \quad r = P(a)$$

PROOF Theorem 9-2 guarantees the existence of unique polynomials $Q(x)$ and $R(x)$ such that $P(x) = (x - a)Q(x) + R(x)$. Since r must be of a lower degree than $D(x)$ and $D(x) = x - a$ is of degree 1, then r must be of degree 0, and a polynomial of degree 0 is a constant. Hence, $P(x) = (x - a)Q(x) + r$. Furthermore, r must be a real number, because both $P(x)$ and $D(x)$ are polynomials over $\mathbb{R}$.

To show that $r = P(a)$, note that the equation $P(x) = (x - a)Q(x) + r$ must hold for all $x \in \mathbb{R}$. In particular, for $x = a$,

$$\begin{aligned} P(a) &= (a - a)Q(a) + r \\ &= 0 \cdot Q(a) + r \\ &= r \end{aligned}$$ ∎

In other words, the value of $P(x)$ for $x = a$ is r.

EXAMPLE 9-5 Consider $D(x) = x - 1$, $Q(x) = x^2 + 3x + 5$, and $r = 4$. Then there exists a polynomial, $P(x)$, such that $P(x) = (x - 1)(x^2 + 3x + 5) + 4$. Expanding, we obtain

$$P(x) = x^3 + 2x^2 + 2x - 1$$

From the Remainder Theorem, for $x = 1$, $P(1)$ should equal $r = 4$. As a check, let $x = 1$ in the expanded form of $P(x)$. This yields

$$P(1) = (1)^3 + 2(1)^2 + 2(1) - 1$$
$$= 1 + 2 + 2 - 1$$
$$= 4$$

We now use Theorem 9-3 to prove the Factor Theorem.

THEOREM 9-4 (Factor Theorem) Let P be a polynomial function over $\mathbb{R}$, and let $a \in \mathbb{R}$. Then $P(a) = 0$ if and only if $(x - a)$ is a factor of $P(x)$.

PROOF   Assume that $P(a) = 0$. The Remainder Theorem gives $P(x) = (x - a)Q(x) + r$. Since $r = P(a) = 0$, then $P(x) = (x - a)Q(x)$, and $(x - a)$ is a factor of $P(x)$.

Conversely, assume that $x - a$ is a factor of $P(x)$. Then there exists a polynomial, $Q(x)$, such that $P(x) = (x - a)Q(x)$. In particular, for $x = a$, we have $P(a) = (a - a)Q(a) = 0$. ∎

EXAMPLE 9-6 Find the third-degree polynomial, $P(x)$, such that $(x - 1)$ and $(x^2 + 3x + 5)$ are factors of $P(x)$.

The product of $(x - 1)$ and $(x^2 + 3x + 5)$ is

$$(x - 1)(x^2 + 3x + 5) = x^3 + 3x^2 + 5x - x^2 - 3x - 5$$

Simplifying yields

$$P(x) = (x - 1)(x^2 + 3x + 5) = x^3 + 2x^2 + 2x - 5$$

When $(x - a)$ is a factor of $P(x)$, so that $P(x) = (x - a)Q(x)$, it is possible for $(x - a)$ to be a factor of $Q(x)$ as well. In this case, $(x - a)^2$ is a factor of $P(x)$, and if no higher power of $(x - a)$ is a factor of $P(x)$, then a is said to be a zero of *multiplicity* 2 of $P(x)$. In general, if $(x - a)^k$ is a factor of $P(x)$ and no higher power of $(x - a)$ is a factor of $P(x)$, then a is a zero of *multiplicity k*.

Zeros of Polynomials

The concept of multiplicity, along with repeated applications of the Fundamental Theorem of Algebra and the Factor Theorem to $P(x)$, leads to the following theorem:

THEOREM 9-5 Every nth-degree polynomial function, $P(x)$, in one variable over $\mathbb{R}$ possesses exactly n zeros (not necessarily all real), where zeros of multiplicity k are counted k times.

PROOF By the Fundamental Theorem of Algebra, $P(x)$ has at least one zero, $z_1 \in \mathbb{C}$. By the Factor Theorem, there exists a polynomial function, $Q_1(x)$, such that

$$P(x) = (x - z_1)Q_1(x)$$

Again by the Fundamental Theorem of Algebra, $Q_1(x)$ has at least one zero, $z_2 \in \mathbb{C}$. Then by the Factor Theorem, $P(x)$ can be written as

$$P(x) = (x - z_1)(x - z_2)Q_2(x)$$

We can keep applying the Fundamental Theorem of Algebra and the Factor Theorem until we obtain a polynomial, $Q_n(x)$, of the form $z_0(x - z_n)$, where $z_0, z_n \in \mathbb{C}$ and $z_0 \neq 0$. Then $P(x)$ will be of the form

$$P(x) = z_0(x - z_1)(x - z_2)(x - z_3)\cdots(x - z_n)$$

This equation shows that $P(x) = 0$ for any $x = z_i$ $(i = 1, 2, 3, \ldots, n)$, because for $x = z_i$ the factor $x - z_i = 0$. Hence, $P(x)$ has exactly n zeros, which are not necessarily real. ∎

EXAMPLE 9-7 Show that $(x - 1)$, $(x + 2i)$, and $(x - 2i)$ are factors of

$$P(x) = x^3 - x^2 + 4x - 4$$

By algebraic multiplication, we obtain

$$(x - 1)(x + 2i)(x - 2i) = (x - 1)(x^2 + 4)$$
$$= x^3 - x^2 + 4x - 4 = P(x)$$

Consider the factored form of $P(x)$,

$$P(x) = z_0(x - z_1)(x - z_2)(x - z_3)\cdots(x - z_n)$$

where $z_0, z_i \in \mathbb{C}$ $(i = 1, 2, 3, \ldots, n)$. By definition, the coefficients of a real polynomial $P(x)$ are *all* real. If the zeros are complex, the question arises how the product of complex values can yield real numbers. As we saw in Chapter 8, the product of a complex number and its conjugate is a real number. If $z_1 = a_1 + b_1 i$ and $z_2 = a_2 + b_2 i$, then the product $z_1 z_2 = (a_1 a_2 - b_1 b_2) + (a_1 b_2 + a_2 b_1)i$ is real only if

$$\frac{b_2}{a_2} = \frac{-b_1}{a_1}$$

Since

$$z_2 = a_2 + b_2 i = a_2\left(1 + \frac{b_2 i}{a_2}\right)$$

we obtain, by substitution,

$$z_2 = a_2\left(1 - \frac{b_1 i}{a_1}\right)$$

$$= \frac{a_2}{a_1}(a_1 - b_1 i)$$

$$= \frac{a_2}{a_1}\bar{z}_1$$

Thus, since a_1, $a_2 \in \mathbb{R}$, z_2 is some real multiple of $\bar{z}_1$. Hence, $P(x)$ can have real coefficients only if the complex zeros of $P(x)$ occur in conjugate pairs. That is, if $z_1 \in \mathbb{C}$ is a zero of $P(x)$, then $\bar{z}_1$ must also be a zero of $P(x)$. The factor a_2/a_1 is part of z_0. In fact, z_0 must be real if $P(x)$ has real coefficients, so in this case, we use the symbol k_0 instead of z_0.

We conclude that if $P(x)$ has any real zeros, they can result only from factors of the form

$$(x - a)^m, \qquad a \in \mathbb{R},\, 1 \leqslant m \leqslant n$$

and hence, the factored form of $P(x)$ must be

$$P(x) = k_0(x - a_1)^{m_1}\cdots(x - a_K)^{m_K}(x - z_1)(x - \bar{z}_1)\cdots(x - z_L)(x - \bar{z}_L)$$

where

$$k_0, a_i \in \mathbb{R}, \qquad i = 1, 2, \ldots, K$$
$$z_j, \bar{z}_j \in \mathbb{C}, \qquad j = 1, 2, \ldots, L$$

and

$$m_1 + m_2 + \cdots + m_K + 2L = n$$

We have established the following theorem:

THEOREM 9-6 Let P be an nth-degree polynomial function over $\mathbb{R}$ in one variable. Then the n zeros of $P(x)$ are given in factored form by

$$P(x) = k_0(x - a_1)^{m_1}\cdots(x - a_K)^{m_K}(x - z_1)(x - \bar{z}_1)\cdots(x - z_L)(x - \bar{z}_L)$$

where

$$k_0, a_i \in \mathbb{R}, \qquad i = 1, 2, 3, \ldots, K$$
$$z_j, \bar{z}_j \in \mathbb{C}, \qquad j = 1, 2, 3, \ldots, L$$

and

$$m_1 + m_2 + \cdots + m_K + 2L = n$$

As we have already stated, we wish to find only the real zeros, so the techniques that follow will be presented only for real zeros.

Synthetic Division and Graphing of Polynomials

Although the Remainder Theorem guarantees the existence of the polynomials $Q(x)$ and $R(x)$, it does not show how they are calculated. The following example shows how $Q(x)$ and $R(x)$ can be found by algebraic division:

EXAMPLE 9-8 Divide $3x^4 + 2x^2 - 4x + 3$ by $x - 2$.
The usual long division technique yields

$$
\begin{array}{r}
3x^3 + 6x^2 + 14x + 24 \\
x - 2 \overline{)\ 3x^4 + 0x^3 + 2x^2 - 4x + 3} \\
\end{array}
$$

$$
\begin{array}{r}
-\quad + \\
\oplus\ 3x^4 \ominus 6x^3 \\
\hline
6x^3 + 2x^2 \\
-\quad + \\
\oplus\ 6x^3 \ominus 12x^2 \\
\hline
14x^2 - 4x \\
-\quad + \\
\oplus\ 14x^2 \ominus 28x \\
\hline
24x + 3 \\
-\quad + \\
\oplus\ 24x \ominus 48 \\
\hline
51
\end{array}
$$

Algebraic multiplication shows that if $P(x) = 3x^4 + 2x^2 - 4x + 3$, $D(x) = x - 2$, $Q(x) = 3x^3 + 6x^2 + 14x + 24$, and $r = 51$, then

$$P(x) = D(x)Q(x) + r$$

In other words, $Q(x)$ is the real polynomial quotient obtained from division of $P(x)$ by $D(x)$, and r is the remainder from this division. In particular, if $D(x)$ is of the form $(x - a)$ for $a \in \mathbb{R}$, then $r \in \mathbb{R}$. This process indicates a way of finding whether a given real number, a, is a zero of $P(x)$: Simply divide $P(x)$ by $(x - a)$; if the remainder, r, is 0, then a is a real zero of $P(x)$.

EXAMPLE 9-9 Find whether $x = 3$ and $x = 1$ are real zeros of $P(x) = x^4 - 4x^2 + 2x - 3$.
We divide $P(x)$ by $x - 3$ and $x - 1$ and see whether $r = 0$ in each case. For $x = 3$, we have

$$
\begin{array}{r}
x^3 + 3x^2 + 5x + 17 \\
x - 3 \overline{)\ x^4 + 0x^3 - 4x^2 + 2x - 3} \\
+\ x^4 - 3x^3 \\
\hline
3x^3 - 4x^2 \\
+\ 3x^3 - 9x^2 \\
\hline
5x^2 + 2x \\
+\ 5x^2 - 15x \\
\hline
17x - 3 \\
+\ 17x - 51 \\
\hline
48
\end{array}
$$

For $x = 1$, we have

$$
\require{enclose}
\begin{array}{r}
x^3 + x^2 - 3x - 1 \\[2pt]
x - 1 \enclose{longdiv}{x^4 + 0x^3 - 4x^2 + 2x - 3} \\
\end{array}
$$

$$
\begin{array}{r}
x^3 + x^2 - 3x - 1 \\
\hline
x^4 + 0x^3 - 4x^2 + 2x - 3 \\
+\,x^4 - x^3 \\
\hline
x^3 - 4x^2 \\
+\,x^3 - x^2 \\
\hline
-3x^2 + 2x \\
-3x^2 + 3x \\
\hline
-\,x - 3 \\
-\,x + 1 \\
\hline
-4
\end{array}
$$

For $x = 3$, $r = 48$; for $x = 1$, $r = -4$. Clearly, these are not real zeros of $P(x)$.

This division process can be shortened considerably by the use of *synthetic division*. The next example illustrates this technique. (The reader should refer to Example 9-9 to verify that the numerical values resulting from this method turn out to be the leading coefficients of each line of the division, the remainder, and the coefficients of the quotient polynomial.)

EXAMPLE 9-10 Use synthetic division to find r for $x = 3$ in the polynomial $P(x) = x^4 - 4x^2 - 2x - 3$.

Step 1 Arrange the terms of the polynomial so that the powers of x are decreasing from left to right. Next, form an array of the coefficients of $P(x)$, including zeros for the coefficients of any powers of x that do not occur. For the given equation, the array is

$$1 \quad 0 \quad -4 \quad 2 \quad -3$$

Step 2 Draw lines as shown below. (The box placed below the last coefficient is called the remainder box.) Place the value of x for which we wish to find r outside the array, as shown. The value in this case is $x = 3$.

$$
3 \,\big|\, 1 \quad 0 \quad -4 \quad 2 \quad -3
$$

Step 3 Bring down the leading coefficient of the array and multiply this coefficient by the value of x. Place the product beneath the next coefficient and add them. Place the sum next to the leading coefficient, which was brought down.

$$
\begin{array}{r|rrrrr}
3 & 1 & 0 & -4 & 2 & -3 \\
  &   & 3 &   &   &   \\
\hline
  & 1 & 3 &   &   &
\end{array}
$$

Step 4 Repeat the process with the sum obtained in Step 3.

$$
\begin{array}{r|rrrrr}
3 & 1 & 0 & -4 & 2 & -3 \\
  &   & 3 & 9 &   &   \\
\hline
  & 1 & 3 & 5 &   &
\end{array}
$$

Step 5 Continue the process until a number results in the remainder box.

$$\begin{array}{r|rrrrr} 3 & 1 & 0 & -4 & 2 & -3 \\ & & 3 & 9 & 15 & 51 \\ \hline & 1 & 3 & 5 & 17 & 48 \end{array}$$

$\leftarrow$ Remainder, r

Coefficients of quotient polynomial, $Q(x)$

The value in the remainder box is the same as the value obtained for r by long division. Note as well that by the Remainder Theorem, $r = P(a)$. Hence, the ordered pair $(a, P(a))$ is a point on the graph of the polynomial function P, so the information obtained from the synthetic division can be used to graph P.

We now calculate some other ordered pairs, $(a, P(a))$, by synthetic division.

$$\begin{array}{r|rrrrr} -4 & 1 & 0 & -4 & 2 & -3 \\ & & -4 & 16 & -48 & 184 \\ \hline & 1 & -4 & 12 & -46 & 181 \end{array} \quad (-4, 181)$$

$$\begin{array}{r|rrrrr} -3 & 1 & 0 & -4 & 2 & -3 \\ & & -3 & 9 & -15 & 39 \\ \hline & 1 & -3 & 5 & -13 & 36 \end{array} \quad (-3, 36)$$

$$\begin{array}{r|rrrrr} -2 & 1 & 0 & -4 & 2 & -3 \\ & & -2 & 4 & 0 & -4 \\ \hline & 1 & -2 & 0 & 2 & -7 \end{array} \quad (-2, -7)$$

$$\begin{array}{r|rrrrr} -1 & 1 & 0 & -4 & 2 & -3 \\ & & -1 & 1 & 3 & -5 \\ \hline & 1 & -1 & -3 & 5 & -8 \end{array} \quad (-1, -8)$$

$$\begin{array}{r|rrrrr} 0 & 1 & 0 & -4 & 2 & -3 \\ & & 0 & 0 & 0 & 0 \\ \hline & 1 & 0 & -4 & 2 & -3 \end{array} \quad (0, -3)$$

$$\begin{array}{r|rrrrr} 1 & 1 & 0 & -4 & 2 & -3 \\ & & 1 & 1 & -3 & -1 \\ \hline & 1 & 1 & -3 & -1 & -4 \end{array} \quad (1, -4)$$

$$\begin{array}{r|rrrrr} 2 & 1 & 0 & -4 & 2 & -3 \\ & & 2 & 4 & 0 & 4 \\ \hline & 1 & 2 & 0 & 2 & 1 \end{array} \quad (2, 1)$$

The ordered pairs just found are listed in Table 9-1. It happens that none of the real values tested are zeros, since none of the remainders are 0.

TABLE 9-1

x	y
−4	181
−3	36
−2	−7
−1	−8
0	−3
1	−4
2	1
3	48

However, we can find approximate values for the real zeros by graphing the function P and noting where the graph crosses or touches the D axis. When we plot the ordered pairs in the DR plane and connect them with a smooth curve, we obtain the graph shown in Figure 9-1. From this graph, we see that there are two real zeros for $P(x)$, one between -3 and -2 and another between 1 and 2.

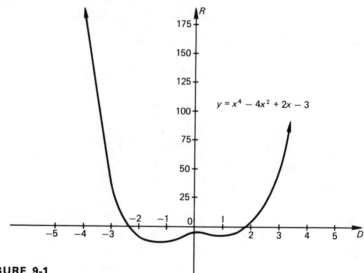

$$y = x^4 - 4x^2 + 2x - 3$$

FIGURE 9-1

EXAMPLE 9-11 Graph the function

$$y = P(x) = x^5 - 2x^3 + 4x^2 - 7$$

and locate the real zeros.

We calculate the ordered pairs by synthetic division.

$$
\begin{array}{r|rrrrrr}
-4 & 1 & 0 & -2 & 4 & 0 & -7 \\
   &   & -4 & 16 & -56 & 208 & -832 \\
\hline
   & 1 & -4 & 14 & -52 & 208 & -839
\end{array}
\quad (-4, -839)
$$

$$
\begin{array}{r|rrrrrr}
-3 & 1 & 0 & -2 & 4 & 0 & -7 \\
   &   & -3 & 9 & -21 & 51 & -153 \\
\hline
   & 1 & -3 & 7 & -17 & 51 & -160
\end{array}
\quad (-3, -160)
$$

$$
\begin{array}{r|rrrrrr}
-2 & 1 & 0 & -2 & 4 & 0 & -7 \\
   &   & -2 & 4 & -4 & 0 & 0 \\
\hline
   & 1 & -2 & 2 & 0 & 0 & -7
\end{array}
\quad (-2, -7)
$$

$$
\begin{array}{r|rrrrrr}
-1 & 1 & 0 & -2 & 4 & 0 & -7 \\
   &   & -1 & 1 & 1 & -5 & 5 \\
\hline
   & 1 & -1 & -1 & 5 & -5 & -2
\end{array}
\quad (-1, -2)
$$

$$
\begin{array}{r|rrrrrr}
0 & 1 & 0 & -2 & 4 & 0 & -7 \\
  &   & 0 & 0 & 0 & 0 & 0 \\
\hline
  & 1 & 0 & -2 & 4 & 0 & -7
\end{array}
\quad (0, -7)
$$

$$
\begin{array}{r|rrrrrr}
1 & 1 & 0 & -2 & 4 & 0 & -7 \\
  &   & 1 & 1 & -1 & 3 & 3 \\
\hline
  & 1 & 1 & -1 & 3 & 3 & -4
\end{array}
\quad (1, -4)
$$

$$
\begin{array}{r|rrrrrr}
2 & 1 & 0 & -2 & 4 & 0 & -7 \\
  &   & 2 & 4 & 4 & 16 & 32 \\
\hline
  & 1 & 2 & 2 & 8 & 16 & 25
\end{array}
\quad (2, 25)
$$

$$
\begin{array}{r|rrrrrr}
3 & 1 & 0 & -2 & 4 & 0 & -7 \\
  &   & 3 & 9 & 21 & 75 & 225 \\
\hline
  & 1 & 3 & 7 & 25 & 75 & 218
\end{array}
\quad (3, 218)
$$

These ordered pairs are listed in Table 9-2. Figure 9-2 shows the

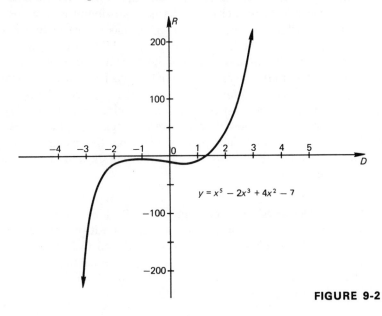

$$y = x^5 - 2x^3 + 4x^2 - 7$$

FIGURE 9-2

ordered pairs plotted in the *DR* plane and connected with a smooth curve. From the graph, we see that there is one real zero, near $x = 1$.

TABLE 9-2

x	y
-4	-839
-3	-160
-2	-7
-1	-2
0	-7
1	-4
2	25
3	218

Location of Real Zeros

Since any nth-degree polynomial over $\mathbb{R}$ in one variable possesses n zeros (not necessarily real) and complex zeros must occur in complex conjugate pairs, an nth-degree polynomial function over $\mathbb{R}$ can have at most n real zeros. Moreover, because the complex roots occur in conjugate pairs, the number of possible real zeros decreases from the maximum by stages of two.

For example, if $P(x)$ is a fifth-degree polynomial with real coefficients, the maximum number of real zeros $P(x)$ can have is five. Since nonreal zeros always occur in conjugate pairs, the next possibility is three real zeros. The next possibility would be one real zero. Since the least number of real zeros any polynomial can have is none, the possibility of one real zero cannot be diminished by two any further without the number of real zeros being less than 0. So a fifth-degree polynomial always has at least one real zero. In general, a similar argument will show that any polynomial whose degree is odd must have at least one real zero. (This is not always true, however, for polynomials whose degree is even.) In summary, the number of possible real zeros always diminishes by two from the maximum of n and cannot be less than 0. This justifies the following theorem, known as Descartes' Rule of Signs.

THEOREM 9-7 (Descartes' Rule of Signs) Let $P(x)$ be an nth-degree polynomial over $\mathbb{R}$. Then the maximum number of positive real zeros of $P(x)$ is equal to the number of sign changes in the coefficients of $P(x)$. The maximum number of negative real zeros of $P(x)$ is equal to the number of sign changes in the coefficients of $P(-x)$. These possibilities are diminished in stages of two and are never less than 0.

EXAMPLE 9-12 Find all possibilities for the numbers of positive and negative real zeros of

$$y = 3x^7 - 4x^6 + 2x^4 - 3x^3 - 7x^2 + 4x - 9$$

From Descartes' Rule of Signs, we have

$$P(x) = 3x^7 - 4x^6 + 2x^4 - 3x^3 - 7x^2 + 4x - 9$$

The number of sign changes is five, so there are at most five positive real zeros. The next possibilities are three positive real zeros and one positive real zero. Since the number of positive zeros cannot be less than 0, at least one positive real zero exists.

We find $P(-x)$ by changing the signs of those terms involving odd powers of x:

$$P(-x) = -3x^7 - 4x^6 + 2x^4 + 3x^3 - 7x^2 - 4x - 9$$

There are two sign changes in $P(-x)$, so there are at most two negative real zeros. The next possibility is that no negative real zeros exist.

A valuable method for locating a real zero is given by the following law:

THEOREM 9-8 (Zero Location Law) Let $P(x)$ be an nth-degree polynomial function over $\mathbb{R}$ in one variable. Then if the values of $P(a)$ and $P(b)$ have opposite signs, there exists at least one value, $\bar{x}$, such that $a < \bar{x} < b$ and $P(\bar{x}) = 0$.

The proof of this law is beyond the scope of this book. However, to see why this law is plausible, consider the graphs shown in Figure 9-3. If

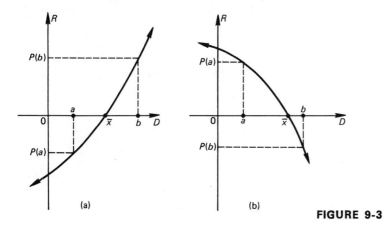

FIGURE 9-3

$P(a)$ and $P(b)$ have opposite signs, then either $P(a) < 0$ and $P(b) > 0$, or $P(a) > 0$ and $P(b) < 0$. In either case, since the graph of $P(x)$ must be smooth, it must pass through a point where $P(x) = 0$ to go from the value $P(a)$ to the value $P(b)$. So at least one real zero exists between any two x values for which the values of $P(x)$ have opposite signs.

We now present, without proof, another theorem that is useful in determining the boundaries in which the real zeros of a polynomial exist.

THEOREM 9-9 **(Real Zero Bounding Theorem)** Let $P(x)$ be a polynomial function over $\mathbb{R}$ in one variable, and let $\bar{x}$ be any real zero of $P(x)$.

(a) If there exists an $M \in \mathbb{R}$ ($M \geq 0$) such that the remainder, r, and the coefficients of $Q(x)$ have the same sign in the expression $P(x) = (x - M)Q(x) + r$, then $\bar{x} \leq M$; that is, M is an *upper bound* on the real zeros of $P(x)$.

(b) If there exists an $m \in \mathbb{R}$ ($m \leq 0$) such that in the expression $P(x) = (x - m)Q(x) + r$, the coefficients of $Q(x)$ and the remainder r alternate in sign (with a coefficient of 0 denoted either $+0$ or -0), then $m \leq \bar{x}$; that is, m is a *lower bound* on the real zeros of $P(x)$.

This theorem, when combined with the process of synthetic division, provides an easy way to determine when the process should terminate. In Example 9-11 the synthetic division could have terminated at $x = 2$, since all the coefficients of $Q(x)$ and r were of the same sign. Hence, 2 is an upper bound on the real zeros of the polynomial. Similarly, the process could have terminated at $x = -2$, since the signs of the coefficients of $Q(x)$ and r alternated (with the zero coefficients properly chosen as $+0$ and -0). Hence, -2 is a lower bound on the real zeros of the polynomial.

EXAMPLE 9-13 Locate the real zeros of

$$y = 3x^4 - 9x^3 + 4x^2 + x - 6$$

If we let

$$P(x) = 3x^4 - 9x^3 + 4x^2 + x - 6$$

then

$$P(-x) = 3x^4 + 9x^3 + 4x^2 - x - 6$$

From Descartes' Rule of Signs, the maximum number of positive real zeros is three, and the next possibility for the number of positive real zeros is one. This cannot be diminished further, so at least one

TABLE 9-3

x	$y = P(x)$
-3	513
-2	128
-1	9
0	-6
1	-7
2	-12
3	$+33$
4	$+254$

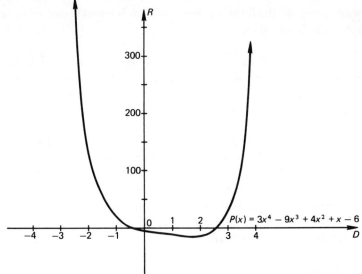

$$P(x) = 3x^4 - 9x^3 + 4x^2 + x - 6$$

FIGURE 9-4

positive real zero must exist. The maximum number of negative real zeros is one. Since this cannot be diminished further, one negative real zero must exist as well. We find several points on the curve (for example, by synthetic division), as listed in Table 9-3, and obtain the graph shown in Figure 9-4. Clearly, $P(x)$ changes sign between $x = -1$ and $x = 0$ and between $x = 2$ and $x = 3$, so zeros exist between those values of x. Note that these are the zeros guaranteed by Descartes' Rule of Signs: The positive real zero guaranteed by Descartes' Rule has some value between $x = 2$ and $x = 3$, and the negative real zero is between $x = -1$ and $x = 0$. The other two zeros of this fourth-degree polynomial must be a complex conjugate pair, because by Theorem 9-9 $x = -1$ and $x = 3$ are, respectively, the lower and upper bounds on the real zeros of P.

Rational Zeros of Polynomials

The next task is to develop a method of calculating the values of the zeros. There are many standard techniques available for finding the rational zeros of a polynomial. These involve forming all possible ratios of the *integral factors* of the constant term, a_n, with all possible integral factors of the leading coefficient, a_0, and then using synthetic division to find which values result in a remainder of 0.

The technique of determining the *possible* rational zeros of $P(x)$ is described by the Rational Zero Theorem, which we present without proof.

THEOREM 9-10 (Rational Zero Theorem) Let $P(x) = a_0 x^n + a_1 x^{n-1} + \cdots + a_n$ be an nth-degree polynomial over $\mathbb{R}$ in one variable. Then, all *possible* rational zeros of $P(x)$ are given by all possible ratios, in lowest terms, of the form p/q, where p is an integral factor of a_n and q is an integral factor of a_0.

These ratios are all the *possible* rational zeros of $P(x)$. If none of the possible rational zeros actually satisfy $P(x) = 0$, then any real zeros that exist are irrational. The following examples illustrate the use of this technique.

> **EXAMPLE 9-14** List all possible rational zeros of the polynomial $y = 2x^3 - 7x^2 + 9$. Then, use synthetic division to determine which of the possibilities are zeros. Determine whether any of the zeros are irrational and where these irrational zeros are located.
>
> For this polynomial, $a_0 = 2$ and $a_n = 9$, so the values of p are ± 1, ± 3, and ± 9, and the values of q are ± 2 and ± 1. Thus, the ratios p/q to be considered are
>
> $$\pm \tfrac{1}{2}, \quad \pm 1, \quad \pm \tfrac{3}{2}, \quad \pm 3, \quad \pm \tfrac{9}{2}, \quad \pm 9$$
>
> These are all *possible* rational zeros of $y = 2x^3 - 7x^2 + 9$.
>
> We can now use synthetic division to determine which of the possible zeros, if any, are actual zeros. The zeros turn out to be $x = 3$, -1, and $\tfrac{3}{2}$. The synthetic divisions for these values follow.

$$
\begin{array}{r|rrrr}
3 & 2 & -7 & 0 & 9 \\
  &   & 6 & -3 & -9 \\
\hline
  & 2 & -1 & -3 & \;0 \\
\end{array}
$$

$$
\begin{array}{r|rrrr}
-1 & 2 & -7 & 0 & -9 \\
   &   & -2 & 9 & -9 \\
\hline
   & 2 & -9 & 9 & \;0 \\
\end{array}
$$

$$
\begin{array}{r|rrrr}
\tfrac{3}{2} & 2 & -7 & 0 & 9 \\
   &   & 3 & -6 & -9 \\
\hline
   & 2 & -4 & -6 & \;0 \\
\end{array}
$$

Remember that if a value is a zero, the remainder will be 0. To show what happens with a possible value that is not a zero, we carry out the synthetic division for $x = -3$:

$$
\begin{array}{r|rrrr}
-3 & 2 & -7 & 0 & 9 \\
   &   & -6 & 39 & -117 \\
\hline
   & 2 & -13 & 39 & -108 \\
\end{array}
$$

Since the polynomial $y = 2x^3 - 7x^2 + 9$ is of the third degree, it can have at most three real zeros. We have just found the three zeros, $x = 3$, -1, and $\tfrac{3}{2}$, so no other zeros exist. Thus, the zeros of this polynomial are all rational.

> **EXAMPLE 9-15** List all possible rational zeros of the polynomial $y = 4x^4 - 6x^3 + 3x - 12$. Then use synthetic division to determine

which of the possibilities are actual zeros. Determine whether any of the zeros are irrational and where these irrational zeros are located.

For this polynomial, $a_0 = 4$ and $a_n = -12$, so the values of p are ± 1, ± 2, ± 3, ± 4, ± 6, and ± 12, and the values of q are ± 1, ± 2, and ± 4. Thus, the ratios p/q to be considered are

$$\pm\tfrac{1}{4}, \quad \pm\tfrac{1}{2}, \quad \pm\tfrac{3}{4}, \quad \pm 1, \quad \pm\tfrac{3}{2}, \quad \pm 2, \quad \pm 3, \quad \pm 4, \quad \pm 6, \quad \pm 12$$

These are all possible rational zeros of the polynomial $y = 4x^4 - 6x^3 + 3x - 12$. It would be inconvenient to check so many possibilities, but we can eliminate many of them by graphing the function and using Theorem 9-9. This also gives us a general idea of what zero values to try. The ordered pairs for this function are listed in Table 9-4, and the graph is shown in Figure 9-5. This graph is coarse in

TABLE 9-4

x	y
-2	94
-1	-5
0	-12
1	-11
2	10
3	159

that only integer values were used to construct it. By Theorem 9-9, $x = 2$ is an upper bound and $x = -2$ is a lower bound. The curve also shows that there are at least two real zeros (we say *at least* because in the region between -2 and 2, there are many fractional values that were not used in drawing the graph but may still be zeros);

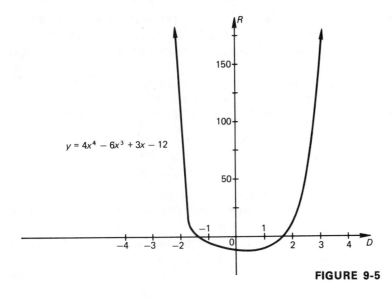

$y = 4x^4 - 6x^3 + 3x - 12$

FIGURE 9-5

one zero must lie between -1 and -2, and another must lie between 1 and 2. So the only possible zeros are those values of p/q between -2 and 2.

When we perform synthetic division with the possible zeros between -2 and 2, we see that none are zeros, so any real zeros of this polynomial must be irrational. Therefore, the two real zeros whose existence is indicated by the graph must be irrational, and the two remaining zeros must be a complex conjugate pair. (The reader should carry out the synthetic division for the rational zero possibilities between -2 and 2 and check the results.) In Section 9-2, we compute the irrational zeros of this polynomial.

Multiplicity of Zeros

So far, we have not considered any cases of polynomials with zeros of multiplicity greater than 1. The following example illustrates how such polynomials are treated.

EXAMPLE 9-16 Find all rational zeros of the polynomial function $y = P(x) = x^4 - x^3 - x^2 + 1$.

Using Descartes' Law of Signs, we find that $P(x)$ has either two positive real zeros or no positive real zeros, and no negative real zeros. By the Rational Zero Theorem, the only possible rational zero values are $x = 1$ and $x = -1$. Since $P(x)$ has no negative real zeros, the value $x = -1$ need not be considered. Use of synthetic division to test the value $x = 1$ yields

$$
\begin{array}{r|rrrrr}
1 & 1 & -1 & 0 & -1 & 1 \\
  &   & 1 & 0 & 0 & -1 \\
\hline
  & 1 & 0 & 0 & -1 & 0 \\
\end{array}
$$

This verifies that $x = 1$ is a zero of $P(x)$; hence, $x - 1$ is a factor of $P(x)$. There exists one more positive real zero, but we have exhausted our rational zero possibilities, so it seems that the remaining positive real zero must be irrational.

However, this is not the case. Recall that the values to the left of the remainder box are the coefficients of $Q_1(x)$. Since $x - 1$ is a factor of $P(x)$, then $Q_1(x)$ must be the remaining factor. Hence,

$$
\begin{aligned}
y = P(x) &= x^4 - x^3 - x^2 + 1 \\
&= (x - 1)Q_1(x) \\
&= (x - 1)(x^3 - 1)
\end{aligned}
$$

Now any zero (or factor) of $Q_1(x)$ is also a zero (or factor) of $P(x)$. By application of Descartes' Law of Signs and the Rational Zero Theorem to $Q_1(x)$, we find that

(a) $Q_1(x)$ has at most one positive real zero (guaranteed) and no negative real zeros.

(b) The only possible rational zero values of $Q_1(x)$ are $x = 1$ and $x = -1$.

As mentioned earlier, the value $x = -1$ need not be considered. Use of synthetic division on $Q_1(x)$ for $x = 1$ yields

$$\begin{array}{r|rrrr} 1 & 1 & 0 & 0 & -1 \\ & & 1 & 1 & 1 \\ \hline & 1 & 1 & 1 & 0 \end{array}$$

This verifies that $x = 1$ is a zero of $Q_1(x)$, and hence of $P(x)$. Moreover, $x - 1$ is a factor of $Q_1(x)$, and hence of $P(x)$. Therefore, using the results of this last synthetic division, we get

$$\begin{aligned} Q_1(x) &= (x - 1)Q_2(x) \\ &= (x - 1)(x^2 + x + 1) \end{aligned}$$

Hence, $P(x)$ becomes

$$\begin{aligned} y = P(x) = x^4 - x^3 - x^2 + 1 \\ = (x - 1)Q_1(x) \\ = (x - 1)(x - 1)(x^2 + x + 1) \\ = (x - 1)^2(x^2 + x + 1) \end{aligned}$$

This shows that $x = 1$ is a zero of $P(x)$ of multiplicity 2. The nonreal zeros are calculated by solving the equation $Q_2(x) = 0$ with the quadratic formula.

EXERCISES 9-1

Set A

Using Theorems 9-7, 9-8, 9-9, and synthetic division, sketch the graphs of the following polynomials. Give the values of any integer zeros; for each non-integer zero, give the two successive integers between which the zero lies.

1. $P(x) = 2x^3 - x^2 - 7x + 6$
2. $P(x) = 4x^3 - 8x^2 + x + 3$
3. $P(x) = 6x^4 + 13x^3 - 47x^2 - 10x + 8$
4. $P(x) = 12x^4 + 8x^3 - 7x^2 - 2x + 1$
5. $P(x) = x^3 + 2x^2 - 5x - 10$
6. $P(x) = x^4 - x^3 - 8x^2 - 9x - 7$
7. $P(x) = x^4 + 2x^3 - 8x - 16$
8. $P(x) = 2x^3 - 11x^2 + 32x - 30$
9. $P(x) = 3x^4 - 11x + 2$
10. $P(x) = 4x^3 - 3x + 7$
11. $P(x) = x^5 - 2x^4 - 12$
12. $P(x) = 2x^6 - 9x^4 + 2x - 6$

Set B

13. For the polynomials in Exercises 1 through 4, use the Rational Zero Theorem to list all the possible rational zeros of $P(x)$ that need to be tested. Find all the rational zeros.

14. Find all the real zeros of the following polynomial functions:
    (a) $y = x^3 - 3x^2 + 4$
    (b) $y = x^5 + 7x^4 + 23x^3 + 37x^2 + 28x + 8$

15. Using three stakes, a girl scout lays out a triangular plot such that one side is 2 yards longer than the shortest side and the remaining side is 1 yard longer than the shortest side. She has determined that the product of the lengths of the three sides equals five times their sum. Find the lengths of the sides of this triangular plot.

Set C

16. The motion of a particle is such that the distance (or distances) traveled from a fixed reference point is given by

    $$s = 4t^4 - 34t^3 + 85t^2 - 81t + 30, \qquad t \geqslant 0$$

    For what values of t will the particle return to the reference point?

17. In the theory of electronic feedback control systems, polynomial zeros play a major role in the time response of the electrical system. Using the methods developed in this section, find *all* zeros (real and complex) of the polynomial

    $$F(s) = 2s^4 + 17s^3 + 61s^2 + 160s + 150$$

    (*Hint*: Use the Factor Theorem.)

9-2 ITERATIVE METHODS OF FINDING ZEROS OF POLYNOMIALS

Introduction

In the many applications of polynomials, functions with rational zeros are much less common than those having only irrational zeros. As we saw in Chapter 1, it is not possible to determine precisely the decimal value of an irrational number. The calculation must end when the desired level of accuracy is reached. This automatically "rationalizes" an irrational value. (Even a computer calculation of an irrational zero eventually terminates the answer when the digit capacity of the machine is reached.) So the answers become rational approximations to the true (irrational) zero. The error in this approximation depends on the degree of accuracy of the approximate answer.

In Section 4-2, we derived a formula for the zeros of a second-degree polynomial. There also exist formulas for determining the zeros for the third- and fourth-degree polynomials. However, they are complicated and really not worth the effort involved in their derivations. Instead, we examine methods that work for polynomials of any degree and lead to answers with any desired accuracy. Calculating zeros with these methods usually takes no longer than it takes to use the complicated zero formulas. No zero formulas exist for polynomials of degree five or more, so in these cases, other methods *must* be employed.

In the two numerical methods for finding approximate zero values that we will discuss, the underlying concept is called *iteration*. Basically, this involves choosing a value near the actual zero and using this value to obtain a better approximation. The better approximation is then used to find a still better answer. We repeat the process until the difference between two successive answers meets certain criteria determined by the desired accuracy; then the last answer obtained is the approximation sought. (*An electronic calculator is invaluable in carrying out the calculations involved in these approximation methods.*)

Method of Successive Approximation

The basis of this technique is simple. We locate the zero between two values and then use a series of successively smaller similar triangles to approach the true zero value. By the Zero Location Law, whenever the value of $P(x)$ changes sign between two points, the curve must have passed through the D axis. That is, if $P(x_0)$ and $P(x_1)$ have opposite signs, there is a value $\bar{x}$ between x_0 and x_1 such that $P(\bar{x}) = 0$. Thus the zero, $\bar{x}$, is located between x_0 and x_1. Figure 9-6 shows four possible types of curvature that $P(x)$ can exhibit in passing through the point $(\bar{x}, 0)$.

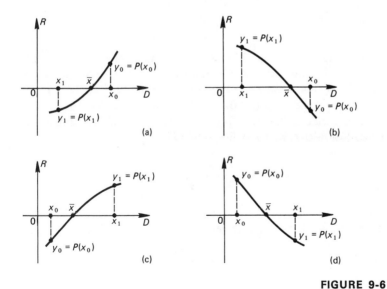

FIGURE 9-6

In Figure 9-6(a) and (b), x_1 is to the left of $\bar{x}$ and x_0 is to the right of $\bar{x}$, whereas in Figure 9-6(c) and (d), x_0 is to the left and x_1 is to the right. The technique requires that one of the two points be the anchor point of the iteration, and when the points are labeled as in Figure 9-6, x_0 is *always* chosen as the anchor point. So before beginning the iteration process, we must graph $P(x)$ and decide which of the four orientations the curve has at $\bar{x}$. (There are two instances not illustrated in Figure 9-6 where this method fails. They will be mentioned later.)

In Figure 9-6(a) and (b), the iterations will approach $\bar{x}$ from the left. We carry out the derivation for the case shown in Figure 9-6(a), and the reader can show that the same iteration scheme results for Figure 9-6(b). In Figure 9-7, which is an enlarged version of Figure 9-6(a), x_0 and x_1 are,

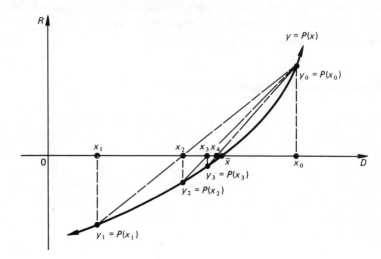

FIGURE 9-7

respectively, the initial right and left bounding values, $\bar{x}$ is the zero value, and y_0 and y_1 are, respectively, the values of $P(x)$ at x_0 and x_1. Now, if we draw the line between the points (x_0, y_0) and (x_1, y_1), this line intersects the D axis at the point $(x_2, 0)$, which is nearer to $\bar{x}$ than either x_0 or x_1 is. We can calculate the value of x_2 by using the properties of similar triangles. From Figure 9-7, we have the proportion

$$\frac{|y_1|}{x_2 - x_1} = \frac{|y_0|}{x_0 - x_2}, \quad \text{for } x_1 < x_2 < x_0$$

The absolute value signs are needed so that all terms will be related to distances. Solving for x_2, we get

$$x_2 = \frac{x_0|y_1| + x_1|y_0|}{|y_1| + |y_0|}$$

Thus, $x_2 \neq \bar{x}$, so we evaluate $y_2 = P(x_2)$ and thus locate a new point, (x_2, y_2), on the curve. Next, we draw a new line, between (x_0, y_0) and (x_2, y_2), which intersects the D axis at $(x_3, 0)$. Since x_3 is nearer to $\bar{x}$ than was x_2, it is a better approximation to $\bar{x}$. Now, using this smaller set of similar triangles, we calculate x_3 from the proportion

$$\frac{|y_2|}{x_3 - x_2} = \frac{|y_0|}{x_0 - x_3}, \quad \text{for } x_2 < x_3 < x_0$$

Solving for x_3 yields

$$x_3 = \frac{x_0|y_2| + x_2|y_0|}{|y_2| + |y_0|}$$

As before $x_3 \neq \bar{x}$ (but x_3 is closer to $\bar{x}$), so we evaluate $y_3 = P(x_3)$ and locate another point, (x_3, y_3), on the curve. We draw another line between (x_0, y_0) and (x_3, y_3), intersecting the D axis at $(x_4, 0)$; then x_4 is an even better approximation to $\bar{x}$ than was x_3. The value of x_4 is calculated from the proportion

$$\frac{|y_3|}{x_4 - x_3} = \frac{|y_0|}{x_0 - x_4}, \quad \text{for } x_3 < x_4 < x_0$$

Solving for x_4 yields

$$x_4 = \frac{x_0|y_3| + x_3|y_0|}{|y_3| + |y_0|}$$

Thus, each calculation yields an answer closer to $\bar{x}$ than the previous answer was. We repeat the process until we obtain the desired accuracy. Note that the anchor point, (x_0, y_0), is the same in each iteration and that the previous answer is always used to find the next value. In general, the result of each successive iteration can be written as

$$\blacktriangleright \quad x_{n+1} = \frac{x_0|y_n| + x_n|y_0|}{|y_n| + |y_0|}, \quad \text{where} \quad y_n = P(x_n)$$

Clearly, the approximations approach $\bar{x}$ from the left.

Next, we consider the curvatures shown in Figure 9-6(c) and (d). The iteration answers will approach $\bar{x}$ from the right. The major difference is that in these cases, the anchor point is to the left of $\bar{x}$. We present only the derivation for the case shown in Figure 9-6(c), but the reader should carry out the derivation for Figure 9-6(d) and show that the result is the same.

Figure 9-8 shows an enlarged version of Figure 9-6(c). As in the previous case, we begin by drawing the line between the points (x_0, y_0) and (x_1, y_1), which intersects the D axis at $(x_2, 0)$. The proportion is

$$\frac{|y_0|}{x_2 - x_0} = \frac{|y_1|}{x_1 - x_2}, \quad \text{for } x_0 < x_2 < x_1$$

Solving for x_2 yields

$$x_2 = \frac{x_0|y_1| + x_1|y_0|}{|y_1| + |y_0|}$$

To obtain a better approximation, we evaluate $y_2 = P(x_2)$. This locates a

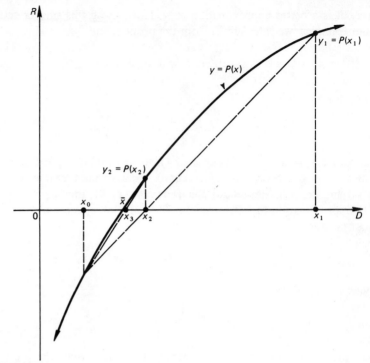

FIGURE 9-8

new point, (x_2, y_2), on the curve. If we draw the line between (x_0, y_0) and (x_2, y_2), which intersects the D axis at $(x_3, 0)$, then x_3 will be a better approximation to $\bar{x}$ than x_2 was. The proportion is now

$$\frac{|y_0|}{x_3 - x_0} = \frac{|y_2|}{x_2 - x_3}, \quad \text{for } x_0 < x_3 < x_2$$

Solving for x_3 yields

$$x_3 = \frac{x_0|y_2| + x_2|y_0|}{|y_2| + |y_0|}$$

Clearly, the results of these iterations are exactly the same as those obtained in the first case. Therefore, the general iteration equation can be written as

$$x_{n+1} = \frac{x_0|y_n| + x_n|y_0|}{|y_n| + |y_0|} \quad \text{where} \quad y_n = P(x_n)$$

and we need only a single, general iteration form. The generality of this equation is the result of careful selection of the anchor point and of recognizing that the four possible curvatures can be made to fit the same iteration equation if the proper anchor point is chosen.

There are several limitations to this method of approximation. First, the speed of convergence to $\bar{x}$ may be slow if the desired accuracy is high, so many iterations may be needed. Second, there are two cases in which this method fails to find a zero. One case occurs when the curvature of the graph changes near $\bar{x}$, as shown in Figure 9-9(a). This means that there exists a *point of inflection* at or near the zero. (The reader should show that the iterations will not converge in this case by constructing such a curve and attempting to use the triangle method.) The other case occurs when the curve touches but does not cross the D axis, as shown in Figure 9-9(b). In this instance, there is no way of knowing that a zero exists at the point, since $P(x)$ does not change sign near $\bar{x}$. The existence of this zero could very well go undetected.

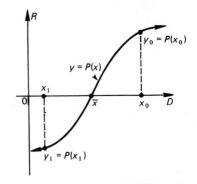

FIGURE 9-9a

An Example of Successive Approximations

As an example of the use of the technique of successive approximations, consider the polynomial

$$y = P(x) = 4x^4 - 6x^3 + 3x - 12$$

In Section 9-1, we saw that this polynomial has two irrational zeros, one between -2 and -1 and the other between 1 and 2. Suppose we wish to calculate the values of the zeros to two decimal places of accuracy. We proceed in two steps.

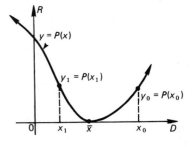

FIGURE 9-9b

1. From the graph of $P(x)$, shown in Figure 9-5, determine which type of curvature exists at each of the zeros by comparing the curve to those in Figure 9-6. Then select the proper anchor point and begin the iterations.
2. In order to obtain two decimal places of accuracy, we must have two successive iterations whose results agree to three decimal places. Terminate the process when this happens.

To find the zero between $x = 1$ and $x = 2$, note that this part of the curve has a curvature like that shown in Figure 9-6(a). Thus the point to the right, $x = 2$, is the anchor point, and the point $x = 1$ is the other starting point. Therefore,

$$x_0 = 2, \quad y_0 = 10, \quad x_1 = 1, \quad y_1 = -11$$

Then

$$x_2 = \frac{2|-11| + 1|10|}{|-11| + |10|}$$

$$= 1.523809$$

Now, $y_2 = P(x_2) = -7.091592$, so

$$x_3 = \frac{2|-7.09159\ldots| + (1.52380\ldots)|10|}{|-7.09159\ldots| + |10|}$$

$$= 1.721389$$

Since x_2 and x_3 do not agree to any decimal places, we continue, calculating

$y_3 = P(x_3) = -2.318800\ldots$ Then

$$x_4 = \frac{2|-2.3188\ldots| + (1.72138\ldots)|10|}{|-2.3188\ldots| + |10|}$$

$$= 1.773832$$

Since x_4 and x_3 agree to only one decimal place, the process must be continued. Table 9-5 gives a summary of the iteration results for this zero.

TABLE 9-5

n	x_n	$y_n = P(x_n)$
2	1.523809	-7.091592
3	1.721389	-2.318800
4	1.773832	-0.565094
5	1.785929	-0.127241
6	1.788619	-0.028131
7	1.789212	-0.006194
8	1.789342	

Since x_7 and x_8 agree to three decimal places, we terminate the iteration process after finding x_8. Therefore, the value of the zero between $x = 1$ and $x = 2$ is, to two decimal places of accuracy,

$$x = 1.79$$

In this case, the convergence was slow, requiring eight iterations just to obtain two decimal places of accuracy. Greater accuracy would require even more iterations.

To find the zero between $x = -2$ and $x = -1$, note that this part of the graph has a curvature like that shown in Figure 9-6(d). Thus, the point to the left is the anchor point. We have

$$x_0 = -2, \quad y_0 = 94, \quad x_1 = -1, \quad y_1 = -5$$

and

$$x_2 = \frac{-2|-5| + -1|94|}{|-5| + |94|}$$

$$= -1.050505$$

so

$$y_2 = P(x_2) = -3.324351$$

We continue the process, obtaining

$$x_3 = \frac{-2|-3.324\cdots| + (-1.0505\cdots)|94|}{|-3.324\cdots| + |94|}$$

$$= -1.082937$$

Since we do not yet have agreement to three decimal places, we must still continue the iteration process. Table 9-6 shows a summary of the iterations

TABLE 9-6

9-2 *Iterative Methods*
of Finding Zeros
of Polynomials **311**

n	x_n	$y_n = P(x_n)$
2	-1.050505	-3.324351
3	-1.082937	-2.127299
4	-1.103231	-1.327563
5	-1.115720	-0.815415
6	-1.123325	-0.495933
7	-1.127926	-0.299812
8	-1.130699	-0.180587
9	-1.132365	-0.108534
10	-1.133366	-0.065143
11	-1.133966	

for this zero. We finally terminate the process after calculating x_{10} and x_{11}, which are two successive answers that agree to three decimal places. Therefore, the value of the second zero to two decimal places of accuracy is

$$x = -1.13$$

Note that these results substantiate our earlier warning about the speed of convergence to the true zero. The next technique to be covered provides a faster convergence, but it requires a somewhat deeper understanding and more preliminary work.

Method of Functional Difference

If a function $y = H(x)$ has a zero at $x = \bar{x}$, then $H(\bar{x}) = 0$. Now suppose we rewrite $H(x)$ as the difference of two functions,

$$H(x) = f(x) - g(x)$$

then when $H(\bar{x}) = 0$, the expression becomes

$$0 = f(\bar{x}) - g(\bar{x}) \quad \text{or} \quad f(\bar{x}) = g(\bar{x})$$

If we graph both $f(x)$ and $g(x)$ on the same set of axes, the point $x = \bar{x}$ is the intersection of these curves. Furthermore, if we select $f(x)$ and $g(x)$ so that in the region near $\bar{x}$ the *magnitude* of the *slope* of $f(x)$ is *greater* than that of $g(x)$, a simple iteration scheme allows us to evaluate the unknown zero. Figure 9-10 shows the case where the slopes are of the same sign and $f(x)$ has the slope of greater *magnitude*. This case will illustrate how the iteration proceeds.

We know that we have a zero value when $f(x) = g(x)$. If we make a guess at the zero value, say, x_0, then the point $A = (x_0, g(x_0))$ is on the graph of g. If we let x_1 be the value such that $f(x_1) = g(x_0)$, this brings us to the point $B = (x_1, f(x_1))$. Clearly, x_1 is closer to the zero, $\bar{x}$. But x_1 is the solution to the equation

$$f(x_1) = g(x_0)$$

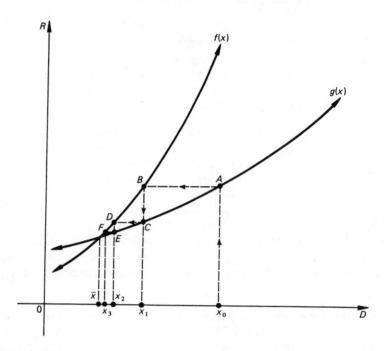

FIGURE 9-10

Next, we substitute the value x_1 into $g(x)$, obtaining the point C on the graph of g. As before, the value x_2 such that $f(x_2) = g(x_1)$ leads us to point D, which is even closer to $\bar{x}$. But x_2 is the solution to

$$f(x_2) = g(x_1)$$

Again, we substitute x_2 into $g(x)$, which brings us to point E on the graph. Setting $f(x_3) = g(x_2)$ brings us to point F, whose first coordinate, x_3, is even closer to $\bar{x}$. And x_3 is the solution to

$$f(x_3) = g(x_2)$$

We continue this process until we obtain an answer with the desired accuracy. Note that starting with an initial guess, x_0, we calculate a better guess, x_1. Then we use x_1 to get an even better guess, x_2. The iteration always goes from the function with smaller slope *magnitude*, $g(x)$, to the one with larger slope *magnitude*, $f(x)$. Then we use $f(x)$ to calculate a better approximation, which will be used in $g(x)$ to obtain an even closer value.

To use this method successfully, we must observe two criteria:

1. The choice of $f(x)$ and $g(x)$ should be such that near the zero values, the magnitude of the slope of $f(x)$ is greater than that of $g(x)$.
2. The function $f(x)$ should be such that the zero, x_{n+1}, of the iterative equation

$$\blacktriangleright \quad f(x_{n+1}) = g(x_n)$$

can be calculated easily for any x_n.

The following examples illustrate the technique.

EXAMPLE 9-17 Use an electronic calculator and the method of functional difference to find the real zeros of

$$y = P(x) = x^3 - 2x - 7$$

First, from Descartes' Law of Signs, we know that there exists one positive real zero and either two negative real zeros or no negative real zeros. Table 9-7 lists the values used to graph $P(x)$, as shown in

TABLE 9-7

x	y
-4	-63
-3	-28
-2	-11
-1	-6
0	-7
1	-8
2	-3
3	14
4	49

Figure 9-11. The graph shows that $P(x)$ has only one real zero, located between $x = 2$ and $x = 3$. This is also shown by the sign change in the values of $P(x)$ in Table 9-7.

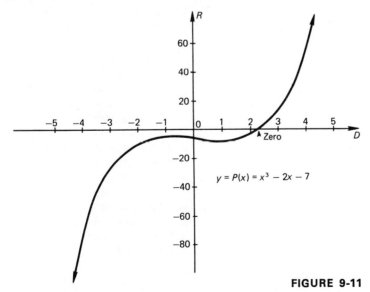

$$y = P(x) = x^3 - 2x - 7$$

FIGURE 9-11

In choosing $f(x)$ and $g(x)$, a good rule of thumb is to let $f(x)$ be the term of $P(x)$ containing the highest power of x, if the zero to be calculated has an absolute value greater than 1. If the zero has an absolute value less than 1, let $f(x)$ be the term of $P(x)$ containing the lowest power of x. Since the desired zero value is greater than 1, we write $P(x)$ as

$$P(x) = x^3 - (2x + 7)$$

letting

$$f(x) = x^3 \quad \text{and} \quad g(x) = 2x + 7$$

The iteration equation is

$$x_{n+1}^3 = 2x_n + 7$$

which, when solved for x_{n+1}, becomes

$$x_{n+1} = \sqrt[3]{2x_n + 7}$$

where x_n is the value used to obtain the better approximation x_{n+1}.

Figure 9-12 shows $f(x)$ and $g(x)$ plotted on the same set of axes. The graphs intersect only once (indicating only one real zero), at approximately $x = 2.3$. This value will be our initial estimate, x_0. Therefore,

$$x_1 = \sqrt[3]{2x_0 + 7} = \sqrt[3]{2(2.3) + 7}$$
$$= 2.263702391924$$

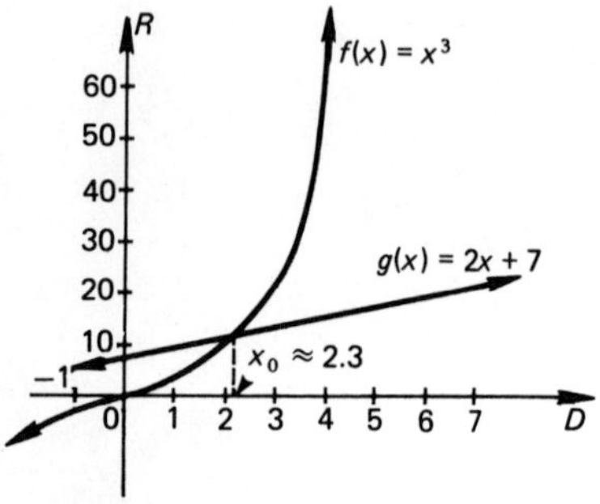

Using x_1 in the next iteration, we obtain

$$x_2 = \sqrt[3]{2x_1 + 7} = \sqrt[3]{2(2.263\cdots) + 7}$$
$$= 2.258970266253$$

We continue the iterations until we obtain the desired degree of accuracy. Table 9-8 shows the resulting values.

FIGURE 9-12

TABLE 9-8

x_0	$= 2.300000000000$
x_1	$= 2.263702391924$
x_2	$= 2.258970266253$
x_3	$= 2.258351875662$
x_4	$= 2.258271039823$
x_5	$= 2.258260472558$
x_6	$= 2.258259091145$
x_7	$= 2.258258910559$
x_8	$= 2.258258886951$
x_9	$= 2.258258883866$
x_{10}	$= 2.258258883462$
x_{11}	$= 2.258258883410$
x_{12}	$= 2.258258883403$
x_{13}	$= 2.258258883401$
x_{14}	$= 2.258258883401$

We have carried out a large number of iterations to illustrate how fast this technique converges. With the method of functional difference, we achieved accuracy to two decimal places after only three iterations. After 14 iterations, we have agreement between two successive answers to 12 decimal places (the maximum number of digits available on the calculator used).

The next example illustrates how to approximate zeros whose absolute values are less than 1.

● **EXAMPLE 9-18** Use an electronic calculator and the method of functional difference to calculate the irrational zeros of

$$y = P(x) = x^4 - 3x^2 + 12x - 7$$

Using the Zero Location Law, we find that $P(x)$ has only two real zeros, both irrational, one between $x = -3$ and $x = -2$ and the other between $x = 0$ and $x = 1$.

To find the zero between $x = 0$ and $x = 1$: This zero has absolute value less than 1, so we choose $f(x)$ as the term of $P(x)$ containing the lowest power of x. Thus, we write

$$y = P(x) = 12x - (-x^4 + 3x^2 + 7)$$

and let

$$f(x) = 12x \quad \text{and} \quad g(x) = -x^4 + 3x^2 + 7$$

These functions are graphed in Figure 9-13. The zero of interest is near $x = 0.7$; this will be our first estimate, x_0. The iteration equation is

$$12x_{n+1} = -x_n^4 + 3x_n^2 + 7$$

or

$$x_{n+1} = \frac{-x_n^4 + 3x_n^2 + 7}{12}$$

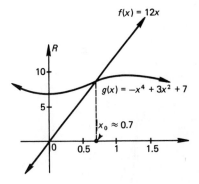

FIGURE 9-13

Table 9-9 shows the results of carrying out the iterations until agreement to twelve decimal places is reached.

To find the zero between $x = -3$ and $x = -2$: This zero has absolute value greater than 1, so we write

$$y = P(x) = x^4 - (3x^2 - 12x + 7)$$

and let

$$f(x) = x^4 \quad \text{and} \quad g(x) = 3x^2 - 12x + 7$$

The iteration equation is

$$x_{n+1}^4 = 3x_n^2 - 12x_n + 7$$

Solving for x_{n+1} yields

$$x_{n+1} = \sqrt[4]{3x_n^2 - 12x_n + 7}$$

TABLE 9-9

$x_0 = 0.7000000000000$
$x_1 = 0.6858250000000$
$x_2 = 0.6824860908668$
$x_3 = 0.6817003347637$
$x_4 = 0.6815154738376$
$x_5 = 0.6814719856691$
$x_6 = 0.6814617553394$
$x_7 = 0.6814593487257$
$x_8 = 0.6814587825874$
$x_9 = 0.6814586494077$
$x_{10} = 0.6814586180779$
$x_{11} = 0.6814586107080$
$x_{12} = 0.6814586089743$
$x_{13} = 0.6814586085660$
$x_{14} = 0.6814586084700$
$x_{15} = 0.6814586084475$
$x_{16} = 0.6814586084424$
$x_{17} = 0.6814586084409$
$x_{18} = 0.6814586084406$
$x_{19} = 0.6814586084406$

TABLE 9-10

$x_0 = -2.800000000000$
$x_1 = -2.829752018760$
$x_2 = -2.839187760800$
$x_3 = -2.842172792790$
$x_4 = -2.843116373270$
$x_5 = -2.843414568410$
$x_6 = -2.843508798150$
$x_7 = -2.843538574020$
$x_8 = -2.843547982900$
$x_9 = -2.843550956000$
$x_{10} = -2.843551895470$
$x_{11} = -2.843552192330$
$x_{12} = -2.843552286136$
$x_{13} = -2.843552315770$
$x_{14} = -2.843552325140$
$x_{15} = -2.843552328100$
$x_{16} = -2.843552329030$
$x_{17} = -2.843552329320$
$x_{18} = -2.843552329420$
$x_{19} = -2.843552329450$
$x_{20} = -2.843552329460$
$x_{21} = -2.843552329460$

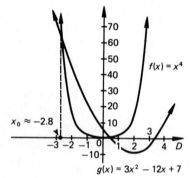

$f(x) = x^4$

$x_0 \approx -2.8$

$g(x) = 3x^2 - 12x + 7$

FIGURE 9-14

Since the answer we seek is negative, we use the negative fourth root. The graphs of $f(x)$ and $g(x)$ are shown in Figure 9-14. They intersect near $x = -2.8$, so this is our initial estimate, x_0. Table 9-10 shows the results of carrying out 21 iterations to twelve decimal places of accuracy; again, these figures illustrate the speed of convergence of this method.

Note that in each of the examples just worked, it takes only four or five iterations to obtain a result accurate to three or four decimal places.

Summary: Finding Zeros of Polynomials

General Techniques:

1. *Synthetic division* is used to obtain ordered pairs so that the polynomial can be graphed.
2. *Descartes' Rule of Signs* gives maximum numbers of real positive zeros and real negative zeros.
3. *The Zero Location Law* determines values between which zeros lie.
4. *The Real Zero Bounding Theorem* gives upper and lower bounds on the real zeros of a polynomial.

The *Rational Zero Law* determines the possible rational zeros of a polynomial. It can be used in combination with the four general techniques to reduce the number of possible rational zeros that must be tested by substitution or synthetic division.

Determining Irrational Zeros:

1. *The method of successive approximations* is a rather mechanical method requiring only determination of the proper anchoring point. It is slow to converge to any degree of accuracy but easy to use. Under certain conditions, this method fails to give an answer.
2. *The method of functional difference* is a more difficult method conceptually. It requires more skill and preparatory work than the method of successive approximations, but it converges more rapidly than most methods. Accuracy is limited by the digital capacity of the device used.

In actual practice, iteration methods are used to evaluate *all* real zeros of polynomial functions, whether rational or irrational. The study of differential calculus will further refine the techniques already developed.

EXERCISES 9-2

Set A

● 1. Consider the polynomical $P(x) = x^2 - 3$ for $x \geqslant 0$. Find the real zero, accurate to four significant digits, of $P(x)$ by the method of
   (a) successive approximations;
   (b) functional difference.

● 2. For the polynomial $Q(x) = x^2 + x - 7$, find the real zeros of $Q(x)$, to three significant digits, by the method of
   (a) successive approximations;
   (b) functional difference.

● 3. Given the polynomials
   (a) $P(x) = x^3 - 3x^2 - 1$
   (b) $P(x) = x^3 + 5x + 1$
   Find the real zero by the method of successive approximations with answers accurate to three significant digits.

● 4. For the polynomials in Exercise 3, find the real zeros by the method of functional difference with answers accurate to three significant digits.

Set B

● 5. For the polynomial $P(x) = 2x^3 + 5x^2 + 24x + 36$, find the real zero, precise to two decimal places. (*Hint:* Use functional difference.)

● 6. Find the real zero(s) to two decimal places of the polynomial $P(x) = x^4 - 6x^2 - 11x + 3$ by the method of successive approximations.

● 7. For the same polynomial in Exercise 6, find the zero(s) to four decimal places using the method of functional difference.

9-3 RATIONAL FUNCTIONS

Introduction

Our discussion of polynomial functions leads naturally to discussion of a second class of functions, called *real rational functions*. These are obtained as ratios of polynomials.

> **DEFINITION** A **real rational function**, Q, is a function defined by an equation of the form
>
> $$Q(x) = \frac{N(x)}{D(x)}, \qquad D(x) \neq 0$$
>
> where $N(x)$ and $D(x)$ are polynomial functions over $\mathbb{R}$ in one variable.

EXAMPLE 9-19 For $N(x) = x - 4$ and $D(x) = x^2 + 4x + 3$,

$$Q(x) = \frac{x - 4}{x^2 + 4x + 3}, \quad \text{for all } x \neq -3, -1$$

In the remainder of this section, we assume that all rational functions discussed are real and refer to them simply as rational functions. We also assume, for simplicity, that $N(x)$ and $D(x)$ have no common factors. The major topic of this section is the graphical behavior of rational functions; we will use calculations only to find certain specific critical values.

Since rational functions are ratios of polynomials and polynomials can have real zeros, an infinite discontinuity will occur whenever the denominator polynomial, $D(x)$, assumes the value 0. (Our assumption that $N(x)$ and $D(x)$ have no common factors implies that $N(x)$ and $D(x)$ cannot simultaneously be 0.) Near these values, the function becomes unbounded in either the positive or the negative direction. The graphs of the rational functions approach but never reach these points of discontinuity, so the line $x = a$, where $D(a) = 0$ and $N(a) \neq 0$, is a vertical asymptote of $Q(x) = N(x)/D(x)$.

The equation of the general rational function is

$$\blacktriangleright \quad Q(x) = \frac{N(x)}{D(x)} = \frac{b_0 x^n + b_1 x^{n-1} + \cdots + b_n}{a_0 x^m + a_1 x^{m-1} + \cdots + a_m}$$

where $m, n \in \mathbb{J}$, $m \geq 0$, $n \geq 0$, $a_i, b_j \in \mathbb{R}$ $(i = 0, 1, 2, \ldots, m, \ j = 0, 1, 2, \ldots, n)$, $a_0 \neq 0$, and $b_0 \neq 0$. If the degree of $N(x)$ is n and the degree of $D(x)$ is m, then there are two cases to consider: $n < m$ and $n \geq m$.

When $n < m$, the horizontal asymptote is always the D axis, the line $y = 0$. This is easily shown by considering the value of the general rational function as x increases without bound in either the positive or the negative direction. In this case, the highest powers of x in $N(x)$ and $D(x)$ dominate the values of these polynomials, so

$$y = Q(x) \approx \frac{b_0 x^n}{a_0 x^m}$$

for large (positive or negative) x. Since $n < m$, this reduces to

$$y = Q(x) \approx \frac{b_0}{a_0 x^{m-n}}$$

Clearly, as the value of x increases without bound, the value of the denominator also increases without bound, and the value of the ratio approaches 0. Therefore, the line $y = 0$ (the D axis) is a horizontal asymptote of $Q(x)$.

As stated earlier, the vertical asymptotes occur at those values of x for which $D(x) = 0$ and $N(x) \neq 0$. The zeros of $N(x)$ determine the points where the graph of the function either touches or crosses the D axis; this follows from the fact that if the numerator of a fraction is 0, the fraction's value is 0. The points at which $N(x) = 0$ and the vertical asymptotes divide the D axis into regions in which the value of $y = Q(x)$ is either always positive or always negative. If we determine the sign of y for each region, we know whether the graph of $Q(x)$ is above or below the D axis in each region. This knowledge and the smoothness of the curve in each of the regions will be very helpful in constructing the graph. (Since both $N(x)$ and $D(x)$ are polynomials with smooth curves, their ratio, where it exists, also produces a smooth curve.)

EXAMPLE 9-20 Sketch the graph of the rational function

$$y = \frac{3}{x - 3}$$

Step 1 Since the degree of the numerator is less than the degree of the denominator, the D axis is the horizontal asymptote.

Step 2 The denominator has only one zero, at $x = 3$. Therefore, the line $x = 3$ is the only vertical asymptote.

Step 3 The numerator cannot take on the value 0, so the graph will not touch or cross the D axis at any point.

Figure 9-15 reflects the information we have so far. The D axis is divided into two distinct regions by the vertical asymptote.

Step 4 Now we determine the sign of y in each region. For $x > 3$,

$$y = \frac{\text{positive}}{\text{positive}} = \text{positive}$$

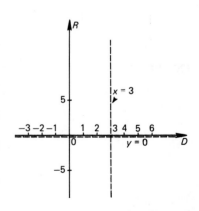

FIGURE 9-15

For $x < 3$,

$$y = \frac{\text{positive}}{\text{negative}} = \text{negative}$$

So for $x > 3$, the curve is always above the D axis, and for $x < 3$, the curve is always below the D axis.

For $x > 3$, as x gets closer to 3, the value of $x - 3$ gets closer to 0 (while remaining positive), so the value of $3/(x - 3)$ increases without bound in the positive sense. Thus, the curve must approach the vertical asymptote in an increasing positive direction as it gets closer to the line $x = 3$. For large positive values of x, the value of $3/(x - 3)$ becomes smaller and smaller (while remaining positive), so the curve must approach the D axis from above.

For $x < 3$, the curve must approach the vertical asymptote in a decreasing negative direction as x gets closer to 3; and as x gets large and negative, the curve must approach the D axis from below. The completed graph is shown in Figure 9-16. To help give some scale perspective to the graph, we have calculated one additional point, the R axis intercept, the point for which $x = 0$.

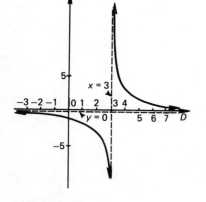

FIGURE 9-16

EXAMPLE 9-21 Sketch the graph of the rational function

$$y = \frac{x - 1}{x^2 + x - 6} = \frac{x - 1}{(x + 3)(x - 2)}$$

Since $n < m$, the horizontal asymptote is $y = 0$ (the D axis). The denominator has two zeros, one at $x = 2$ and one at $x = -3$. Therefore, the vertical asymptotes are at these points. The numerator is 0 at $x = 1$, so the graph either touches or crosses the D axis at $x = 1$. Figure 9-17 shows these critical points and how they divide the D axis.

The D axis has been divided into four regions: $x > 2$, $1 \leqslant x < 2$, $-3 < x \leqslant 1$, and $x < -3$. Now we find the sign of y in each region. For $x > 2$,

$$y = \frac{\text{positive}}{\text{positive}} = \text{positive}$$

For $1 \leqslant x < 2$,

$$y = \frac{\text{positive}}{\text{negative}} = \text{negative}$$

For $-3 < x \leqslant 1$,

$$y = \frac{\text{negative}}{\text{negative}} = \text{positive}$$

For $x < -3$,

$$y = \frac{\text{negative}}{\text{positive}} = \text{negative}$$

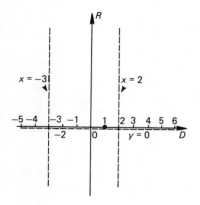

FIGURE 9-17

So for $x > 2$, the curve must approach $x = 2$ in an increasing positive direction, and as x grows large and positive, the curve must approach the D axis from above.

For $1 \leqslant x < 2$, the curve approaches $x = 2$ in a decreasing negative direction and must meet the D axis at $x = 1$ from below.

For $-3 < x \leqslant 1$, the curve must approach $x = -3$ in an increasing positive direction and must meet the D axis at $x = 1$ from above. Since the curve also crosses the R axis in this region, we calculate the R axis intercept by letting $x = 0$; the value of this intercept is $\frac{1}{6}$. This will give some scale perspective to the graph in that region.

For $x < -3$, the curve must approach the line $x = -3$ in a decreasing negative direction, and as x becomes large and negative, the curve approaches the D axis from below. The completed sketch is shown in Figure 9-18.

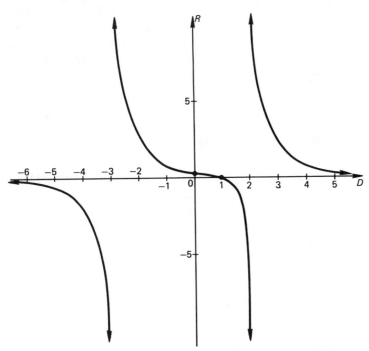

FIGURE 9-18

EXAMPLE 9-22 Sketch the curve of the rational function given by

$$y = \frac{x - 4}{x^2 - 4x + 4} = \frac{x - 4}{(x - 2)^2}$$

Since $n < m$, the D axis ($y = 0$) is the horizontal asymptote. The denominator has only one real zero, $x = 2$, so there is one vertical asymptote, at that point. The numerator is 0 at $x = 4$, so the curve either touches or crosses the D axis at that point. Figure 9-19 shows the division of the D axis.

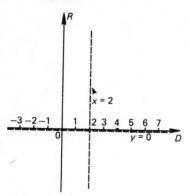

FIGURE 9-19

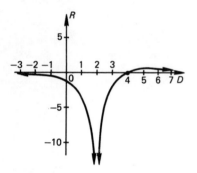

FIGURE 9-20

For $x \geqslant 4$,

$$y = \frac{\text{positive}}{\text{positive}} = \text{positive}$$

For $2 < x \leqslant 4$,

$$y = \frac{\text{negative}}{\text{positive}} = \text{negative}$$

For $x < 2$,

$$y = \frac{\text{negative}}{\text{positive}} = \text{negative}$$

For $x \geqslant 4$, the curve must approach the D axis from above for large positive values of x and meet the D axis at $x = 4$ from above.

For $2 < x \leqslant 4$, the curve approaches $x = 2$ in a decreasing negative direction and must meet the D axis at $x = 4$ from below.

For $x < 2$, the curve approaches $x = 2$ in a decreasing negative direction, crosses the R axis at -1, and approaches the D axis from below for large negative values of x. The completed graph is shown in Figure 9-20.

Graphing Rational Functions When $n \geqslant m$

If the rational function

$$Q(x) = \frac{N(x)}{D(x)}$$

is such that the degree of $N(x)$ is greater than or equal to that of $D(x)$ polynomial division can always be used to reduce this to the form

▶ $$y = \frac{N(x)}{D(x)} = P(x) + \frac{R(x)}{D(x)}$$

where $P(x)$ is a polynomial, $R(x)$ is the remainder polynomial, and $R(x)/D(x)$ is a rational function for which the degree of the numerator is less than that of the denominator. Then we can obtain the graph of $N(x)/D(x)$ as the graphical sum of the graphs of $P(x)$ and $R(x)/D(x)$. (These graphs can be drawn by methods already discussed.) By simply graphing each function on the same set of axes and algebraically adding the ordinate values for the same abscissa value, we can construct the graph of y.

EXAMPLE 9-23 Sketch the graph of the rational function

$$y = \frac{x^2}{x^2 - 4x + 4}$$

Using polynomial division, we rewrite this as

$$y = 1 + \frac{4x - 4}{x^2 - 4x + 4}$$

so $P(x) = 1$ and

$$\frac{R(x)}{D(x)} = \frac{4x - 4}{x^2 - 4x + 4}$$

The graphs of $P(x)$ and $R(x)/D(x)$ are shown in Figure 9-21 as dashed curves. The graph of y is the sum of these graphs. The unbroken curve shows this sum, which is the desired sketch.

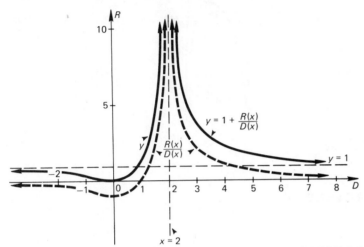

FIGURE 9-21

EXAMPLE 9-24   Sketch the graph of the rational function

$$y = \frac{x^3 + 4x^2 - 2x - 12}{x^2 + x - 6}$$

Using polynomial division, we can rewrite this as

$$y = x + 3 + \frac{x + 6}{x^2 + x - 6}$$

Now,

$$P(x) = x + 3$$

and

$$\frac{R(x)}{D(x)} = \frac{x + 6}{x^2 + x - 6}$$

The graphs of $P(x)$ and $R(x)/D(x)$ are shown in Figure 9-22 as dashed curves, and y, which is the sum of these two functions, is shown as an unbroken curve.

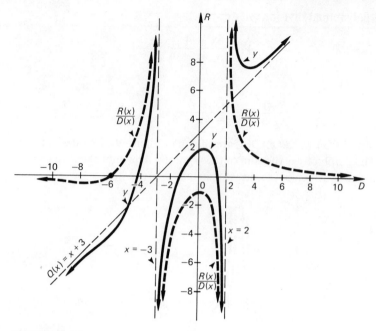

FIGURE 9-22

EXERCISES 9-3

Set A

Sketch the graphs of the following rational functions:

1. $y = \dfrac{3}{x^2 - 4x - 12}$

2. $y = \dfrac{4x}{x^2 + 6x + 5}$

3. $y = \dfrac{x}{x^2 - 16}$

4. $y = \dfrac{x + 2}{x^3 - x^2}$

5. $y = \dfrac{x + 3}{x^2 + 6x + 5}$

6. $y = \dfrac{x + 1}{x^3 + 4x^2 + 4x}$

7. $y = \dfrac{x^2 - 9}{x^3 + 16x}$

8. $y = \dfrac{x^2 + 3x + 2}{x^3 - 27}$

Set B

Sketch the graphs of the following rational functions:

9. $y = \dfrac{4x^2 - 16}{x^2 - 1}$

10. $y = \dfrac{x^3 - 6x^2 - 10x}{x^2 - 6x + 9}$

11. $y = \dfrac{x^3 + 8x^2 + 10x}{x^2 + 6x + 9}$

12. $y = \dfrac{2x^3 - 5x^2 - 5x - 25}{x^2 - 2x - 8}$

1. Determine all the rational zeros and locate any irrational zeros of the following polynomial functions:
   (a) $P(x) = 2x^4 - 5x^3 + 3x^2 - x$
   (b) $P(x) = x^6 - 4x^2 + 2x - 5$
   (c) $P(x) = 2x^6 - 5x^5 + 3x^4 - 7x^2 + 1$
   (d) $P(x) = x^5 - x^4 - x^3 - x^2 - x + 1$

2. Use the method of successive approximations to find the value, to two significant digits, of the irrational zeros of the polynomial in Exercise 1(a).

3. Use the method of functional difference to find, to three significant digits, the irrational zero of the polynomial in Exercise 1(a).

4. Sketch the graphs of the following rational functions:

   (a) $f(x) = \dfrac{x}{x^2 - 1}$

   (b) $g(x) = \dfrac{x^2 - 16}{x^2 + 7x + 12}$

   (c) $h(x) = \dfrac{x^3 - 1}{x^2 - x - 6}$

5. Use the method of functional difference to find the real zeros of the polynomial:

$$P(x) = x^4 - 6.2x + 2.3$$

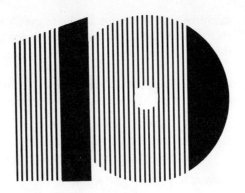

Induction—Sequences and Series

10-1 MATHEMATICAL INDUCTION

The child who observes that the sun rises every morning knows that the sun will again rise the next morning. Even if the sky is clouded, the child knows that the sun has risen because of the presence of daylight. This conclusion is continually reinforced—on the one hand, by daily occurrence, and on the other hand, by the absence of any contradictions to the conclusion. This is an example of a form of induction called *incomplete induction*, because the child has no way of knowing absolutely that the conclusion holds from one day to the next. In contrast, induction in which we know with certainty that a conclusion always holds is called *complete induction*.

In mathematics, we use a form of complete induction called **mathematical induction**. To understand the basic principles of mathematical induction, suppose a set of thin rectangular tiles are placed on end, as shown in Figure 10-1. Clearly, if the tiles are properly placed, then when the first tile is pushed in the indicated direction, all the tiles will fall. To be absolutely sure that all the tiles will fall, it is sufficient to know that

FIGURE 10-1

(a) The first tile falls.
(b) In the event that any tile should fall, its successor necessarily falls.

This is the underlying principle of mathematical induction. Suppose that $s_1, s_2, \ldots, s_n, \ldots$ is an ordered set of statements that are to be tested to see whether they all possess some property, P. (For example, the property might be that all the numbers are evenly divisible by 3.) Then the formal statement of the mathematical induction principle for this test is given in the following axiom:

AXIOM (Principle of Mathematical Induction) Let $s_1, s_2, \ldots, s_n, \ldots$ be an ordered set of statements, numbers, or objects. Suppose

(a) It is known that s_1 has property P.

(b) For any $k \in \mathbb{N}$, whenever s_k is assumed to have property P, it can be proved that s_{k+1} must also have property P $(1 < k < n)$.

Then s_n has property P for all $n \in \mathbb{N}$.

We illustrate the principle of mathematical induction by several examples.

EXAMPLE 10-1 Using mathematical induction, show that the sum of the first n positive integers is given by

$$1 + 2 + 3 + 4 + \cdots + n = \frac{n(n + 1)}{2} = S_n$$

(a) The property holds for $n = 1$, since

$$S_1 = \frac{(1)(1 + 1)}{2} = \frac{(1)(2)}{2} = 1$$

(b) Assume that the property holds for $n = k$; that is, assume that

$$S_k = \frac{k(k + 1)}{2} = 1 + 2 + 3 + \cdots + k$$

We wish to show that

$$S_{k+1} = \frac{(k + 1)(k + 1 + 1)}{2}$$

$$= \frac{(k + 1)(k + 2)}{2}$$

Then for $n = k + 1$,

$$S_{k+1} = (1 + 2 + 3 + \cdots + k) + k + 1 = S_k + k + 1$$

$$= \frac{k(k + 1)}{2} + k + 1$$

$$= (k + 1)\left(\frac{k}{2} + 1\right)$$

$$= (k + 1)\frac{(k + 2)}{2} = \frac{(k + 1)(k + 2)}{2}$$

If $k + 1 = n$, then $k + 2 = n + 1$. Therefore,

$$S_n = \frac{n(n + 1)}{2}, \qquad \text{for all } n \in \mathbb{N}$$

EXAMPLE 10-2 Using mathematical induction, show that the sum of the first n positive odd integers is

$$S_n = 1 + 3 + 5 + \cdots + (2n - 1) = n^2$$

(a) The property holds for $n = 1$, since

$$S_1 = (1)^2 = 1$$

(b) Assume that the property holds for $n = k$. That is, assume that

$$S_k = 1 + 3 + 5 + \cdots + (2k - 1) = k^2$$

Then we wish to show that the property must also hold for $n = k + 1$. We have

$$S_{k+1} = S_k + [2(k + 1) - 1] = S_k + (2k + 2 - 1)$$
$$= k^2 + 2k + 1$$

which is a perfect square. Hence,

$$S_{k+1} = (k + 1)^2$$

Thus, $S_n = n^2$ for all $n \in \mathbb{N}$.

EXAMPLE 10-3 Using mathematical induction, show that for $n \geqslant 1$ ($n \in \mathbb{N}$) and $x \neq a$, $x^n - a^n$ is divisible by $x - a$.

(a) The property holds for $n = 1$, since certainly $x - a$ is divisible by $x - a$.

(b) Assume that the property holds for $n = k$, i.e., $x^k - a^k$ is divisible by $x - a$. Then we wish to show that the property must also hold for $n = k + 1$. We have

$$x^{k+1} - a^{k+1} = x^{k+1} - xa^k + xa^k - a^{k+1}$$
$$= x(x^k - a^k) + a^k(x - a)$$

Therefore,

$$\frac{x^{k+1} - a^{k+1}}{(x - a)} = \frac{x(x^k - a^k)}{(x - a)} + \frac{a^k(x - a)}{(x - a)}$$

Now, by assumption the term containing $x^k - a^k$ is divisible by $x - a$, and the term $a^k(x - a)$ is obviously divisible by $x - a$. Hence, $x^{k+1} - a^{k+1}$ must also be divisible by $x - a$. Thus, $x^n - a^n$ is divisible by $x - a$ for all $n \in \mathbb{N}$.

EXERCISES 10-1

Set A

Use mathematical induction to show that the following mathematical statements are true:

1. The sum of the first n positive even integers is given by

$$S(n) = 2 + 4 + 6 + 8 + \cdots + 2n = n(n + 1)$$

2. The sum of the positive integers that are multiples of 3 is given by
$$S(n) = 3 + 6 + 9 + 12 + \cdots + 3n = \tfrac{3}{2}n(n + 1)$$

3. The sum of the first n positive integer powers of 2 is given by
$$S(n) = 2^1 + 2^2 + 2^3 + \cdots + 2^n = 2(2^n - 1)$$

4. The following holds for all $n \in \mathbb{N}$:
$$S(n) = \frac{1}{1 \cdot 2} + \frac{1}{2 \cdot 3} + \frac{1}{3 \cdot 4} + \cdots + \frac{1}{n(n + 1)} = \frac{n}{n + 1}$$

5. The following holds for all $n \in \mathbb{N}$:
$$S(n) = 1 + \tfrac{1}{2} + (\tfrac{1}{2})^2 + (\tfrac{1}{2})^3 + \cdots + (\tfrac{1}{2})^n = 2[1 - (\tfrac{1}{2})^{n+1}]$$

Set B

Prove the following by mathematical induction:

6. $S(n) = 1^2 + 2^2 + 3^2 + \cdots + n^2 = \dfrac{n(n + 1)(2n + 1)}{6}$

7. $S(n) = a + ar + ar^2 + ar^3 + \cdots + ar^{n-1} = \dfrac{a(1 - r^n)}{1 - r}$ for $r \neq 1$

8. $S(n) = a + (a + d) + (a + 2d) + \cdots + [a + (n - 1)d]$
$= \dfrac{n[2a + (n - 1)d]}{2}$ for constants a and d.

9. $S(n) = 1^3 + 2^3 + 3^3 + \cdots + n^3 = \dfrac{n^2(n + 1)^2}{4}$

10. $x^{2n} - 2x^n a^n + a^{2n}$ is divisible by $x - a$.

Set C

11. The expression $n!$, read n factorial, is defined as
$$n! = n(n - 1)(n - 2) \cdots 3 \cdot 2 \cdot 1$$
for all $n \in \mathbb{N}$. Prove by mathematical induction that
$$n! = n(n - 1)!$$

12. Use mathematical induction to prove that the following laws of exponents hold for $m, n \in \mathbb{N}$, where x and y are positive real numbers:

(a) $(xy)^n = x^n y^n$ (b) $\left(\dfrac{x}{y}\right)^n = \dfrac{x^n}{y^n}$

10-2   FINITE SEQUENCES AND SERIES

Sequence Functions

In earlier chapters, we considered functions whose domains consisted of all real numbers, possibly with certain restrictions. In the remainder of this chapter, we discuss functions whose domains are restricted to the set of natural numbers.

DEFINITION A function f is a **sequence function** if its domain is the set $\mathbb{N}$, i.e.,

$$\blacktriangleright \quad f: k \to f(k)$$

for all $k \in \mathbb{N}$.

Sequence functions map the set of natural numbers to images that are elements of the set of real numbers. Thus,

$$\blacktriangleright \quad f: \mathbb{N} \to \mathbb{R}$$

EXAMPLE 10-4 For the sequence function f, $f(k) = f_k = (3k - 1)/2$, find f_1, f_2, f_4, and f_7.

We have

$$f_1 = f(1) = 1, \qquad f_2 = f(2) = \tfrac{5}{2}$$
$$f_4 = f(4) = \tfrac{11}{2}, \qquad f_7 = f(7) = 10$$

Finite Sequences

A sequence function generates a set of ordered pairs, $(k, f(k))$, where $f(k) = f_k$ for $k \in \mathbb{N}$. For some fixed $n \in \mathbb{N}$, if the range elements of the function, f_k, are arranged in the order $f_1, f_2, f_3, \ldots, f_k, \ldots, f_n$, then the arrangement is a *finite sequence*.

DEFINITION Let f be a sequence function and let $1 \leqslant k \leqslant n$ for $k, n \in \mathbb{N}$. Then the arrangement

$$f_1, f_2, \ldots, f_k, \ldots, f_n$$

is called a **finite sequence**, denoted $\{f_k\}$.

By this definition, $\{f_k\}$ is considered an "ordered set" of elements. The element f_k of $\{f_k\}$ is called the kth *term* of the sequence.

EXAMPLE 10-5 Find the finite sequence $\{a_k\}$ to seven terms if $a_k = f(k) = 2k^2$.

The terms of the sequence are $a_1 = 2$, $a_2 = 8$, $a_3 = 18, \ldots, a_7 = 98$. Hence,

$$\{a_k\} = 2, 8, 18, 32, 50, 72, 98$$

EXAMPLE 10-6 Calculate the fifth term of the sequence $\{F_k\}$ if

$$F_k = F(k) = \frac{(-1)^k(k-1)^2}{\sqrt{k^2 + 3}}$$

The fifth term is

$$F_5 = \frac{(-1)^5(5-1)^2}{\sqrt{5^2 + 3}} = \frac{-16}{\sqrt{28}} = \frac{-8\sqrt{7}}{7}$$

EXAMPLE 10-7 Find the finite sequence $\{b_k\}$ to 72 terms if

$$b_k = g(k) = \frac{5k + 3}{2}$$

The terms are $b_1 = 4$, $b_2 = \frac{13}{2} = 6.5$, $b_3 = 9$, $b_4 = \frac{23}{2} = 11.5$, $b_5 = 14, \ldots, b_{71} = 179$, $b_{72} = \frac{363}{2} = 181.5$. So

$$\{b_k\} = 4, 6.5, 9, 11.5, 14, \ldots, 179, 181.5$$

Arithmetic Sequences

In the last example, it was possible to find the terms of the sequence without actually calculating $(5k + 3)/2$ for each value of k. Instead, if we recognized that any two successive elements of the sequence differ by a constant, 2.5, we could calculate each term by adding this number to the preceding term. Sequences of this type are called *arithmetic sequences* or *arithmetic progressions*.

DEFINITION Let f define a sequence function such that

$$f_{k+1} - f_k = d$$

for all $k \in \mathbb{N}$, where d is a constant, called the common difference. Then the sequence $\{f_k\}$ is called an **arithmetic sequence** or **arithmetic progression.**

The definition of an arithmetic sequence can be used to determine any element of the sequence, once the first element and the difference are known. For example, suppose a certain amount of money, P, is borrowed at a simple yearly interest rate, r. For each year the interest, I, is calculated as $I = Pr$. If we let A_k be the amount owed at the beginning of the kth year, then

$$A_1 = P$$
$$A_2 = P + I$$
$$A_3 = P + 2I$$
$$A_4 = P + 3I$$

and so on. At the beginning of the kth year,

$$A_k = P + (k - 1)I$$

which is the general term of sequence $\{A_k\}$. To determine whether the sequence is arithmetic, we form the difference between A_k and A_{k+1}.

$$A_{k+1} - A_k = [P + (k + 1 - 1)I] - [P + (k - 1)I]$$
$$= P + kI - P - kI + I$$
$$= I$$

which is a constant. Hence, the sequence defined by $A_k = P + (k - 1)I$ is arithmetic.

THEOREM 10-2 Let $\{a_k\}$ be an arithmetic sequence with initial element a_1 and common difference d. Then the kth element of this sequence is given by

▶ $a_k = a_1 + (k - 1)d$

PROOF We proceed by mathematical induction. The formula is true for $k = 1$, since $a_1 = a_1 + (1 - 1)d = a_1$. Now, assume that it is true for some $j \in \mathbb{N}$. Then $a_j = a_1 + (j - 1)d$ and

$$a_{j+1} = a_j + d = [a_1 + (j - 1)d] + d = a_1 + jd$$

Thus,

$$a_{j+1} = a_1 + [(j + 1) - 1]d$$

So the formula is true for $k = j + 1$, and the theorem is proved. ∎

EXAMPLE 10-8 Find the fifth term of the arithmetic progression having initial term 8 and common difference 6.

We know that $a_k = a_1 + (k - 1)d$, so

$$a_5 = 8 + (5 - 1)6 = 8 + 4(6) = 8 + 24 = 32$$

EXAMPLE 10-9 How many terms are there in the arithmetic sequence $7, 4, 1, -2, -5, \ldots, -1265$?

In this case, $a_1 = 7$, $d = -3$, and $a_k = -1265$. We can rewrite the equation $a_k = a_1 + (k - 1)d$ as

$$a_k - a_1 = (k - 1)d \quad \text{or} \quad k - 1 = \frac{a_k - a_1}{d}$$

Then

$$k - 1 = \frac{-1265 - 7}{-3} = \frac{-1272}{-3} = 424$$

Therefore, the sequence has 425 terms.

Geometric Sequences

In the biological sciences, the multiplication of bacteria is a well-known phenomenon. Assume that a particular class of bacteria have an initial population of A_1, which doubles every hour. Let A_k be the number of bacteria present at the beginning of the kth hour. The record of microscopic observation of the bacterial count would proceed as follows:

Hour	Amount
1	A_1
2	$A_2 = 2A_1$
3	$A_3 = 2A_2 = 2^2 A_1$
4	$A_4 = 2A_3 = 2^3 A_1$
5	$A_5 = 2A_4 = 2^4 A_1$

After k hours, the count is given by

$$A_k = 2^{k-1}A_1$$

This sequence, $\{A_k\} = A_1, 2A_1, 2^2A_1, 2^3A_1, 2^4A_1, \ldots$, has the characteristic that the *ratio* between any two consecutive terms is always a constant. Such a sequence is called a *geometric sequence* or *geometric progression*.

DEFINITION Let f define a sequence function such that

$$\frac{f_{k+1}}{f_k} = r, \qquad f_k \neq 0$$

where $k \in \mathbb{N}$ and r is a constant, called the common ratio. Then the sequence $\{f_k\}$ is called a **geometric sequence** or **geometric progression.**

By this definition, we can determine the entire sequence $\{f_k\} = f_1, f_2, f_3, \ldots, f_k, \ldots$ if we know any one term of $\{f_k\}$ and the ratio, r. This is true because $f_{k+1} = rf_k$. The following theorem results:

THEOREM 10-3 Let $\{a_k\}$ be a geometric sequence with initial element a_1 and common ratio r. Then the kth element of this sequence is given by

$$\blacktriangleright \quad a_k = a_1 r^{k-1}, \qquad r \neq 0$$

PROOF The proof is left as an exercise. ∎

EXAMPLE 10-10 Find the sixth term of a geometric progression having initial term 3 and common ratio 2.
Since $a_k = a_1 r^{k-1}$, then

$$a_6 = 3(2^{6-1}) = 3(2^5) = 3(32) = 96$$

EXAMPLE 10-11 If a geometric sequence of ten terms has common ratio $\frac{1}{2}$ and tenth term $\frac{1}{128}$, find the initial term.
Solving the general geometric sequence equation for a_1 yields

$$a_1 = a_k r^{-(k-1)} = a_k r^{1-k} = \tfrac{1}{128}(\tfrac{1}{2})^{1-10} = \tfrac{1}{128}(\tfrac{1}{2})^{-9}$$
$$= \tfrac{1}{128}(2)^9 = \tfrac{512}{128} = 4$$

Summation Notation

Sequences are important in many areas of analysis. A special application of sequences is found in their use in developing series. Before giving the definition of a series, we must introduce summation notation. The symbol Σ (the Greek letter *sigma*) is used to denote summation. For example, suppose we wish to sum all the values x_k for $1 \leqslant k \leqslant 7$. This sum is written

$$x_1 + x_2 + x_3 + x_4 + x_5 + x_6 + x_7$$

Summation (or sigma) notation provides a more compact way of writing this, namely,

$$\sum_{k=1}^{7} x_k$$

which is read "the sum of values x_k from $k = 1$ to $k = 7$." The integer k, called the *index of summation*, is a "dummy" variable in the sense that if any other letter were used, the result would be the same. In general, for $k, q, n \in \mathbb{J}, n \geqslant q$,

$$\sum_{k=q}^{n} x_k = x_q + x_{q+1} + x_{q+2} + \cdots + x_n$$

EXAMPLE 10-12 Express the sum $f_1 + (f_2)^2 + (f_3)^3 + (f_4)^4$ in summation notation.

Since each term in the sum is raised to an exponent that is also its subscript index, we can write

$$f_1 + (f_2)^2 + (f_3)^3 + (f_4)^4 = \sum_{k=+1}^{4} (f_k)^k$$

EXAMPLE 10-13 Express the sum $x_1 y_2 + x_2 y_3 + x_3 y_4 + x_4 y_5$ in summation notation.

Now there are two subscripts in each term, one for x and the other for y. Since the y subscript is always 1 more than the x subscript, we can write

$$x_1 y_2 + x_2 y_3 + x_3 y_4 + x_4 y_5 = \sum_{k=1}^{4} x_k y_{k+1}$$

Finite Series

The summation of a sequence of terms is of special interest. For example, if the sequence $\{a_k\}$ is defined by $a_k = f(k) = k^2$, then the sum of the first five terms of the sequence is

$$\sum_{k=1}^{5} k^2 = 1^2 + 2^2 + 3^2 + 4^2 + 5^2 .$$

DEFINITION Let $\{f_k\}$ define a finite sequence for $1 \leqslant k \leqslant n\,(k, n \in \mathbb{N})$. The sum

$$\sum_{k=1}^{n} f_k = f_1 + f_2 + f_3 + \cdots + f_n$$

is called a **finite series.**

An individual element in the summation, f_k, is called a *term* of the series and is the same as the corresponding term in the sequence.

EXAMPLE 10-14   Find the sum of the series

$$\sum_{k=1}^{6} k(k + 1)$$

Here the elements of the summation are the terms of a sequence function, whose values depend on the index, k. Thus,

$$\sum_{k=1}^{6} k(k + 1) = (1)(2) + (2)(3) + (3)(4) + (4)(5) + (5)(6) + (6)(7)$$
$$= 2 + 6 + 12 + 20 + 30 + 42$$
$$= 112$$

EXAMPLE 10-15   The series

$$\sum_{k=1}^{5} (-1)^k k^3 = -(1)^3 + (2)^3 - (3)^3 + (4)^3 - (5)^3$$
$$= 2^3 + 4^3 - (1^3 + 3^3 + 5^3)$$
$$= 8 + 64 - (1 + 27 + 125)$$
$$= 72 - 153 = -81$$

has a sum equal to -81.

Since the sum of a series is often lengthy or awkward to calculate, a formula for computing the sum would be very useful. For example, suppose we wish to find the sum of the cubes of the first 20 counting numbers. This is represented by a series of the form

$$\sum_{k=1}^{20} k^3 = 1^3 + 2^3 + 3^3 + \cdots + 19^3 + 20^3$$

which is certainly not a simple computation. However, suppose we knew that this sum could be computed by the formula

$$\sum_{k=1}^{n} k^3 = \frac{n^2(n + 1)^2}{4}$$

Then we could calculate the sum as

$$\sum_{k=1}^{20} k^3 = \frac{(20)^2(21)^2}{4} = \frac{(400)(441)}{4} = 44{,}100$$

which is a rather simple computation. One way of arriving at such a formula is by the use of *partial sums*.

DEFINITION   Let f_k represent the elements of a finite series. Then the *n*th **partial sum** of the series, denoted S_n, is defined as

$$\blacktriangleright \quad S_n = \sum_{k=1}^{n} f_k$$

For the series just described, we have

$$S_1 = \sum_{k=1}^{1} k^3 = 1$$

$$S_2 = \sum_{k=1}^{2} k^3 = 1^3 + 2^3 = 9$$

$$S_3 = \sum_{k=1}^{3} k^3 = 1^3 + 2^3 + 3^3 = 36$$

$$S_4 = \sum_{k=1}^{4} k^3 = 1^3 + 2^3 + 3^3 + 4^3 = 100$$

If a pattern could be recognized, then it would be possible to find an expression for S_n. Although the pattern is not immediately obvious, if we rewrite the partial sums as

$$S_1 = 1 = 1^2 \cdot \frac{2^2}{4}$$

$$S_2 = 9 = 2^2 \cdot \frac{3^2}{4}$$

$$S_3 = 36 = 3^2 \cdot \frac{4^2}{4}$$

$$S_4 = 100 = 4^2 \cdot \frac{5^2}{4}$$

we can immediately see a pattern, namely,

$$S_n = \frac{n^2(n+1)^2}{4}$$

Recognition of this pattern does *not* constitute a proof. However, the reader can show by mathematical induction that

$$S_n = \sum_{k=1}^{n} k^3 = \frac{n^2(n+1)^2}{4}$$

is true for all $n \in \mathbb{N}$. (See Exercise 14 at the end of this section.)

Note that the ordered set

$$S_1, S_2, S_3, S_4, \ldots, S_n, \ldots$$

forms a sequence of partial sums, denoted $\{S_n\}$. Each term of this sequence determines the value of the corresponding finite series. Hence, we have the following alternative definition of a finite series:

DEFINITION   A **finite series** is a finite sequence of partial sums.

In Section 10-3, we will generalize this definition to define an infinite series.

EXAMPLE 10-16   Let $S_n = n(n + 1)$ define the *n*th partial sum of a series. Construct the first five terms of this series from S_n.

We have

$$S_1 = 1(1 + 1) = 2$$
$$S_2 = 2(3) = 6$$
$$S_3 = 3(4) = 12$$
$$S_4 = 4(5) = 20$$
$$S_5 = 5(6) = 30$$

Thus,

$$S_1 = a_1 = 2$$
$$S_2 = a_1 + a_2 = S_1 + a_2 = 2 + a_2 = 6$$
$$S_3 = a_1 + a_2 + a_3 = S_2 + a_3 = 6 + a_3 = 12$$
$$S_4 = a_1 + a_2 + a_3 + a_4 = S_3 + a_4 = 12 + a_4 = 20$$
$$S_5 = a_1 + a_2 + a_3 + a_4 + a_5 = S_4 + a_5 = 20 + a_5 = 30$$

Hence, $a_1 = 2$, $a_2 = 4$, $a_3 = 6$, $a_4 = 8$, and $a_5 = 10$. The series is

$$2 + 4 + 6 + 8 + 10 = \sum_{k=1}^{5} 2k$$

Arithmetic Series

A special application of partial sums is in determining the sum of an arithmetic sequence, called an *arithmetic series*. First, we have the following theorem:

THEOREM 10-4   Let $\{a_k\}$ be an arithmetic sequence with initial term a_1 and common difference d; that is, $a_k = a_1 + (k - 1)d$. The *n*th partial sum, S_n, of this sequence is given by

$$\blacktriangleright \quad S_n = \frac{n(a_1 + a_n)}{2} \quad \text{or} \quad S_n = \frac{n[2a_1 + (n - 1)d]}{2}$$

PROOF   The *n*th partial sum of this series can be written in two ways, in terms of a_1 or in terms of a_n. Hence

$$S_n = a_1 + (a_1 + d) + (a_1 + 2d) + \cdots + [a_1 + (n - 1)d]$$

and

$$S_n = a_n + (a_n - d) + (a_n - 2d) + \cdots + [a_n - (n - 1)d]$$

Adding these partial sums together gives

$$2S_n = (a_1 + a_n) + (a_1 + a_n) + (a_1 + a_n) + \cdots + (a_1 + a_n) = n(a_1 + a_n)$$

Therefore,

$$S_n = \frac{n(a_1 + a_n)}{2}$$

By substituting $a_1 + (n - 1)d$ for a_n, we obtain

$$S_n = \frac{n[2a_1 + (n - 1)d]}{2}$$

EXAMPLE 10-17 Find the sum of the positive numbers 1 through 99.
This is an arithmetic sequence with $a_1 = 1$, $a_n = 99$, $n = 99$, and $d = 1$. The sum equation $S_n = n(n + 1)/2$ yields

$$S_{99} = \tfrac{99}{2}(99 + 1)$$
$$= \tfrac{99}{2}(100) = 4950$$

EXAMPLE 10-18 In an arithmetic sequence, the sum of the first 12 terms is 144, and the twelfth term is 96. Find a_1 and d.
From the formula for S_n, we have

$$S_{12} = \tfrac{12}{2}(a_1 + 96) = 144$$

Therefore,

$$a_1 + 96 = \tfrac{144}{6} = 24 \quad \text{and} \quad a_1 = -72$$

Furthermore, since

$$a_{12} = a_1 + (12 - 1)d$$

we have

$$96 = -72 + 11d$$
$$168 = 11d$$
$$d = \tfrac{168}{11}$$

Geometric Series

Partial sums are also used in obtaining the sum of a geometric sequence, called a *geometric series*. We have the following theorem:

THEOREM 10-5 Let $\{a_k\}$ be a geometric sequence with initial term a_1 and common ratio r, where $a_k = a_1 r^{k-1}$. Then the nth partial sum of this sequence is given by

▶ $$S_n = \frac{a_1(1 - r^n)}{1 - r} \quad \text{for } r \neq 1$$

or

▶ $$S_n = na_1 \qquad \text{for } r = 1$$

PROOF The partial sum can be written in expanded form as

$$S_n = a_1 + a_1 r + a_1 r^2 + a_1 r^3 + \cdots + a_1 r^{n-1}$$

If we multiply this equation by r, we have

$$rS_n = a_1 r + a_1 r^2 + a_1 r^3 + a_1 r^4 + \cdots + a_1 r^n$$

The difference between these equations is

$$S_n - rS_n = a_1 - a_1 r^n$$

Solving for S_n yields

$$S_n = a_1\left(\frac{1 - r^n}{1 - r}\right), \qquad r \neq 1$$

The proof that $S_n = na_1$ for $r = 1$ is left as an exercise. ∎

EXAMPLE 10-19 Find the sum of the first six terms of the geometric sequence for which $a_1 = 3$ and $r = 2$.

Using the sum formula, we obtain

$$S_6 = \frac{3(1 - 2^6)}{1 - 2} = \frac{3(1 - 64)}{-1}$$

$$= \frac{3(-63)}{-1} = 189$$

EXAMPLE 10-20 If the sum of the first five terms of a geometric sequence is 2046, and $r = 4$, find the first five terms.

From the sum formula,

$$2046 = a_1 \frac{(1 - 4^5)}{1 - 4} = a_1 \frac{(1 - 1024)}{-3}$$

Solving for a_1 gives

$$a_1 = \frac{-3}{-1023}(2046) = 3(2) = 6$$

So the first five terms of the sequence are

$$6, 24, 96, 384, 1536$$

EXERCISES 10-2

Set A

1. Which of the following are sequence functions?
    (a) $f(k) = k$ (b) $g(k) = k^2 - 7k + 4$
    (c) $f(k) = \dfrac{1}{k - 4}$ (d) $h(k) = \sqrt{10.3 - k}$
    (e) $\phi(k) = \dfrac{4}{k - 2}$ (f) $\psi(k) = \dfrac{7}{\sqrt{2 + k}}$

2. Find the first six terms of the following sequences, $\{f_k\}$:
    (a) $f_k = 1/2k$ (b) $f_k = 5(3 - 1/k)$
    (c) $f_k = 3(k^2 - 1)/k^2$ (d) $f_k = 3(k^2 + k^3)$
    (e) $f_k = \dfrac{(-1)^k(2k - 1)}{k^2}$ (f) $f_k = \dfrac{(-1)^{k+1}(k^2 - k)}{k + 2}$

3. Find $\sum_{k=1}^{5} f_k$ for each of the f_k described in Exercise 2.

4. Find the first six terms of the arithmetic sequence $\{a_k\}$ with initial term a_1 and common difference d.
   (a) $a_1 = 3, d = 4$
   (b) $a_1 = \frac{1}{2}, d = \frac{3}{2}$
   (c) $a_1 = -\frac{1}{3}, d = -\frac{4}{3}$
   (d) $a_1 = -\frac{2}{3}, d = \frac{4}{3}$

5. Find the first six terms of the geometric sequence $\{b_k\}$ with initial term b_1 and common ratio r.
   (a) $b_1 = 2, r = 2$
   (b) $b_1 = 4, r = \frac{1}{3}$
   (c) $b_1 = \frac{1}{5}, r = -\frac{1}{2}$
   (d) $b_1 = -\frac{2}{3}, r = -\frac{1}{4}$

6. Find $\sum_{k=1}^{6} a_k$ for each of the a_k described in Exercise 4.

7. Find $\sum_{k=1}^{6} b_k$ for each of the b_k described in Exercise 5.

Set B

8. Calculate the following sums:

   (a) $\sum_{k=1}^{8} k^2(k^2 - 3k + 4)$
   (b) $\sum_{k=1}^{5} \frac{1}{k}$

   (c) $\sum_{k=1}^{8} \frac{1}{k^2}$
   (d) $\sum_{k=1}^{10} \frac{1}{k^2 + k}$

9. Find the number of terms in each of the following series for the given conditions:
   (a) Geometric: sum $= 124, r = 2, b_1 = 4$
   (b) Geometric: sum $= 104, r = \frac{1}{5}, b_1 = \frac{1000}{12}$
   (c) Arithmetic: sum $= 168, a_1 = 3, d = 2$

10. For each of the functions in Exercises 2(a) and 2(b), find the sequence of partial sums $\{S_n\}$ for $n \in \mathbb{N}$ and $1 \leq n \leq 5$. (Note that it is not necessary to find the generalized function, S_n.)

11. Find the formula for the nth term of the following sequences:
    (a) $6, 8.5, 11, 13.5, 16, \ldots$
    (b) $-12, -2, 8, 18, 28, \ldots$
    (c) $1, 2, 4, 8, 16, \ldots$
    (d) $-1, 2, -4, 8, -16, \ldots$
    (e) $16, 15, 14, 13, \ldots$
    (f) $3, 0.3, 0.03, 0.003, \ldots$

12. For the sequences in Exercise 11, find the nth partial sum. Then find the sum of the first 20 terms.

13. Show by mathematical induction that the kth element of a geometric sequence with initial element a_1 and common ratio r is given by
$$a_k = a_1 r^{k-1}, \qquad r \neq 0$$

14. Use mathematical induction to show that
$$\sum_{k=1}^{n} k^3 = \frac{n^2(n + 1)^2}{4}$$

15. Show by mathematical induction that for a geometric sequence with initial term a_1 and common ratio $r = 1$, the nth partial sum is given by
$$S_n = na_1$$

Set C

16. The well-known Fibonacci "series" (which is actually a sequence) has the pattern

$$1, 1, 2, 3, 5, 8, 13, 21, \ldots$$

Find a sequence function, a_k, that will identify any element in this sequence. (*Hint:* Consider the terms such that $k > 2$.)

17. Prove that if f_k and g_k are sequence functions and a and b are real constants, then

(a) $\sum_{k=1}^{n} (af_k + bg_k) = a\left(\sum_{i=1}^{n} f_i\right) + b\left(\sum_{j=1}^{n} g_j\right)$

(b) $\sum_{k=1}^{n} f_{k+1} = \left(\sum_{k=1}^{n+1} f_k\right) - f_1$

18. Use the equations given in Exercises 15 and 17(a) and the results of this section to evaluate the following sums. (*Hint:* Find partial sums.)

(a) $\sum_{k=1}^{42} 12k$ (b) $\sum_{j=1}^{12} 7$

(c) $\sum_{n=1}^{30} (16 - 3n)$ (d) $\sum_{k=1}^{90} (50k - 100)$

(e) $\sum_{k=1}^{12} 12(2^k)$ (f) $\sum_{k=1}^{6} [6 + 4(3^k)]$

(g) $\sum_{k=1}^{10} [25 + 3k - 13(2^k)]$

10-3 INFINITE SEQUENCES AND SERIES

Introduction

About the year 350 BC, the Greek philosopher and mathematician Zeno posed a paradox to his contemporaries. He claimed that the act of walking across a room is just an illusion. His reasoning went this way: First, one travels across half the distance; then one travels across half the remaining distance. One continues traveling by always traversing half the remaining distance. Zeno reasoned that because there is always some distance remaining to traverse and since one is always traversing half of this remaining distance, one can never reach the end of the room. This paradox is probably one of the earliest recorded examples of an infinite series. In mathematical terms, we can describe the paradox by writing

$$\text{Distance traveled} = \tfrac{1}{2} + \tfrac{1}{2}(\tfrac{1}{2}) + \tfrac{1}{2}(\tfrac{1}{4}) + \tfrac{1}{2}(\tfrac{1}{8}) + \tfrac{1}{2}(\tfrac{1}{16}) + \cdots$$

where the three dots mean that the process continues without terminating. If the products are simplified, the distance traveled can be written

$$\text{Distance traveled} = \tfrac{1}{2} + \tfrac{1}{4} + \tfrac{1}{8} + \tfrac{1}{16} + \tfrac{1}{32} + \cdots$$

Such nonterminating sums are the main subject of this section.

Infinite Sequences

We can use the concept of a sequence, which was developed in Section 10-2, to define an *infinite sequence*.

> **DEFINITION** Let f be a sequence function defined for all $k \in \mathbb{N}$. Then the sequence $f_1, f_2, f_3, \ldots, f_k, \ldots$, denoted $\{f_k\}$, is an **infinite sequence.**

Note that this is similar to a finite sequence, except that the terms of the sequence are in a one-to-one correspondence with *all* elements of $\mathbb{N}$, which is an infinite set.

> **EXAMPLE 10-21** Consider the special type of harmonic sequence defined by $f_k = 1/k$ for $k \in \mathbb{N}$. The sequence $\{f_k\}$ is

$$1, \frac{1}{2}, \frac{1}{3}, \frac{1}{4}, \frac{1}{5}, \ldots, \frac{1}{k}, \ldots$$

Infinite Series

Some of the questions we can ask about infinite sequences are

1. Can the sum of an infinite sequence be formulated?
2. If so, what is the meaning of this infinite series?
3. Does the sum of this infinite series exist?

To begin, the sum of the terms of an infinite sequence can always be formulated. However, the summation notation must be modified, since the upper limit of the summation index is not a natural number. When expressing the sum $x_1 + x_2 + x_3 + \cdots$ in summation notation, the three dots indicate that the sum continues indefinitely, with the subscript increasing by 1 at each step. In other words, k increases with infinity as its upper limit. The convenience of the summation notation can now be appreciated. This infinite sum is written as

$$x_1 + x_2 + x_3 + \cdots = \sum_{k=1}^{\infty} x_k$$

It is now possible to define an infinite series. The definition is an extension of that given for finite series.

> **DEFINITION** An **infinite series** is an infinite sequence of partial sums, whose sum is denoted by S.

Note that the definitions for the finite and infinite series are the same, the major difference being that the upper summation index is different. Thus for *any* sequence $\{a_k\}$, $k \in \mathbb{N}$, the nth partial sum is given as

$$S_n = \sum_{k=1}^{n} a_k \quad \text{for } n \in \mathbb{N}$$

and the infinite series as

$$S = \sum_{k=1}^{\infty} a_k$$

The sequence of partial sums is

$$S_1 = a_1$$
$$S_2 = a_1 + a_2$$
$$S_3 = a_1 + a_2 + a_3$$
$$S_4 = a_1 + a_2 + a_3 + a_4$$
$$\vdots \qquad \vdots$$
$$S_n = a_1 + a_2 + a_3 + a_4 + \cdots + a_n = \sum_{k=1}^{n} a_k$$
$$\vdots \qquad \vdots$$
$$S = a_1 + a_2 + a_3 + a_4 + \cdots = \sum_{k=1}^{\infty} a_k$$

Hence, the sequence $\{S_n\}$ denotes the sum of an infinite series if $n \in \mathbb{N}$ approaches ∞.

Convergence and Divergence

The sum of any series exists if the sum is a finite value. If each term of a sequence exists and if the series is finite, the sum *always* exists. If the series is infinite, the sum may or may not exist. If the sum exists, the series is said to be *convergent*; otherwise, it is *divergent*.

DEFINITION   A series is **convergent** if its sequence of partial sums approaches a finite value.

EXAMPLE 10-22   The infinite arithmetic series

$$\sum_{k=1}^{\infty} [a_1 + (k-1)d]$$

has an nth partial sum $S_n = n[2a_1 + (n-1)d]/2$. Clearly, as n grows larger and larger, the sequence

$$S_1, S_2, S_3, \ldots, S_n, \ldots$$

does *not* approach a finite value. Therefore, the series diverges.

EXAMPLE 10-23   Consider the infinite series

$$\sum_{k=1}^{\infty} \frac{1}{k^2}$$

If we calculate the values of the partial sums for $n = 10, 20, 30, 40$, and 50, we obtain the values listed in Table 10-1. Although this listing does not constitute a proof, it seems that

$$\sum_{k=1}^{\infty} \frac{1}{k^2}$$

is always less than 2.

TABLE 10-1

n	Partial sum $\sum_{k=1}^{n} \frac{1}{k^2}$
10	1.54977
20	1.59616
30	1.61215
40	1.62024
50	1.62513

Infinite Geometric Series

In general, the techniques needed to study infinite series require the use of the calculus and thus are beyond the scope of this book. However, in some cases it is possible to use "ordinary" means to approximate the sum of an infinite series. Consider the nth partial sum of a geometric progression given as

$$S_n = \frac{a_1(1 - r^n)}{1 - r}, \qquad r \neq 1$$

We can rewrite this as

$$S_n = \frac{a_1}{1 - r} - \frac{a_1 r^n}{1 - r}, \qquad r \neq 1$$

The first term is independent of index n. The second term can be written as

$$\frac{a_1}{1 - r}(r^n)$$

Since n is increasing to infinity, when $|r| > 1$, r^n will not approach a finite value; when $|r| < 1$, r^n approaches 0 (e.g., if $r = \frac{1}{2}$, r^n becomes $\frac{1}{2}, \frac{1}{4}, \frac{1}{8}, \frac{1}{16}, \frac{1}{32}, \ldots$, and these values get closer and closer to 0). Hence, the second term approaches 0, and the infinite sum S becomes

$$S = \frac{a_1}{1 - r}, \qquad |r| < 1$$

For $r = 1$, $S_n = na_1$. Clearly, as n becomes larger without bound, S_n also increases without bound; hence, the corresponding infinite series diverges.

These results are summarized in the following theorem, which we present without proof:

THEOREM 10-6 Let a_k describe a geometric sequence, where $a_k = a_1 r^{k-1}$. Then the infinite series $\sum_{k=1}^{\infty} a_1 r^{k-1}$

▶   converges to $S = a_1/(1 - r)$ if $|r| < 1$
    diverges   if $|r| \geqslant 1$

Now we can return to Zeno's paradox. The reader will recognize this as an infinite geometric sequence, where $a_1 = \frac{1}{2}$ and $r = \frac{1}{2}$. Therefore, the sum of the sequence

$$\tfrac{1}{2}, \tfrac{1}{4}, \tfrac{1}{8}, \tfrac{1}{16}, \tfrac{1}{32}, \tfrac{1}{64}, \ldots$$

can be calculated as

$$S = \frac{\frac{1}{2}}{1 - \frac{1}{2}} = \frac{\frac{1}{2}}{\frac{1}{2}} = 1$$

Therefore, it does seem that one can cross the room, but it would take an infinite number of steps. *What do you think?*

EXERCISES 10-3

Set A

1. Write the following infinite series in condensed form by using the Σ notation with initial index $n = 1$:
   (a) $S = (\tfrac{2}{3})^2 + (\tfrac{2}{3})^3 + (\tfrac{2}{3})^4 + (\tfrac{2}{3})^5 + \cdots$
   (b) $S = \tfrac{1}{6} + \tfrac{1}{9} + \tfrac{1}{12} + \tfrac{1}{15} + \cdots$
   (c) $S = \dfrac{1\cdot3}{2\cdot4} + \dfrac{3\cdot5}{4\cdot6} + \dfrac{5\cdot7}{6\cdot8} + \dfrac{7\cdot9}{8\cdot10} + \cdots$
   (d) $S = 1 + \tfrac{1}{4} + \tfrac{1}{9} + \tfrac{1}{16} + \tfrac{1}{25} + \cdots$
   (e) $S = \dfrac{1}{1\cdot2} + \dfrac{1}{2\cdot3} + \dfrac{1}{3\cdot4} + \dfrac{1}{4\cdot5} + \cdots$

2. Find the sums of the following infinite geometric series:
   (a) $S = \displaystyle\sum_{n=1}^{\infty} \dfrac{8}{5^n}$ (b) $S = 1 - \displaystyle\sum_{n=1}^{\infty} \dfrac{4}{7^n}$ (c) $S = 4 + \displaystyle\sum_{n=1}^{\infty} \dfrac{5}{4^n}$

● 3. In Chapter 5, we mentioned that finding the sine and cosine of most angle values requires the use of calculus. Application of the calculus results in the following infinite series:

$$\cos x = 1 - \frac{x^2}{2!} + \frac{x^4}{4!} - \frac{x^6}{6!} + \frac{x^8}{8!} - \cdots$$

$$\sin x = x - \frac{x^3}{3!} + \frac{x^5}{5!} - \frac{x^7}{7!} + \cdots$$

where $x \in \mathbb{R}$ and ! denotes the factorial function. For example, $7! = 7$ factorial, $6! = 6$ factorial, and $3! = 3$ factorial are defined by

$$7! = 7 \cdot 6 \cdot 5 \cdot 4 \cdot 3 \cdot 2 \cdot 1 = 5040$$
$$6! = 6 \cdot 5 \cdot 4 \cdot 3 \cdot 2 \cdot 1 = 720$$
$$3! = 3 \cdot 2 \cdot 1 = 6$$

For these series, find the number of terms required in order to find the sine and cosine values accurate to four decimal places (that is, two successive answers must agree to five decimal places) for the following real argument values:

(a) 0.0189   (b) 0.1743   (c) 0.9314
(d) 1.178   (e) 1.439

4. For the series given in Exercise 3, what conclusion can be made about the number of terms needed to get the required precision, as the value of the argument increases?

5. Using the series given in Exercise 3, verify that

$$\sin x = -\sin(-x) \quad \text{and} \quad \cos x = \cos(-x)$$

6. Show that the infinite series

$$r + (r^2 - r) + (r^3 - r^2) + \cdots + (r^n - r^{n-1}) + \cdots$$

converges to 0 if $|r| < 1$ and converges to 1 if $r = 1$.

Set B

7. Use the results of Exercise 4 in Section 10-1 to show, by the method of partial sums, that the infinite series

$$\sum_{n=1}^{\infty} \frac{1}{n(n+1)}$$

converges to 1 as $n \in \mathbb{N}$ increases to infinity.

8. (a) Use mathematical induction to show that

$$S_n = \sum_{k=1}^{n} (\tfrac{1}{3})^{k-1} = \tfrac{3}{2}[1 - (\tfrac{1}{3})^n]$$

(b) Then use the method of partial sums to find the value to which the infinite series

$$\sum_{k=1}^{\infty} (\tfrac{1}{3})^{k-1}$$

converges.

Set C

9. Use the result of Exercise 7 and the results given in the text for the infinite geometric series

$$\sum_{n=1}^{\infty} \frac{1}{2^n}$$

to find whether the series

$$\sum_{n=1}^{\infty} \left[\frac{1}{n(n+1)} + \frac{1}{2^n} \right]$$

converges and, if so, to what value. Knowing that each of the individual series converges, what general conclusion can be made about the sum of two convergent series? (*Hint:* Find the partial sums of each series.)

10. In Section 8-2, Euler's Identity was given as $e^{i\theta} = \cos \theta + i \sin \theta$. If

$$e^x = 1 + x + \frac{x^2}{2!} + \frac{x^3}{3!} + \frac{x^4}{4!} + \cdots$$

prove Euler's Identity using the information in Exercise 3.

11. Show that the harmonic series $\sum_{k=1}^{\infty} \frac{1}{k}$ diverges. (*Hint:* Use the fact that for $n \in \mathbb{N}$, the series can be separated into groups of n terms of the form

$$\frac{1}{2^n + 1} + \frac{1}{2^n + 2} + \frac{1}{2^n + 3} + \cdots + \frac{1}{2^{n+1}}.)$$

REVIEW EXERCISES FOR CHAPTER 10

1. Use mathematical induction to verify the following formulas for the summation of a sequence of n terms:

    (a) $2 + 2 + 2 + \cdots + 2 = 2n$

    (b) $7 + 10 + 13 + 16 + \cdots = \dfrac{n[14 + 3(n-1)]}{2}$

    (c) $3 + 2 + \dfrac{4}{3} + \dfrac{8}{9} + \cdots = 9\left[1 - \left(\dfrac{2}{3}\right)^n\right]$

    (d) $1 + r + r^2 + r^3 + \cdots = \dfrac{1 - r^n}{1 - r}, r \neq 1$

2. Find the first five terms of the sequence $\{a_k\}$.

    (a) $a_k = \dfrac{1}{3k}$

    (b) $a_k = 7 - \dfrac{1}{k^2}$

    (c) $a_k = \dfrac{(-1)^k k^2}{k + 1}$

    (d) $a_k = \sqrt{1 + k^2}$

3. Write the first seven terms of the arithmetic sequence $\{a_k\}$ for the given initial term, a_1, and common difference, d.

    (a) $a_1 = 2, d = -2$
    (b) $a_1 = -4, d = -3$

    (c) $a_1 = -12, d = \frac{2}{3}$

4. For the sequences $\{a_k\}$ given in Exercise 3, find

$$\sum_{k=1}^{27} a_k$$

5. Write the first five terms of the geometric sequence $\{b_k\}$ for the given initial term, b_1, and common ratio, r.

    (a) $b_1 = 7, r = \frac{1}{3}$
    (b) $b_1 = -2, r = 2$

    (c) $b_1 = 4, r = -\frac{1}{2}$

6. For the sequences $\{b_k\}$ given in Exercise 5, find

$$\sum_{k=1}^{10} b_k$$

7. If possible, identify the following sequences as arithmetic or geometric:
   (a) $8, 6.5, 5, 3.5, 2, \ldots$ (b) $1, -\frac{1}{2}, \frac{1}{4}, -\frac{1}{8}, \ldots$
   (c) $1, 2, 4, 7, 11, 16, 22, \ldots$ (d) $4, 0.4, 0.04, 0.004, 0.0004, \ldots$
   (e) $3, -0.3, 0.03, -0.003, 0.0003, \ldots$

8. Determine whether the following series diverge or converge. Calculate the
   sum for those that converge.

   (a) $\displaystyle\sum_{n=25}^{\infty} n$

   (b) $\displaystyle\sum_{k=1}^{\infty} \frac{2}{3^k}$

   (c) $\left(\displaystyle\sum_{k=1}^{\infty} \frac{7}{(-2)^k}\right) - 1$

APPENDIXES

ROTATION OF AXES

A JUSTIFICATION OF EULER'S IDENTITY

TABLES

APPENDIX

Rotation of Axes

In Chapter 4, when we discussed the conic sections and their graphs, we made extensive use of the axis translation rules to analyze conic sections that were centered at points other than the origin. We also mentioned rotation of axes, but we postponed the development of this topic, because it depends on trigonometric concepts and involves some complicated algebraic forms that shed no additional light on the properties of these relations. In this appendix, we develop the rotation rules and use two simple examples to illustrate the techniques of axis notation.

Figure A-1 shows a point, $P_0 = (x_0, y_0)$, in the DR plane. This illustration also shows the D and R axes rotated by an angle θ to become the $\bar{D}$ and $\bar{R}$ axes. Since the D and R axes are mutually perpendicular, so are the $\bar{D}$ and $\bar{R}$ axes. Therefore, these rotated axes determine a new coordinate system, which we call the $\bar{D}\bar{R}$ plane. In the $\bar{D}\bar{R}$ system, the coordinates of P_0 are designated $(\bar{x}_0, \bar{y}_0)$; that is, $\bar{x}_0$ is the perpendicular distance from P_0 to $\bar{R}$, and $\bar{y}_0$ is the perpendicular distance from P_0 to $\bar{D}$. We wish to develop a set of formulas that relate $\bar{x}_0$ and $\bar{y}_0$ to x_0, y_0, and θ, when the values of x_0, y_0, and θ are known and when both systems have the same origin.

Using the fact that the distance, r, from the origin to P_0 is the same in either system, we can write the values of $x_0, y_0, \bar{x}_0$, and $\bar{y}_0$ as follows. In the DR system,

$$x_0 = r \cos(\theta + \psi), \qquad y_0 = r \sin(\theta + \psi)$$

In the $\bar{D}\bar{R}$ system,

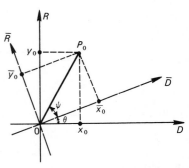

FIGURE A-1

$$\bar{x}_0 = r \cos \psi, \qquad \bar{y}_0 = r \sin \psi$$

We can expand the equations for x_0 and y_0 with the formulas for the sine and cosine of the sum of two angles. This yields

$$x_0 = r \cos \theta \cos \psi - r \sin \theta \sin \psi$$

and

$$y_0 = r \sin \theta \cos \psi + r \cos \theta \sin \psi$$

Regrouping terms, we obtain

$$x_0 = (r \cos \psi) \cos \theta - (r \sin \psi) \sin \theta$$

and

$$y_0 = (r \cos \psi) \sin \theta + (r \sin \psi) \cos \theta$$

On substitution of $\bar{x}_0 = r \cos \psi$ and $\bar{y}_0 = r \sin \psi$, these equations become

$$\blacktriangleright \quad x_0 = \bar{x}_0 \cos \theta - \bar{y}_0 \sin \theta$$

and

$$\blacktriangleright \quad y_0 = \bar{x}_0 \sin \theta + \bar{y}_0 \cos \theta$$

These are the equations for x_0 and y_0 in terms of $\bar{x}_0$ and $\bar{y}_0$. To solve for $\bar{x}_0$, we multiply the first equation by $\cos \theta$ and the second equation by $\sin \theta$, which yields

$$x_0 \cos \theta = \bar{x}_0 \cos^2 \theta + \bar{y}_0 \sin \theta \cos \theta$$
$$y_0 \sin \theta = \bar{x}_0 \sin^2 \theta - \bar{y}_0 \cos \theta \sin \theta$$

Adding these equations, we obtain

$$x_0 \cos \theta + y_0 \sin \theta = \bar{x}_0(\cos^2 \theta + \sin^2 \theta) = \bar{x}_0$$

This is the first transformation equation. To find the equation for $\bar{y}_0$, we multiply the y_0 equation by $\cos \theta$ and the x_0 equation by $\sin \theta$ and subtract. The equations become

$$y_0 \cos \theta = \bar{x}_0 \sin \theta \cos \theta + \bar{y}_0 \cos^2 \theta$$
$$x_0 \sin \theta = \bar{x}_0 \sin \theta \cos \theta - \bar{y}_0 \sin^2 \theta$$

Subtraction yields

$$y_0 \cos \theta - x_0 \sin \theta = \bar{y}_0(\cos^2 \theta + \sin^2 \theta) = \bar{y}_0$$

which is the second transformation formula. Thus,

$$\blacktriangleright \quad \bar{x}_0 = x_0 \cos \theta + y_0 \sin \theta \quad \text{and} \quad \bar{y}_0 = x_0 \sin \theta - y_0 \cos \theta$$

are the equations for $\bar{x}_0$ and $\bar{y}_0$ in terms of x_0 and y_0. Examples A-1 and A-2 illustrate how these equations are used.

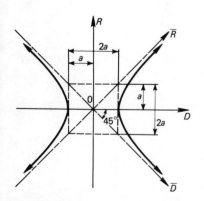

FIGURE A-2

EXAMPLE A-1 Suppose the $\bar{D}\bar{R}$ system is located at an angle of $-45°\,(-\pi/4$ radians) with respect to the DR system. Find the equation in the $\bar{D}\bar{R}$ system of the equilateral hyperbola whose equation in the DR system is

$$\frac{x^2}{a^2} - \frac{y^2}{a^2} = 1$$

The hyperbola and both sets of axes are shown in Figure A-2. For $\theta = -45°$, the transformation equations become

$$\bar{x} = x\left(\frac{\sqrt{2}}{2}\right) + y\left(\frac{-\sqrt{2}}{2}\right) = \frac{\sqrt{2}}{2}(x - y)$$

and

$$\bar{y} = -x\left(\frac{-\sqrt{2}}{2}\right) + y\left(\frac{\sqrt{2}}{2}\right) = \frac{\sqrt{2}}{2}(x + y)$$

or

$$\sqrt{2}\bar{x} = x - y \quad \text{and} \quad \sqrt{2}\bar{y} = x + y$$

The equation of the hyperbola in the DR system, which is

$$\frac{x^2}{a^2} - \frac{y^2}{a^2} = 1$$

can be rewritten as

$$x^2 - y^2 = a^2$$

which in turn can be factored as

$$(x + y)(x - y) = a^2$$

If we substitute $\sqrt{2}\bar{y} = x + y$ and $\sqrt{2}\bar{x} = x - y$, this equation becomes

$$(\sqrt{2}\bar{y})(\sqrt{2}\bar{x}) = a^2$$

or

$$2\bar{y}\bar{x} = a^2$$

or

$$\bar{y}\bar{x} = \frac{a^2}{2}$$

If we let $a^2/2 = k$, then the final form of the equation for the hyperbola in the $\bar{D}\bar{R}$ system is

$$\bar{y}\bar{x} = k$$

This is exactly the form that we derived in Chapter 4 for the rectangular hyperbola oriented as shown in Figure A-3.

We can reverse the process just outlined if the equation in the rotated system is known and the angle of rotation is unknown. Knowledge of the

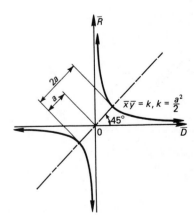

FIGURE A-3

rotation angle then enables us to eliminate the xy term from a second-degree equation.

THEOREM A-1 Consider the general quadratic equation

$$Ax^2 + Bxy + Cy^2 + Dx + Ey + F = 0$$

where $A, B, C, D, E, F \in \mathbb{R}$, $B \neq 0$, and A and C are not both 0, which is the equation of a rotated conic section. Then the angle of rotation, θ, is given by

$$\text{Cot } 2\theta = \frac{A - C}{B}$$

PROOF The proof omits many algebraic steps, which are left to the reader to complete. We reexpress x and y in terms of $\bar{x}$, $\bar{y}$, and θ with the equations

$$x = \bar{x} \cos \theta - \bar{y} \sin \theta \quad \text{and} \quad y = \bar{x} \sin \theta + \bar{y} \cos \theta$$

Next, we substitute these expanded forms into the general quadratic equation and collect the terms for $\bar{x}^2$, $\bar{x}\bar{y}$, $\bar{y}^2$, $\bar{x}$, $\bar{y}$, and the constant. Since there will be no rotational term in the $\bar{D}\bar{R}$ coordinate system, the coefficient, $\bar{B}$, of the $\bar{x}\bar{y}$ term should be 0. The coefficients of the general quadratic equation in the $\bar{D}\bar{R}$ coordinate system are

$$\bar{A} = A \cos^2 \theta + B \cos \theta \sin \theta + C \sin^2 \theta$$
$$\bar{B} = B(\cos^2 \theta - \sin^2 \theta) + 2(C - A) \sin \theta \cos \theta$$
$$\bar{C} = A \sin^2 \theta - B \sin \theta \cos \theta + C \cos^2 \theta$$
$$\bar{D} = D \cos \theta - E \sin \theta$$
$$\bar{E} = E \cos \theta - D \sin \theta$$
$$\bar{F} = F$$

Setting $\bar{B} = 0$ yields

$$\bar{B} = B(\cos^2 \theta - \sin^2 \theta) + (C - A)(2 \cos \theta \sin \theta) = 0$$

and since

$$\cos^2 \theta - \sin^2 \theta = \cos 2\theta \quad \text{and} \quad 2 \cos \theta \sin \theta = \sin 2\theta$$

the condition on $\bar{B}$ becomes

$$\bar{B} = 0 = B \cos 2\theta + (C - A) \sin 2\theta$$

Solving for the ratio $\cos 2\theta / \sin 2\theta$ yields

$$\frac{\cos 2\theta}{\sin 2\theta} = \frac{A - C}{B}$$

where $B \neq 0$, or

$$\cot 2\theta = \frac{A - C}{B} \quad \blacksquare$$

EXAMPLE A-2 Describe the following conic section by determining the angle of rotation, θ, and using the transformation equations to eliminate the rotational term. The equation for the unrotated conic

$$x^2 - 2\sqrt{3}xy + 3y^2 + 2\sqrt{3}x + 2y = 0$$

Here, $A = 1$, $C = 3$, and $B = -2\sqrt{3}$; therefore,

$$\cot 2\theta = \frac{1 - 3}{-2\sqrt{3}} = \frac{-2}{-2\sqrt{3}} = \frac{1}{\sqrt{3}} = \frac{\sqrt{3}}{3}$$

so

$$2\theta = \text{Arccot} \frac{\sqrt{3}}{3}$$

Hence, $2\theta = \frac{\pi}{3}$, so $\theta = \frac{\pi}{6}$, and the equations relating x and y to $\bar{x}$ and $\bar{y}$ are

$$x = \frac{\sqrt{3}}{2}\bar{x} - \frac{\bar{y}}{2} \quad \text{and} \quad y = \frac{\bar{x}}{2} + \frac{\sqrt{3}}{2}\bar{y}$$

Substitution of these forms into each term of the untransformed equation yields

$$x^2 = \left(\frac{\sqrt{3}}{2}\bar{x} - \frac{\bar{y}}{2}\right)^2 = \frac{3}{4}\bar{x}^2 - \frac{\sqrt{3}}{2}\bar{x}\bar{y} + \frac{\bar{y}^2}{4}$$

$$3y^2 = 3\left(\frac{\bar{x}}{2} + \frac{\sqrt{3}}{2}\bar{y}\right)^2 = 3\left(\frac{\bar{x}^2}{4} + \frac{\sqrt{3}}{2}\bar{x}\bar{y} + \frac{3}{4}\bar{y}^2\right)$$

$$= \frac{3}{4}\bar{x}^2 + \frac{3\sqrt{3}}{2}\bar{x}\bar{y} + \frac{9\bar{y}^2}{4}$$

$$2\sqrt{3}xy = 2\sqrt{3}\left(\frac{\sqrt{3}}{2}\bar{x} - \frac{\bar{y}}{2}\right)\left(\frac{\bar{x}}{2} + \frac{\sqrt{3}}{2}\bar{y}\right)$$

$$= \frac{3}{2}\bar{x}^2 + \sqrt{3}\bar{x}\bar{y} - \frac{3}{2}\bar{y}^2$$

$$2\sqrt{3}x = 2\sqrt{3}\left(\frac{\sqrt{3}}{2}\bar{x} - \frac{\bar{y}}{2}\right) = 3\bar{x} - \sqrt{3}\bar{y}$$

$$2y = 2\left(\frac{\bar{x}}{2} + \frac{\sqrt{3}}{2}\bar{y}\right) = \bar{x} + \sqrt{3}\bar{y}$$

Therefore,

$$x^2 - 2\sqrt{3}xy + 3y^2 + 2\sqrt{3}x + 2y$$

$$= \left(\frac{3}{4} - \frac{3}{2} + \frac{3}{4}\right)\bar{x}^2 + \left(\frac{-\sqrt{3}}{2} + \frac{3\sqrt{3}}{2} - \sqrt{3}\right)\bar{x}\bar{y} + \left(\frac{1}{4} + \frac{3}{2} + \frac{9}{4}\right)\bar{y}^2$$

$$+ (3 + 1)\bar{x} + (-\sqrt{3} + \sqrt{3})\bar{y} = 0$$

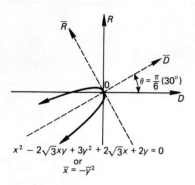

$$x^2 - 2\sqrt{3}xy + 3y^2 + 2\sqrt{3}x + 2y = 0$$
or
$$\bar{x} = -\bar{y}^2$$

FIGURE A-4

Therefore, by substitution the equation

$$x^2 - 2\sqrt{3}xy + 3y^2 + 2\sqrt{3}x + 2y = 0$$

reduces to

$$4\bar{y}^2 + 4\bar{x} = 0$$

Hence, in the $\bar{D}\bar{R}$ coordinate system, the equation of the conic section is

$$\bar{x} = -\bar{y}^2$$

which is the equation of a parabola. Figure A-4 shows the parabola and both sets of coordinate axes.

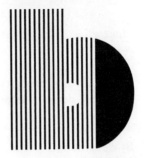

A Justification of Euler's Identity

Consider the exponential function,

$$F(x) = e^x$$

For real values of x, this function is real-valued. However, if the exponent is a complex number, say, $z = x + iy$ (for $x, y \in \mathbb{R}$), then

$$F(z) = e^z = e^{x+iy} = e^x e^{iy}$$

The values of this function for complex arguments are not necessarily real. In the expression $e^x e^{iy}$, the term e^x is always real; thus, since $F(z)$ is a complex number, the term e^{iy} must be a complex number. So let

$$e^{iy} = A(y) + iB(y)$$

where $A(y)$ and $B(y)$ are two real functions of y. We can establish several properties of $A(y)$ and $B(y)$ by using the laws of exponents and of complex number arithmetic.

If $e^{iy} = A(y) + iB(y)$, then since e^{-iy} is the complex conjugate of e^{iy}, we have

$$e^{-iy} = A(y) - iB(y)$$

Furthermore, $e^{iy}e^{-iy} = e^{iy-iy} = e^0$, so

$$e^{iy}e^{-iy} = [A(y) + iB(y)][A(y) - iB(y)] = e^0$$

That is,

$$e^0 = [A(y)]^2 + [B(y)]^2$$

Since $e^0 = 1$, this equation becomes

$$A^2(y) + B^2(y) = 1$$

This is the first property derived for $A(y)$ and $B(y)$.

We can derive a second property by considering the product

$$e^{iy_1}e^{iy_2}$$

By definition,

$$e^{iy_1} = A(y_1) + iB(y_1) \quad \text{and} \quad e^{iy_2} = A(y_2) + iB(y_2)$$

Furthermore, by the laws of exponents,

$$e^{iy_1}e^{iy_1} = e^{i(y_1+y_2)}$$

Using the definitions of the functions A and B, we can rewrite the right side of this equation as

$$e^{i(y_1+y_2)} = A(y_1 + y_2) + iB(y_1 + y_2)$$

Combining these forms and substituting yields

$$A(y_1 + y_2) + iB(y_1 + y_2) = [A(y_1) + iB(y_1)][A(y_2) + iB(y_2)]$$

Expanding the right side yields

$$A(y_1 + y_2) + iB(y_1 + y_2)$$
$$= A(y_1)A(y_2) - B(y_1)B(y_2) + iA(y_1)B(y_2) + iB(y_1)A(y_2)$$

Equating real and imaginary parts yields

$$A(y_1 + y_2) = A(y_1)A(y_2) - B(y_1)B(y_2)$$

and

$$B(y_1 + y_2) = B(y_1)A(y_2) + A(y_1)B(y_2)$$

These are the second and third properties that must be satisfied by $A(y)$ and $B(y)$.

We can carry out the same expansions with the product

$$e^{iy_1}e^{-iy_2} = e^{i(y_1-y_2)}$$

which is equivalent to

$$[A(y_1) + iB(y_1)][A(y_2) - iB(y_2)] = A(y_1 - y_2) + iB(y_1 - y_2)$$

The results are

$$A(y_1 - y_2) = A(y_1)A(y_2) + B(y_1)B(y_2)$$
$$B(y_1 - y_2) = B(y_1)A(y_2) - A(y_1)B(y_2)$$

These are the fourth and fifth properties of the functions $A(y)$ and $B(y)$.

Now consider the case where $y_1 = y_2 = \hat{y}$ for some $\hat{y}$. Then as a special case of the second property, we have

$$A(\hat{y} + \hat{y}) = A(\hat{y})A(\hat{y}) - B(\hat{y})B(\hat{y})$$

or

$$A(2\hat{y}) = A^2(\hat{y}) - B^2(\hat{y})$$

which is now a sixth property. Similarly, a special case of the third property is

$$B(\hat{y} + \hat{y}) = B(\hat{y})A(\hat{y}) + A(\hat{y})B(\hat{y})$$

or

$$B(2\hat{y}) = 2A(\hat{y})B(\hat{y})$$

which is now a seventh property. We can also consider the special case $y_1 = y_2 = \hat{y}$ for the fourth and fifth properties. The fourth property yields

$$A(\hat{y} - \hat{y}) = A(\hat{y})A(\hat{y}) + B(\hat{y})B(\hat{y})$$
$$= A^2(\hat{y}) + B^2(\hat{y})$$

which is equal to 1 by the first property; hence, the eighth property is

$$A(0) = 1$$

The fifth property yields

$$B(\hat{y} - \hat{y}) = B(\hat{y})A(\hat{y}) - A(\hat{y})B(\hat{y})$$
$$= 0$$

Hence, the ninth property is

$$B(0) = 0$$

In summary, then, we have derived nine properties of the functions $A(y)$ and $B(y)$ in the equation $A(y) + iB(y) = e^{iy}$
They are, for all y, y_1, and $y_2 \in \mathbb{R}$,

1. $A^2(y) + B^2(y) = 1$
2. $A(y_1 + y_2) = A(y_1)A(y_2) - B(y_1)B(y_2)$
3. $B(y_1 + y_2) = A(y_1)B(y_2) + B(y_1)A(y_2)$
4. $A(y_1 - y_2) = A(y_1)A(y_2) + B(y_1)B(y_2)$
5. $B(y_1 - y_2) = B(y_1)A(y_2) - A(y_1)B(y_2)$
6. $A(2y) = A^2(y) - B^2(y)$
7. $B(2y) = 2A(y)B(y)$
8. $A(0) = 1$
9. $B(0) = 0$

These properties are identities that $A(y)$ and $B(y)$ must satisfy. Of all the elementary functions discussed in this book, it is clear that only the trigonometric functions have identities corresponding to those just found for $A(y)$ and $B(y)$. These properties are reminiscent of the trigonometric identities if we let

$$A(y) = \cos y \quad \text{and} \quad B(y) = \sin y$$

Then

$$A^2(y) + B^2(y) = 1$$

corresponds to

$$\cos^2 y + \sin^2 y = 1$$

Similarly,

$$A(y_1 + y_2) = A(y_1)A(y_2) - B(y_1)B(y_2)$$

corresponds to

$$\cos(y_1 + y_2) = \cos y_1 \cos y_2 - \sin y_1 \sin y_2$$

and

$$B(y_1 + y_2) = B(y_1)A(y_2) + A(y_1)B(y_2)$$

corresponds to

$$\sin(y_1 + y_2) = \sin y_1 \cos y_2 + \cos y_1 \sin y_2$$

The other correspondences are between

$$A(2y) = A^2(y) - B^2(y) \quad \text{and} \quad \cos 2y = \cos^2 y - \sin^2 y$$

between

$$B(2y) = 2A(y)B(y) \quad \text{and} \quad \sin 2y = 2 \cos y \sin y$$

between

$$A(0) = 1 \quad \text{and} \quad \cos 0 = 1$$

and between

$$B(0) = 0 \quad \text{and} \quad \sin 0 = 0$$

Thus, all nine properties are satisfied by the substitution of the cosine and sine functions, so it is reasonable to conclude that in fact,

$$A(y) = \cos y \quad \text{and} \quad B(y) = \sin y$$

If we return to the original definitions of $A(y)$ and $B(y)$ and make the same substitution, then the defining equation,

$$e^{iy} = A(y) + iB(y)$$

becomes

$$e^{iy} = \cos y + i \sin y$$

which is Euler's Identity.

We emphasize that this is *not* a proof but rather a heuristic justification of Euler's Identity. Our argument makes Euler's Identity plausible, but a formal proof would depend on the theory of Taylor Series, which is studied in calculus.

APPENDIX

Tables

TABLE C-1 The Greek Alphabet

Greek Letter	Name	Greek Letter	Name
A α	Alpha	N ν	Nu
B β	Beta	Ξ ξ	Xi
Γ γ	Gamma	O o	Omicron
Δ δ	Delta	Π π	Pi
E ϵ	Epsilon	P ρ	Rho
Z ζ	Zeta	Σ σ s	Sigma
H η	Eta	T τ	Tau
Θ θ ϑ	Theta	Υ υ	Upsilon
I ι	Iota	Φ ϕ φ	Phi
K κ	Kappa	X χ	Chi
Λ λ	Lambda	Ψ ψ	Psi
M μ	Mu	Ω ω	Omega

TABLE C-2 Powers and Roots

n	n^2	$\sqrt{n}$	n^3	$\sqrt[3]{n}$	n	n^2	$\sqrt{n}$	n^3	$\sqrt[3]{n}$
1	1	1.000	1	1.000	51	2,601	7.141	132,651	3.708
2	4	1.414	8	1.260	52	2,704	7.211	140,608	3.733
3	9	1.732	27	1.442	53	2,809	7.280	148,877	3.756
4	16	2.000	64	1.587	54	2,916	7.348	157,464	3.780
5	25	2.236	125	1.710	55	3,025	7.416	166,375	3.803
6	36	2.449	216	1.817	56	3,136	7.483	175,616	3.826
7	49	2.646	343	1.913	57	3,249	7.550	185,193	3.849
8	64	2.828	512	2.000	58	3,364	7.616	195,112	3.871
9	81	3.000	729	2.080	59	3,481	7.681	205,379	3.893
10	100	3.162	1,000	2.154	60	3,600	7.746	216,000	3.915
11	121	3.317	1,331	2.224	61	3,721	7.810	226,981	3.936
12	144	3.464	1,728	2.289	62	3,844	7.874	238,328	3.958
13	169	3.606	2,197	2.351	63	3,969	7.937	250,047	3.979
14	196	3.742	2,744	2.410	64	4,096	8.000	262,144	4.000
15	225	3.873	3,375	2.466	65	4,225	8.062	274,625	4.021
16	256	4.000	4,096	2.520	66	4,356	8.124	287,496	4.041
17	289	4.123	4,913	2.571	67	4,489	8.185	300,763	4.062
18	324	4.243	5,832	2.621	68	4,624	8.246	314,432	4.082
19	361	4.359	6,859	2.668	69	4,761	8.307	328,509	4.102
20	400	4.472	8,000	2.714	70	4,900	8.367	343,000	4.121
21	441	4.583	9,261	2.759	71	5,041	8.426	357,911	4.141
22	484	4.690	10,648	2.802	72	5,184	8.485	373,248	4.160
23	529	4.796	12,167	2.844	73	5,329	8.544	389,017	4.179
24	576	4.899	13,824	2.884	74	5,476	8.602	405,224	4.198
25	625	5.000	15,625	2.924	75	5,625	8.660	421,875	4.217
26	676	5.099	17,576	2.962	76	5,776	8.718	438,976	4.236
27	729	5.196	19,683	3.000	77	5,929	8.775	456,533	4.254
28	784	5.292	21,952	3.037	78	6,084	8.832	474,552	4.273
29	841	5.385	24,389	3.072	79	6,241	8.888	493,039	4.291
30	900	5.477	27,000	3.107	80	6,400	8.944	512,000	4.309
31	961	5.568	29,791	3.141	81	6,561	9.000	531,441	4.327
32	1,024	5.657	32,768	3.175	82	6,724	9.055	551,368	4.344
33	1,089	5.745	35,937	3.208	83	6,889	9.110	571,787	4.362
34	1,156	5.831	39,304	3.240	84	7,056	9.165	592,704	4.380
35	1,225	5.916	42,875	3.271	85	7,225	9.220	614,125	4.397
36	1,296	6.000	46,656	3.302	86	7,396	9.274	636,056	4.414
37	1,369	6.083	50,653	3.332	87	7,569	9.327	658,503	4.431
38	1,444	6.164	54,872	3.362	88	7,744	9.381	681,472	4.448
39	1,521	6.245	59,319	3.391	89	7,921	9.434	704,969	4.465
40	1,600	6.325	64,000	3.420	90	8,100	9.487	729,000	4.481
41	1,681	6.403	68,921	3.448	91	8,281	9.539	753,571	4.498
42	1,764	6.481	74,088	3.476	92	8,464	9.592	778,688	4.514
43	1,849	6.557	79,507	3.503	93	8,649	9.644	804,357	4.531
44	1,936	6.633	85,184	3.530	94	8,836	9.695	830,584	4.547
45	2,025	6.708	91,125	3.557	95	9,025	9.747	857,375	4.563
46	2,116	6.782	97,336	3.583	96	9,216	9.798	884,736	4.579
47	2,209	6.856	103,823	3.609	97	9,409	9.849	912,673	4.595
48	2,304	6.928	110,592	3.634	98	9,604	9.899	941,192	4.610
49	2,401	7.000	117,649	3.659	99	9,801	9.950	970,299	4.626
50	2,500	7.071	125,000	3.684	100	10,000	10.000	1,000,000	4.642

Angle *u*							
Radians	Degrees	sin *u*	csc *u*	tan *u*	cot *u*	sec *u*	cos *u*
0.00	0°00′	0.0000	No value	0.0000	No value	1.000	1.000
.01	0°34′	.0100	100.0	.0100	100.0	1.000	1.000
.02	1°09′	.0200	50.00	.0200	49.99	1.000	0.9998
.03	1°43′	.0300	33.34	.0300	33.32	1.000	0.9996
.04	2°18′	.0400	25.01	.0400	24.99	1.001	0.9992
0.05	2°52′	0.0500	20.01	0.0500	19.98	1.001	0.9988
.06	3°26′	.0600	16.68	.0601	16.65	1.002	.9982
.07	4°01′	.0699	14.30	.0701	14.26	1.002	.9976
.08	4°35′	.0799	12.51	.0802	12.47	1.003	.9968
.09	5°09′	.0899	11.13	.0902	11.08	1.004	.9960
0.10	5°44′	0.0998	10.02	0.1003	9.967	1.005	0.9950
.11	6°18′	.1098	9.109	.1104	9.054	1.006	.9940
.12	6°53′	.1197	8.353	.1206	8.293	1.007	.9928
.13	7°27′	.1296	7.714	.1307	7.649	1.009	.9916
.14	8°01′	.1395	7.166	.1409	7.096	1.010	.9902
0.15	8°36′	0.1494	6.692	0.1511	6.617	1.011	0.9888
.16	9°10′	.1593	6.277	.1614	6.197	1.013	.9872
.17	9°44′	.1692	5.911	.1717	5.826	1.015	.9856
.18	10°19′	.1790	5.586	.1820	5.495	1.016	.9838
.19	10°53′	.1889	5.295	.1923	5.200	1.018	.9820
0.20	11°28′	0.1987	5.033	0.2027	4.933	1.020	0.9801
.21	12°02′	.2085	4.797	.2131	4.692	1.022	.9780
.22	12°36′	.2182	4.582	.2236	4.472	1.025	.9759
.23	13°11′	.2280	4.386	.2341	4.271	1.027	.9737
.24	13°45′	.2377	4.207	.2447	4.086	1.030	.9713
0.25	14°19′	0.2474	4.042	0.2553	3.916	1.032	0.9689
.26	14°54′	.2571	3.890	.2660	3.759	1.035	.9664
.27	15°28′	.2667	3.749	.2768	3.613	1.038	.9638
.28	16°03′	.2764	3.619	.2876	3.478	1.041	.9611
.29	16°37′	.2860	3.497	.2984	3.351	1.044	.9582
0.30	17°11′	0.2955	3.384	0.3093	3.233	1.047	0.9553
.31	17°46′	.3051	3.278	.3203	3.122	1.050	.9523
.32	18°20′	.3146	3.179	.3314	3.018	1.053	.9492
.33	18°54′	.3240	3.086	.3425	2.920	1.057	.9460
.34	19°29′	.3335	2.999	.3537	2.827	1.061	.9428
.35	20°03′	0.3429	2.916	0.3650	2.740	1.065	0.9394
.36	20°38′	.3523	2.839	.3764	2.657	1.068	.9359
.37	21°12′	.3616	2.765	.3879	2.578	1.073	.9323
.38	21°46′	.3709	2.696	.3994	2.504	1.077	.9287
.39	22°21′	.3802	2.630	.4111	2.433	1.081	.9249
0.40	22°55′	0.3894	2.568	0.4228	2.365	1.086	0.9211
.41	23°29′	.3986	2.509	.4346	2.301	1.090	.9171
.42	24°04′	.4078	2.452	.4466	2.239	1.095	.9131
.43	24°38′	.4169	2.399	.4586	2.180	1.100	.9090
.44	25°13′	.4259	2.348	.4708	2.124	1.105	.9048
0.45	25°47′	0.4350	2.299	0.4831	2.070	1.111	0.9004

Trigonometric Functions of *u* in Radians (*cont.*)

Angle *u*							
Radians	Degrees	sin *u*	csc *u*	tan *u*	cot *u*	sec *u*	cos *u*
0.45	25°47′	0.4350	2.299	0.4831	2.070	1.111	0.9004
.46	26°21′	.4439	2.253	.4954	2.018	1.116	.8961
.47	26°56′	.4529	2.208	.5080	1.969	1.122	.8916
.48	27°30′	.4618	2.166	.5206	1.921	1.127	.8870
.49	28°04′	.4706	2.125	.5334	1.875	1.133	.8823
0.50	28°39′	0.4794	2.086	0.5463	1.830	1.139	0.8776
.51	29°13′	.4882	2.048	.5594	1.788	1.146	.8727
.52	29°48′	.4969	2.013	.5726	1.747	1.152	.8678
.53	30°22′	.5055	1.978	.5859	1.707	1.159	.8628
.54	30°56′	.5141	1.945	.5994	1.668	1.166	.8577
0.55	31°31′	0.5227	1.913	0.6131	1.631	1.173	0.8525
.56	32°05′	.5312	1.883	.6269	1.595	1.180	.8473
.57	32°40′	.5396	1.853	.6410	1.560	1.188	.8419
.58	33°14′	.5480	1.825	.6552	1.526	1.196	.8365
.59	33°48′	.5564	1.797	.6696	1.494	1.203	.8309
0.60	34°23′	0.5646	1.771	0.6841	1.462	1.212	0.8253
.61	34°57′	.5729	1.746	.6989	1.431	1.220	.8196
.62	35°31′	.5810	1.721	.7139	1.401	1.229	.8139
.63	36°06′	.5891	1.697	.7291	1.372	1.238	.8080
.64	36°40′	.5972	1.674	.7445	1.343	1.247	.8021
0.65	37°15′	0.6052	1.652	0.7602	1.315	1.256	0.7961
.66	37°49′	.6131	1.631	.7761	1.288	1.266	.7900
.67	38°23′	.6210	1.610	.7923	1.262	1.276	.7838
.68	38°58′	.6288	1.590	.8087	1.237	1.286	.7776
.69	39°32′	.6365	1.571	.8253	1.212	1.297	.7712
0.70	40°06′	0.6442	1.552	0.8423	1.187	1.307	0.7648
.71	40°41′	.6518	1.534	.8595	1.163	1.319	.7584
.72	41°15′	.6594	1.517	.8771	1.140	1.330	.7518
.73	41°50′	.6669	1.500	.8949	1.117	1.342	.7452
.74	42°24′	.6743	1.483	.9131	1.095	1.354	.7385
0.75	42°58′	0.6816	1.467	0.9316	1.073	1.367	0.7317
.76	43°33′	.6889	1.452	.9505	1.052	1.380	.7248
.77	44°07′	.6961	1.436	.9697	1.031	1.393	.7179
.78	44°41′	.7033	1.422	.9893	1.011	1.407	.7109
.79	45°16′	.7104	1.408	1.009	.9908	1.421	.7038
0.80	45°50′	0.7174	1.394	1.030	0.9712	1.435	0.6967
.81	46°25′	.7243	1.381	1.050	.9520	1.450	.6895
.82	46°59′	.7311	1.368	1.072	.9331	1.466	.6822
.83	47°33′	.7379	1.355	1.093	.9146	1.482	.6749
.84	48°08′	.7446	1.343	1.116	.8964	1.498	.6675
0.85	48°42′	0.7513	1.331	1.138	0.8785	1.515	0.6600
.86	49°16′	.7578	1.320	1.162	.8609	1.533	.6524
.87	49°51′	.7643	1.308	1.185	.8437	1.551	.6448
.88	50°25′	.7707	1.297	1.210	.8267	1.569	.6372
.89	51°00′	.7771	1.287	1.235	.8100	1.589	.6294
0.90	51°34′	0.7833	1.277	1.260	0.7936	1.609	0.6216
.91	52°08′	.7895	1.267	1.286	.7774	1.629	.6137
.92	52°43′	.7956	1.257	1.313	.7615	1.651	.6058
.93	53°17′	.8016	1.247	1.341	.7458	1.673	.5978
.94	53°51′	.8076	1.238	1.369	.7303	1.696	.5898
0.95	54°26′	0.8134	1.229	1.398	0.7151	1.719	0.5817

Angle *u*		sin *u*	csc *u*	tan *u*	cot *u*	sec *u*	cos *u*
Radians	Degrees						
0.95	54°26'	0.8134	1.229	1.398	0.7151	1.719	0.5817
.96	55°00'	.8192	1.221	1.428	.7001	1.744	.5735
.97	55°35'	.8249	1.212	1.459	.6853	1.769	.5653
.98	56°09'	.8305	1.204	1.491	.6707	1.795	.5570
.99	56°43'	.8360	1.196	1.524	.6563	1.823	.5487
1.00	57°18'	0.8415	1.188	1.557	0.6421	1.851	0.5403
1.01	57°52'	.8468	1.181	1.592	.6281	1.880	.5319
1.02	58°27'	.8521	1.174	1.628	.6142	1.911	.5234
1.03	59°01'	.8573	1.166	1.665	.6005	1.942	.5148
1.04	59°35'	.8624	1.160	1.704	.5870	1.975	.5062
1.05	60°10'	0.8674	1.153	1.743	0.5736	2.010	0.4976
1.06	60°44'	.8724	1.146	1.784	.5604	2.046	.4889
1.07	61°18'	.8772	1.140	1.827	.5473	2.083	.4801
1.08	61°53'	.8820	1.134	1.871	.5344	2.122	.4713
1.09	62°27'	.8866	1.128	1.917	.5216	2.162	.4625
1.10	63°02'	0.8912	1.122	1.965	0.5090	2.205	0.4536
1.11	63°36'	.8957	1.116	2.014	.4964	2.249	.4447
1.12	64°10'	.9001	1.111	2.066	.4840	2.295	.4357
1.13	64°45'	.9044	1.106	2.120	.4718	2.344	.4267
1.14	65°19'	.9086	1.101	2.176	.4596	2.395	.4176
1.15	65°53'	0.9128	1.096	2.234	0.4475	2.448	0.4085
1.16	66°28'	.9168	1.091	2.296	.4356	2.504	.3993
1.17	67°02'	.9208	1.086	2.360	.4237	2.563	.3902
1.18	67°37'	.9246	1.082	2.247	.4120	2.625	.3809
1.19	68°11'	.9284	1.077	2.498	.4003	2.691	.3717
1.20	68°45'	0.9320	1.073	2.572	0.3888	2.760	0.3624
1.21	69°20'	.9356	1.069	2.650	.3773	2.833	.3530
1.22	69°54'	.9391	1.065	2.733	.3659	2.910	.3436
1.23	70°28'	.9425	1.061	2.820	.3546	2.992	.3342
1.24	71°03'	.9458	1.057	2.912	.3434	3.079	.3248
1.25	71°37'	0.9490	1.054	3.010	0.3323	3.171	0.3153
1.26	72°12'	.9521	1.050	3.113	.3212	3.270	.3058
1.27	72°46'	.9551	1.047	3.224	.3102	3.375	.2963
1.28	72°20'	.9580	1.044	3.341	.2993	3.488	.2867
1.29	73°55'	.9608	1.041	3.467	.2884	3.609	.2771
1.30	74°29'	0.9636	1.038	3.602	0.2776	3.738	0.2675
1.31	75°03'	.9662	1.035	3.747	.2669	3.878	.2579
1.32	75°38'	.9687	1.032	3.903	.2562	4.029	.2482
1.33	76°12'	.9711	1.030	4.072	.2456	4.193	.2385
1.34	76°47'	.9735	1.027	4.256	.2350	4.372	.2288
1.35	77°21'	0.9757	1.025	4.455	0.2245	4.566	0.2190
1.36	77°55'	.9779	1.023	4.673	.2140	4.779	.2092
1.37	78°30'	.9799	1.021	4.913	.2035	5.014	.1994
1.38	79°04'	.9819	1.018	5.177	.1931	5.273	.1896
1.39	79°38'	.9837	1.017	5.471	.1828	5.561	.1798
1.40	80°13'	0.9854	1.015	5.798	0.1725	5.883	0.1700
1.41	80°47'	.9871	1.013	6.165	.1622	6.246	.1601
1.42	81°22'	.9887	1.011	6.581	.1519	6.657	.1502
1.43	81°56'	.9901	1.010	7.055	.1417	7.126	.1403
1.44	82°30'	.9915	1.009	7.602	.1315	7.667	.1304
1.45	83°05'	0.9927	1.007	8.238	0.1214	8.299	0.1205

Trigonometric Functions of *u* in Radians (*cont.*)

Angle *u*		sin *u*	csc *u*	tan *u*	cot *u*	sec *u*	cos *u*
Radians	Degrees						
1.45	83° 05′	0.9927	1.007	8.238	0.1214	8.299	0.1205
1.46	83° 39′	.9939	1.006	8.989	.1113	9.044	.1106
1.47	84° 13′	.9949	1.005	9.887	.1011	9.938	.1006
1.48	84° 48′	.9959	1.004	10.98	.0910	11.03	.0907
1.49	85° 22′	.9967	1.003	12.35	.0810	12.39	.0807
1.50	85° 57′	0.9975	1.003	14.10	0.0709	14.14	0.0707
1.51	86° 31′	.9982	1.002	16.43	.0609	16.46	.0608
1.52	87° 05′	.9987	1.001	19.67	.0508	19.69	.0508
1.53	87° 40′	.9992	1.001	24.50	.0408	24.52	.0408
1.54	88° 14′	.9995	1.000	32.46	.0308	32.48	.0308
1.55	88° 49′	0.9998	1.000	48.08	0.0208	48.09	0.0208
1.56	89° 23′	.9999	1.000	92.62	.0108	92.63	.0108
1.57	89° 57′	1.000	1.000	1256	.0008	1256	.0008

TABLE C-4 Trigonometric Functions of θ in Degrees

Degrees	Radians	sin θ	csc θ	tan θ	cot θ	sec θ	cos θ		
0° 00′	.0000	.0000	No value	.0000	No value	1.000	1.0000	1.5708	90° 00′
10	029	029	343.8	029	343.8	000	000	679	50
20	058	058	171.9	058	171.9	000	000	650	40
30	087	087	114.6	087	114.6	000	1.0000	621	30
40	116	116	85.95	116	85.94	000	.9999	592	20
50	145	145	68.76	145	68.75	000	999	563	10
1° 00′	.0175	.0175	57.30	.0175	57.29	1.000	.9998	1.5533	89° 00′
10	204	204	49.11	204	49.10	000	998	504	50
20	233	233	42.98	233	42.96	000	997	475	40
30	262	262	38.20	262	38.19	000	997	446	30
40	291	291	34.38	291	34.37	000	996	417	20
50	320	320	31.26	320	31.24	001	995	388	10
2° 00′	.0349	.0349	28.65	.0349	28.64	1.001	.9994	1.5359	88° 00′
10	378	378	26.45	378	26.43	001	993	330	50
20	407	407	24.56	407	24.54	001	992	301	40
30	436	436	22.93	437	22.90	001	990	272	30
40	465	465	21.49	466	21.47	001	989	243	20
50	495	494	20.23	495	20.21	001	988	213	10
3° 00′	.0524	.0523	19.11	.0524	19.08	1.001	.9986	1.5184	87° 00′
10	553	552	18.10	553	18.07	002	985	155	50
20	582	581	17.20	582	17.17	002	983	126	40
30	611	610	16.38	612	16.35	002	981	097	30
40	640	640	15.64	641	15.60	002	980	068	20
50	669	669	14.96	670	14.92	002	978	039	10
4° 00′	.0698	.0698	14.34	.0699	14.30	1.002	.9976	1.5010	86° 00′
10	727	727	13.76	729	13.73	003	974	981	50
20	756	765	13.23	758	13.20	003	971	952	40
30	785	785	12.75	787	12.71	003	969	923	30
40	814	814	12.29	816	12.25	003	967	893	20
50	844	843	11.87	846	11.83	004	964	864	10
5° 00′	.0873	.0872	11.47	.0875	11.43	1.004	.9962	1.4835	85° 00′
10	902	901	11.10	904	11.06	004	959	806	50
20	931	929	10.76	934	10.71	004	957	777	40
30	960	958	10.43	963	10.39	005	954	748	30
40	.0989	.0987	10.13	.0992	10.08	005	951	719	20
50	.1018	.1016	9.839	.1022	9.788	005	948	690	10
6° 00′	.1047	.1045	9.567	.1051	9.514	1.006	.9945	1.4661	84° 00′
10	076	074	9.309	080	9.255	006	942	632	50
20	105	103	9.065	110	9.010	006	939	603	40
30	134	132	8.834	139	8.777	006	936	573	30
40	164	161	8.614	169	8.556	007	932	544	20
50	193	190	8.405	198	8.345	007	929	515	10
7° 00′	.1222	.1219	8.206	.1228	8.144	1.008	.9925	1.4486	83° 00′
10	251	248	8.016	257	7.953	008	922	457	50
20	280	276	7.834	287	7.770	008	918	428	40
30	309	305	7.661	317	7.596	009	914	399	30
40	338	334	7.496	346	7.429	009	911	370	20
50	367	363	7.337	376	7.269	009	907	341	10
8° 00′	.1396	.1392	7.185	.1405	7.115	1.010	.9903	1.4312	82° 00′
		cos θ	sec θ	cot θ	tan θ	csc θ	sin θ	Radians	Degrees
								Angle θ	

Trigonometric Functions of θ in Degrees (*cont.*)

Angle θ		sin θ	csc θ	tan θ	cot θ	sec θ	cos θ		
Degrees	Radians								
8° 00′	.1396	.1392	7.185	.1405	7.115	1.010	.9903	1.4312	82° 00′
10	425	421	7.040	435	6.968	010	899	283	50
20	454	449	6.900	465	827	011	894	254	40
30	484	478	765	495	691	011	890	224	30
40	513	507	636	524	561	012	886	195	20
50	542	536	512	554	435	012	881	166	10
9° 00′	.1571	.1564	6.392	.1584	6.314	1.012	.9877	1.4137	81° 00′
10	600	593	277	614	197	013	872	108	50
20	629	622	166	644	6.084	013	868	079	40
30	658	650	6.059	673	5.976	014	863	050	30
40	687	679	5.935	703	871	014	858	1.4021	20
50	716	708	855	733	769	015	853	1.3992	10
10° 00′	.1745	.1736	5.759	.1763	5.671	1.015	.9848	1.3963	80° 00′
10	774	765	665	793	576	016	843	934	50
20	804	794	575	823	485	016	838	904	40
30	833	822	487	853	396	017	833	875	30
40	862	851	403	883	309	018	827	846	20
50	891	880	320	914	226	018	822	817	10
11° 00′	.1920	.1908	5.241	.1944	5.145	1.019	.9816	1.3788	79° 00′
10	949	937	164	.1974	5.066	019	811	759	50
20	.1978	965	089	.2004	4.989	020	805	730	40
30	.2007	.1994	5.016	035	915	020	799	701	30
40	036	.2022	4.945	065	843	021	793	672	20
50	065	051	876	095	773	022	787	643	10
12° 00′	.2094	.2079	4.810	.2126	4.705	1.022	.9781	1.3614	78° 00′
10	123	108	745	156	638	023	775	584	50
20	153	136	682	186	574	024	769	555	40
30	182	164	620	217	511	024	763	526	30
40	211	193	560	247	449	025	757	497	20
50	240	221	502	278	390	026	750	468	10
13° 00′	.2269	.2250	4.445	.2309	4.331	1.026	.9744	1.3439	77° 00′
10	298	278	390	339	275	027	737	410	50
20	327	306	336	370	219	028	730	381	40
30	356	334	284	401	165	028	724	352	30
40	385	363	232	432	113	029	717	323	20
50	414	391	182	462	061	030	710	294	10
14° 00′	.2443	.2419	4.134	.2493	4.011	1.031	.9703	1.3265	76° 00′
10	473	447	086	524	3.962	031	696	235	50
20	502	476	4.039	555	914	032	689	206	40
30	531	504	3.994	586	867	033	681	177	30
40	560	532	950	617	821	034	674	148	20
50	589	560	906	648	776	034	667	119	10
15° 00′	.2618	.2588	3.864	.2679	3.732	1.035	.9659	1.3090	75° 00′
10	647	616	822	711	689	036	652	061	50
20	676	644	782	742	647	037	644	032	40
30	705	672	742	773	606	038	636	1.3003	30
40	734	700	703	805	566	039	628	1.2974	20
50	763	728	665	836	526	039	621	945	10
16° 00′	.2793	.2756	3.628	.2867	3.487	1.040	.9613	1.2915	74° 00′
		cos θ	sec θ	cot θ	tan θ	csc θ	sin θ	Radians	Degrees
								Angle θ	

Trigonometric Functions of θ in Degrees (*cont.*)

Angle θ									
Degrees	Radians	sin θ	csc θ	tan θ	cot θ	sec θ	cos θ		
16° 00′	.2793	.2756	3.628	.2867	3.487	1.040	.9613	1.2915	74° 00′
10	822	784	592	899	450	041	605	886	50
20	851	812	556	931	412	042	596	857	40
30	880	840	521	962	376	043	588	828	30
40	909	868	487	.2944	340	044	580	799	20
50	938	896	453	.3026	305	045	572	770	10
17° 00′	.2967	.2924	3.420	.3057	3.271	1.046	.9563	1.2741	73° 00′
10	.2996	952	388	089	237	047	555	712	50
20	.3025	.2979	357	121	204	048	546	683	40
30	054	.3007	326	153	172	048	537	654	30
40	083	035	295	185	140	049	528	625	20
50	113	062	265	217	108	050	520	595	10
18° 00′	.3142	.3090	3.236	.3249	3.078	1.051	.9511	1.2566	72° 00′
10	171	118	207	281	047	052	502	537	50
20	200	145	179	314	3.018	053	492	508	40
30	229	173	152	346	2.989	054	483	479	30
40	258	201	124	378	960	056	474	450	20
50	287	228	098	411	932	057	465	421	10
19° 00′	.3316	.3256	3.072	.3443	2.904	1.058	.9455	1.2392	71° 00′
10	345	283	046	476	877	059	446	363	50
20	374	311	3.021	508	850	060	436	334	40
30	403	338	2.996	541	824	061	426	305	30
40	432	365	971	574	798	062	417	275	20
50	462	393	947	607	773	063	407	246	10
20° 00′	.3491	.3420	2.924	.3640	2.747	1.064	.9397	1.2217	70° 00′
10	520	448	901	673	723	065	387	188	50
20	549	475	878	706	699	066	377	159	40
30	578	502	855	739	675	068	367	130	39
40	607	529	833	772	651	069	356	101	20
50	636	557	812	805	628	070	346	072	10
21° 00′	.3665	.3584	2.790	.3839	2.605	1.071	.9336	1.2043	69° 00′
10	694	611	769	872	583	072	325	1.2014	50
20	723	638	749	906	560	074	315	985	40
30	752	665	729	939	539	075	304	956	30
40	782	692	709	.3973	517	076	293	926	20
50	811	719	689	.4006	496	077	283	897	10
22° 00′	.3840	.3746	2.669	.4040	2.475	1.079	.9272	1.1868	68° 00′
10	869	773	650	074	455	080	261	839	50
20	898	800	632	108	434	081	250	810	40
30	927	827	613	142	414	082	239	781	30
40	956	854	595	176	394	084	228	752	20
50	985	881	577	210	375	085	216	723	10
23° 00′	.4014	.3907	2.559	.4245	2.356	1.086	.9205	1.1694	67° 00′
10	043	934	542	279	337	088	194	665	50
20	072	961	525	314	318	089	182	636	40
30	102	.3987	508	348	300	090	171	606	30
40	131	.4014	491	383	282	092	159	577	20
50	160	041	475	417	264	093	147	548	10
24° 00′	.4189	.4067	2.459	.4452	2.246	1.095	.9135	1.1519	66° 00′
		cos θ	sec θ	cot θ	tan θ	csc θ	sin θ	Radians	Degrees
								Angle θ	

Trigonometric Functions of θ in Degrees (*cont.*)

Angle θ		sin θ	csc θ	tan θ	cot θ	sec θ	cos θ		
Degrees	Radians								
24° 00'	.4189	.4067	2.459	.4452	2.246	1.095	.9135	1.1519	66° 00'
10	218	094	443	487	229	096	124	490	50
20	247	120	427	522	211	097	112	461	40
30	276	147	411	557	194	099	100	432	30
40	305	173	396	592	177	100	088	403	20
50	334	200	381	628	161	102	075	374	10
25° 00'	.4363	.4226	2.366	.4663	2.145	1.103	.9063	1.1345	65° 00'
10	392	253	352	699	128	105	051	316	50
20	422	279	337	734	112	106	038	286	40
30	451	305	323	770	097	108	026	257	30
40	480	331	309	806	081	109	013	228	20
50	509	358	295	841	066	111	.9001	199	10
26° 00'	.4538	.4384	2.281	.4877	2.050	1.113	.8988	1.1170	64° 00'
10	567	410	268	913	035	114	975	141	50
20	596	436	254	950	020	116	962	112	40
30	625	462	241	.4986	2.006	117	949	083	30
40	654	488	228	.5022	1.991	119	936	054	20
50	683	514	215	059	977	121	923	1.1025	10
27° 00'	.4712	.4540	2.203	.5095	1.963	1.122	.8910	1.0996	63° 00'
10	741	566	190	132	949	124	897	966	50
20	771	592	178	169	935	126	884	937	40
30	800	617	166	206	921	127	870	908	30
40	829	643	154	243	907	129	857	879	20
50	858	669	142	280	894	131	843	850	10
28° 00'	.4887	.4695	2.130	.5317	1.881	1.133	.8829	1.0821	62° 00'
10	916	720	118	354	868	134	816	792	50
20	945	746	107	392	855	136	802	763	40
30	.4974	772	096	430	842	138	788	734	30
40	.5003	797	085	467	829	140	774	705	20
50	032	823	074	505	816	142	760	676	10
29° 00'	.5061	.4848	2.063	.5543	1.804	1.143	.8746	1.0647	61° 00'
10	091	874	052	581	792	145	732	617	50
20	120	899	041	619	780	147	718	588	40
30	149	924	031	658	767	149	704	559	30
40	178	950	020	696	756	151	689	530	20
50	207	.4975	010	735	744	153	675	501	10
30° 00'	.5236	.5000	2.000	.5774	1.732	1.155	.8660	1.0472	60° 00'
10	265	025	1.990	812	720	157	646	443	50
20	294	050	980	851	709	159	631	414	40
30	323	075	970	890	698	161	616	385	30
40	352	100	961	930	686	163	601	356	20
50	381	125	951	.5969	675	165	587	327	10
31° 00'	.5411	.5150	1.942	.6009	1.664	1.167	.8572	1.0297	59° 00'
10	440	175	932	048	653	169	557	268	50
20	469	200	923	088	643	171	542	239	40
30	498	225	914	128	632	173	526	210	30
40	527	250	905	168	621	175	511	181	20
50	556	275	896	208	611	177	496	152	10
32° 00'	.5585	.5299	1.887	.6249	1.600	1.179	.8480	1.0123	58° 00'
		cos θ	sec θ	cot θ	tan θ	csc θ	sin θ	Radians	Degrees
								Angle θ	

Angle θ									
Degrees	Radians	sin θ	csc θ	tan θ	cot θ	sec θ	cos θ		
32° 00'	.5585	.5299	1.887	.6249	1.600	1.179	.8480	1.0123	58° 00'
10	614	324	878	289	590	181	465	094	50
20	643	348	870	330	580	184	450	065	40
30	672	373	861	371	570	186	434	036	30
40	701	398	853	412	560	188	418	1.0007	20
50	730	422	844	453	550	190	403	.9977	10
33° 00'	.5760	.5446	1.836	.6494	1.540	1.192	.8387	.9948	57° 00'
10	789	471	828	536	530	195	371	919	50
20	818	495	820	577	520	197	355	890	40
30	847	519	812	619	511	199	339	861	30
40	876	544	804	661	501	202	323	832	20
50	905	568	796	703	492	204	307	803	10
34° 00'	.5934	.5592	1.788	.6745	1.483	1.206	.8290	.9774	56° 00'
10	963	616	781	787	473	209	274	743	50
20	.5992	640	773	830	464	211	258	716	40
30	.6021	664	766	873	455	213	241	687	30
40	050	688	758	916	446	216	225	657	20
50	080	712	751	.6959	437	218	208	628	10
35° 00'	.6109	.5736	1.743	.7002	1.428	1.221	.8192	.9599	55° 00'
10	138	760	736	046	419	223	175	570	50
20	167	783	729	089	411	226	158	541	40
30	196	807	722	133	402	228	141	512	30
40	225	831	715	177	393	231	124	483	20
50	254	854	708	221	385	233	107	454	10
36° 00'	.6283	.5878	1.701	.7265	1.376	1.236	.8090	.9425	54° 00'
10	312	901	695	310	368	239	073	396	50
20	341	925	688	355	360	241	056	367	40
30	370	948	681	400	351	244	039	338	30
40	400	972	675	445	343	247	021	308	20
50	429	.5995	668	490	335	249	.8004	279	10
37° 00'	.6458	.6018	1.662	.7536	1.327	1.252	.7986	.9250	53° 00'
10	487	041	655	581	319	255	696	221	50
20	516	065	649	627	311	258	951	192	40
30	545	088	643	673	303	260	934	163	30
40	574	111	636	720	295	263	916	134	20
50	603	134	630	766	288	266	898	105	10
38° 00'	.6632	.6157	1.624	.7813	1.280	1.269	.7880	.9076	52° 00'
10	661	180	618	860	272	272	862	047	50
20	690	202	612	907	265	275	844	.9018	40
30	720	225	606	.7954	257	278	826	.8988	30
40	749	248	601	.8002	250	281	808	959	20
50	778	271	595	050	242	284	790	930	10
39° 00'	.6807	.6293	1.589	.8098	1.235	1.287	.7771	.8901	51° 00'
10	836	316	583	146	228	290	753	872	50
20	865	338	578	195	220	293	735	843	40
30	894	361	572	243	213	296	716	814	30
40	923	383	567	292	206	299	698	785	20
50	952	406	561	342	199	302	679	756	10
40° 00'	.6981	.6428	1.556	.8391	1.192	1.305	.7660	.8727	50° 00'
	cos θ	sec θ	cot θ	tan θ	csc θ	sin θ	Radians	Degrees	
								Angle θ	

Trigonometric Functions of θ in Degrees (*cont.*)

Angle θ Degrees	Angle θ Radians	sin θ	csc θ	tan θ	cot θ	sec θ	cos θ		
40° 00′	.6981	.6428	1.556	.8391	1.192	1.305	.7660	.8727	50° 00′
10	.7010	450	550	441	185	309	642	698	50
20	039	472	545	491	178	312	623	668	40
30	069	494	540	541	171	315	604	639	30
40	098	517	535	591	164	318	585	610	20
50	127	539	529	642	157	322	566	581	10
41° 00′	.7156	.6561	1.524	.8693	1.150	1.325	.7547	.8552	49° 00′
10	185	583	519	744	144	328	528	523	50
20	214	604	514	796	137	332	509	494	40
30	243	626	509	847	130	335	490	465	30
40	272	648	504	899	124	339	470	436	20
50	301	670	499	.8952	117	342	451	407	10
42° 00′	.7330	.6691	1.494	.9004	1.111	1.346	.7431	.8378	48° 00′
10	359	713	490	057	104	349	412	348	50
20	389	734	485	110	098	353	392	319	40
30	418	756	480	163	091	356	373	290	30
40	447	777	476	217	085	360	353	261	20
50	476	799	471	271	079	364	333	232	10
43° 00′	.7505	.6820	1.466	.9325	1.072	1.367	.7314	.8203	47° 00′
10	534	841	462	380	066	371	294	174	50
20	563	862	457	435	060	375	274	145	40
30	592	884	453	490	054	379	254	116	30
40	621	905	448	545	048	382	234	087	20
50	650	926	444	601	042	386	214	058	10
44° 00′	.7679	.6947	1.440	.9657	1.036	1.390	.7193	.8029	46° 00′
10	709	967	435	713	030	394	173	.7999	50
20	738	.6988	431	770	024	398	153	970	40
30	767	.7009	427	827	018	402	133	941	30
40	796	030	423	884	012	406	112	912	20
50	825	050	418	.9942	006	410	092	883	10
45° 00′	.7854	.7071	1.414	1.000	1.000	1.414	.7071	.7854	45° 00′
		cos θ	sec θ	cot θ	tan θ	csc θ	sin θ	Radians	Degrees
									Angle θ

TABLE C-5 **Common Logarithms (Base 10)** *Appendix C* **377**

log x	0	1	2	3	4	5	6	7	8	9
log 1.0	.0000	.0043	.0086	.0128	.0170	.0212	.0253	.0294	.0334	.0374
1.1	.0414	.0453	.0492	.0531	.0569	.0607	.0645	.0682	.0719	.0755
1.2	.0792	.0828	.0864	.0899	.0934	.0969	.1004	.1038	.1072	.1106
1.3	.1139	.1173	.1206	.1239	.1271	.1303	.1335	.1367	.1399	.1430
1.4	.1461	.1492	.1523	.1553	.1584	.1614	.1644	.1673	.1703	.1732
log 1.5	.1761	.1790	.1818	.1847	.1875	.1903	.1931	.1959	.1987	.2014
1.6	.2041	.2068	.2095	.2122	.2148	.2175	.2201	.2227	.2253	.2279
1.7	.2304	.2330	.2355	.2380	.2405	.2430	.2455	.2480	.2504	.2529
1.8	.2553	.2577	.2601	.2625	.2648	.2672	.2695	.2718	.2742	.2765
1.9	.2788	.2810	.2833	.2856	.2878	.2900	.2923	.2945	.2967	.2989
log 2.0	.3010	.3032	.3054	.3075	.3096	.3118	.3139	.3160	.3181	.3201
2.1	.3222	.3243	.3263	.3284	.3304	.3324	.3345	.3365	.3385	.3404
2.2	.3424	.3444	.3464	.3483	.3502	.3522	.3541	.3560	.3579	.3598
2.3	.3617	.3636	.3655	.3674	.3692	.3711	.3729	.3747	.3766	.3784
2.4	.3802	.3820	.3838	.3856	.3874	.3892	.3909	.3927	.3945	.3962
log 2.5	.3979	.3997	.4014	.4031	.4048	.4065	.4082	.4099	.4116	.4133
2.6	.4150	.4166	.4183	.4200	.4216	.4232	.4249	.4265	.4281	.4298
2.7	.4314	.4330	.4346	.4362	.4378	.4393	.4409	.4425	.4440	.4456
2.8	.4472	.4487	.4502	.4518	.4533	.4548	.4564	.4579	.4594	.4609
2.9	.4624	.4639	.4654	.4669	.4683	.4698	.4713	.4728	.4742	.4757
log 3.0	.4771	.4786	.4800	.4814	.4829	.4843	.4857	.4871	.4886	.4900
3.1	.4914	.4928	.4942	.4955	.4969	.4983	.4997	.5011	.5024	.5038
3.2	.5051	.5065	.5079	.5092	.5105	.5119	.5132	.5145	.5159	.5172
3.3	.5185	.5198	.5211	.5224	.5237	.5250	.5263	.5276	.5289	.5302
3.4	.5315	.5328	.5340	.5353	.5366	.5378	.5391	.5403	.5416	.5428
log 3.5	.5441	.5453	.5465	.5478	.5490	.5502	.5514	.5527	.5539	.5551
3.6	.5563	.5575	.5587	.5599	.5611	.5623	.5635	.5647	.5658	.5670
3.7	.5682	.5694	.5705	.5717	.5729	.5740	.5752	.5763	.5775	.5786
3.8	.5798	.5809	.5821	.5832	.5843	.5855	.5866	.5877	.5888	.5899
3.9	.5911	.5922	.5933	.5944	.5955	.5966	.5977	.5988	.5999	.6010
log 4.0	.6021	.6031	.6042	.6053	.6064	.6075	.6085	.6096	.6107	.6117
4.1	.6128	.6138	.6149	.6160	.6170	.6180	.6191	.6201	.6212	.6222
4.2	.6232	.6243	.6253	.6263	.6274	.6284	.6294	.6304	.6314	.6325
4.3	.6335	.6345	.6355	.6365	.6375	.6385	.6395	.6405	.6415	.6425
4.4	.6435	.6444	.6454	.6464	.6474	.6484	.6493	.6503	.6513	.6522
log 4.5	.6532	.6542	.6551	.6561	.6571	.6580	.6590	.6599	.6609	.6618
4.6	.6628	.6637	.6646	.6656	.6665	.6675	.6684	.6693	.6702	.6712
4.7	.6721	.6730	.6739	.6749	.6758	.6767	.6776	.6785	.6794	.6803
4.8	.6812	.6821	.6830	.6839	.6848	.6857	.6866	.6875	.6884	.6893
4.9	.6902	.6911	.6920	.6928	.6937	.6946	.6955	.6964	.6972	.6981
log 5.0	.6990	.6998	.7007	.7016	.7024	.7033	.7042	.7050	.7059	.7067
5.1	.7076	.7084	.7093	.7101	.7110	.7118	.7126	.7135	.7143	.7152
5.2	.7160	.7168	.7177	.7185	.7193	.7202	.7210	.7218	.7226	.7235
5.3	.7243	.7251	.7259	.7267	.7275	.7284	.7292	.7300	.7308	.7316
5.4	.7324	.7332	.7340	.7348	.7356	.7364	.7372	.7380	.7388	.7396
log x	0	1	2	3	4	5	6	7	8	9

Common Logarithms (*cont.*)

log x	0	1	2	3	4	5	6	7	8	9
log 5.5	.7404	.7412	.7419	.7427	.7435	.7443	.7451	.7459	.7466	.7474
5.6	.7482	.7490	.7497	.7505	.7513	.7520	.7528	.7536	.7543	.7551
5.7	.7559	.7566	.7574	.7582	.7589	.7597	.7604	.7612	.7619	.7627
5.8	.7634	.7642	.7649	.7657	.7664	.7672	.7679	.7686	.7694	.7701
5.9	.7709	.7716	.7723	.7731	.7738	.7745	.7752	.7760	.7767	.7774
log 6.0	.7782	.7789	.7796	.7803	.7810	.7818	.7825	.7832	.7839	.7846
6.1	.7853	.7860	.7868	.7875	.7882	.7889	.7896	.7903	.7910	.7917
6.2	.7924	.7931	.7938	.7945	.7952	.7959	.7966	.7973	.7980	.7987
6.3	.7993	.8000	.8007	.8014	.8021	.8028	.8035	.8041	.8048	.8055
6.4	.8062	.8069	.8075	.8082	.8089	.8096	.8102	.8109	.8116	.8122
log 6.5	.8129	.8136	.8142	.8149	.8156	.8162	.8169	.8176	.8182	.8189
6.6	.8195	.8202	.8209	.8215	.8222	.8228	.8235	.8241	.8248	.8254
6.7	.8261	.8267	.8274	.8280	.8287	.8293	.8299	.8306	.8312	.8319
6.8	.8325	.8331	.8338	.8344	.8351	.8357	.8363	.8370	.8376	.8382
6.9	.8388	.8395	.8401	.8407	.8414	.8420	.8426	.8432	.8439	.8445
log 7.0	.8451	.8457	.8463	.8470	.8476	.8482	.8488	.8494	.8500	.8506
7.1	.8513	.8519	.8525	.8531	.8537	.8543	.8549	.8555	.8561	.8567
7.2	.8573	.8579	.8585	.8591	.8597	.8603	.8609	.8615	.8621	.8627
7.3	.8633	.8639	.8645	.8651	.8657	.8663	.8669	.8675	.8681	.8686
7.4	.8692	.8698	.8704	.8710	.8716	.8722	.8727	.8733	.8739	.8745
log 7.5	.8751	.8756	.8762	.8768	.8774	.8779	.8785	.8791	.8797	.8802
7.6	.8808	.8814	.8820	.8825	.8831	.8837	.8842	.8848	.8854	.8859
7.7	.8865	.8871	.8876	.8882	.8887	.8893	.8899	.8904	.8910	.8915
7.8	.8921	.8927	.8932	.8938	.8943	.8949	.8954	.8960	.8965	.8971
7.9	.8976	.8982	.8987	.8993	.8998	.9004	.9009	.9015	.9020	.9025
log 8.0	.9031	.9036	.9042	.9047	.9053	.9058	.9063	.9069	.9074	.9079
8.1	.9085	.9090	.9096	.9101	.9106	.9112	.9117	.9122	.9128	.9133
8.2	.9138	.9143	.9149	.9154	.9159	.9165	.9170	.9175	.9180	.9186
8.3	.9191	.9196	.9201	.9206	.9212	.9217	.9222	.9227	.9232	.9238
8.4	.9243	.9248	.9253	.9258	.9263	.9269	.9274	.9279	.9284	.9289
log 8.5	.9294	.9299	.9304	.9309	.9315	.9320	.9325	.9330	.9335	.9340
8.6	.9345	.9350	.9355	.9360	.9365	.9370	.9375	.9380	.9385	.9390
8.7	.9395	.9400	.9405	.9410	.9415	.9420	.9425	.9430	.9435	.9440
8.8	.9445	.9450	.9455	.9460	.9465	.9469	.9474	.9479	.9484	.9489
8.9	.9494	.9499	.9504	.9509	.9513	.9518	.9523	.9528	.9533	.9538
log 9.0	.9542	.9547	.9552	.9557	.9562	.9566	.9571	.9576	.9581	.9586
9.1	.9590	.9595	.9600	.9605	.9609	.9614	.9619	.9624	.9628	.9633
9.2	.9638	.9643	.9647	.9652	.9657	.9661	.9666	.9671	.9675	.9680
9.3	.9685	.9689	.9694	.9699	.9703	.9708	.9713	.9717	.9722	.9727
9.4	.9731	.9736	.9741	.9745	.9750	.9754	.9759	.9763	.9768	.9773
log 9.5	.9777	.9782	.9786	.9791	.9795	.9800	.9805	.9809	.9814	.9818
9.6	.9823	.9827	.9832	.9836	.9841	.9845	.9850	.9854	.9859	.9863
9.7	.9868	.9872	.9877	.9881	.9886	.9890	.9894	.9899	.9903	.9908
9.8	.9912	.9917	.9921	.9926	.9930	.9934	.9939	.9943	.9948	.9952
9.9	.9956	.9961	.9965	.9969	.9974	.9978	.9983	.9987	.9991	.9996
log x	0	1	2	3	4	5	6	7	8	9

$\log_{10} 10 = 1$

TABLE C-6 **Exponential Functions,** e^x **and** e^{-x} _Appendix C_ **379**

x	e^x	e^{-x}	x	e^x	e^{-x}
0.00	1.0000	1.0000	1.5	4.4817	0.2231
0.01	1.0101	0.9901	1.6	4.9530	0.2019
0.02	1.0202	0.9802	1.7	5.4739	0.1827
0.03	1.0305	0.9702	1.8	6.0496	0.1653
0.04	1.0408	0.9608	1.9	6.6859	0.1496
0.05	1.0513	0.9512	2.0	7.3891	0.1353
0.06	1.0618	0.9418	2.1	8.1662	0.1225
0.07	1.0725	0.9324	2.2	9.0250	0.1108
0.08	1.0833	0.9331	2.3	9.9742	0.1003
0.09	1.0942	0.9139	2.4	11.023	0.0907
0.10	1.1052	0.9048	2.5	12.182	0.0821
0.11	1.1163	0.8958	2.6	13.464	0.0743
0.12	1.1275	0.8869	2.7	14.880	0.0672
0.13	1.1388	0.8781	2.8	16.445	0.0608
0.14	1.1503	0.8694	2.9	18.174	0.0550
0.15	1.1618	0.8607	3.0	20.086	0.0498
0.16	1.1735	0.8521	3.1	22.198	0.0450
0.17	1.1853	0.8437	3.2	24.533	0.0408
0.18	1.1972	0.8353	3.3	27.113	0.0369
0.19	1.2092	0.8270	3.4	29.964	0.0334
0.20	1.2214	0.8187	3.5	33.115	0.0302
0.21	1.2337	0.8106	3.6	36.598	0.0273
0.22	1.2461	0.8025	3.7	40.447	0.0247
0.23	1.2586	0.7945	3.8	44.701	0.0224
0.24	1.2712	0.7866	3.9	49.402	0.0202
0.25	1.2840	0.7788	4.0	54.598	0.0183
0.30	1.3499	0.7408	4.1	60.340	0.0166
0.35	1.4191	0.7047	4.2	66.686	0.0150
0.40	1.4918	0.6703	4.3	73.700	0.0136
0.45	1.5683	0.6376	4.4	81.451	0.0123
0.50	1.6487	0.6065	4.5	90.017	0.0111
0.55	1.7333	0.5769	4.6	99.484	0.0101
0.60	1.8221	0.5488	4.7	109.95	0.0091
0.65	1.9155	0.5220	4.8	121.51	0.0082
0.70	2.0138	0.4966	4.9	134.29	0.0074
0.75	2.1170	0.4724	5.0	148.41	0.0067
0.80	2.2255	0.4493	5.5	244.69	0.0041
0.85	2.3396	0.4274	6.0	403.43	0.0025
0.90	2.4596	0.4066	6.5	665.14	0.0015
0.95	2.5857	0.3867	7.0	1096.6	0.0009
1.0	2.7183	0.3679	7.5	1808.0	0.0006
1.1	3.0042	0.3329	8.0	2981.0	0.0003
1.2	3.3201	0.3012	8.5	4914.8	0.0002
1.3	3.6693	0.2725	9.0	8103.1	0.0001
1.4	4.0552	0.2466	10.0	22026	0.00005

ANSWERS TO SELECTED EXERCISES

EXERCISES 1-1

Set A

1. (a) $\{4, 5, 6\}$ (b) $\{2, 3, 4\}$ (c) $\{2, 3, 4, 5\}$ (d) $\{3, 4, 5, 6\}$
   (e) $\{3\}$ (f) $\varnothing$ (g) $\{2, 3\}$ (h) $\{2, 3\}$
   (i) U (j) $\{2, 3, 4, 6\}$
2. (a) $\{2, 4, 6, 8, 10\}$ (b) $\varnothing, U$ (c) C, B
5. (a) 3 (c) 7 (e) 4
7. (a) $\{2, 3, 6, 7, 8, 11, 12, 14, 19\}$ (b) $\{1, 2, 4, 8, 9, 12, 13, 17, 18, 43\}$
   (c) $\{1, 2, 3, 4, 6, 7, 8, 9, 11, 12, 13, 14, 17, 18, 19, 43\}$
   (d) 9 (e) 10 (f) 3

Set B

11. (d) $A \cup B = U$
12. (a) $\{3\}$ (c) $\{0, 3, 1, 4, 2, 5\}$ (e) $\{0, 1, 2, 3, 4, 5\}$
    (g) Not possible, since $A \cap C \neq \{0\}$; so $A \oplus C = \varnothing$

Set C

14. (b) 175 (c) 88 (d) 29 (e) 200

EXERCISES 1-2

Set A

1. (a) $\mathbb{N}, \mathbb{W}, \mathbb{J}, \mathbb{Q}, \mathbb{R}, \mathbb{C}$ (c) $\mathbb{C}$
   (e) $\mathbb{N}, \mathbb{W}, \mathbb{J}, \mathbb{Q}, \mathbb{R}, \mathbb{C}$ (g) $\mathbb{H}, \mathbb{R}, \mathbb{C}$
   (i) $\mathbb{C}$ (k) $\mathbb{I}, \mathbb{C}$

2. (a) True   (c) True   (e) True   (g) False   (i) False
    (k) False

Set B

3. (a) $x = 1$, a counting number; hence, $x \in \mathbb{N}$
    (c) $x = \pm 2i$, a pure imaginary number, hence, $x \in \mathbb{I}$

Set C

5. (a) Composite   (c) Composite   (e) Composite
    (g) Composite

EXERCISES 1-3

Set A

1. (a) Closure under addition
    (c) Commutativity under multiplication
    (e) Distributivity
    (g) Associativity under addition
    (i) Additive identity
    (k) Multiplicative inverse
    (m) Distributivity
4. (a) True   (c) False   (e) False   (g) Neither
    (i) False   (k) Neither (m) True
5. (a) $x = 3$ (c) $x = \frac{4}{7}$ (e) $x = 9$ (g) $x = 2, x = -1$
6. (a) 17   (c) 45   (e) 176   (g) 290

Set B

9. (a) $35 \cdot 6^{3a}$ (c) 3^{-7n} (e) $4(1 + 2x)$
11. Additive inverse
12. Commutativity under addition

Set C

15. $a^3 + b^3 = 35.711756$; $(a + b)c = 57.592429$; $a + b(c + d) = 225.21372$
16. (a) $\phi = KI_1 + KI_2 + KI_3$ (b) Distributivity
17. (a) $K_2K_1I = K_1K_2I$ (b) Commutativity under multiplication

EXERCISES 1-4

Set A

1. (a) 3   (c) 5   (e) 5   (g) 6   (i) 4   (k) 4
    (m) 5   (o) 4
2. Same as Exercise 1
3. (a) Nearest unit   (c) Nearest tenth
    (e) Nearest ten millionth   (g) Nearest hundred thousandth
    (i) Nearest ten thousand   (k) Nearest hundred millionth
    (m) Nearest unit   (o) Nearest hundred millionth

4. (a) 120 (c) 7900 (e) 0.0038 (g) 3.7
   (i) 72,000,000 (k) 0.000049 (m) 18,000 (o) 0.000049
5. (a) $1.23 \cdot 10^2$ (c) $7.8940 \cdot 10^3$ (e) $3.8217 \cdot 10^{-3}$ (g) 3.74173
   10^0 (i) $7.204 \cdot 10^7$ (k) $4.902 \cdot 10^{-5}$ (m) $1.7601 \cdot 10^4$
   (o) $4.900 \cdot 10^{-5}$
7. (a) 3.0 (c) 22 (e) 0.03
8. (a) 63.8 (c) 0.889 (e) 83.2 (g) 77.8 (i) 0.0764

Set B

9. (a) $7.1 \cdot 10^3$ meters (c) $3 \cdot 10^9$ hertz (e) $7.3 \cdot 10^{-2}$ meters
   (g) $9.26 \cdot 10^{-2}$ liters (i) $1.0 \cdot 10^{-8}$ seconds
11. (a) $1.1 \cdot 10^{11}$ (two significant digits)
    (c) $1.6 \cdot 10^{-9}$ (two significant digits)

Set C

12. (a) $7.5 \cdot 10^{-5}$ grams (c) $2 \cdot 10^{-6}$ meters (e) 2.4 liters
    (g) $6 \cdot 10^{-1}$ grams (i) $3.10 \cdot 10^2$ liters
13. (a) $2 \cdot 10^9$ (one significant digit)
    (b) $1.27 \cdot 10^{-3}$ (three significant digits)

EXERCISES 2-1

Set A

1. (a) See Graph 2-1 (c) See Graph 2-2
2. $Y = -10X$; $Z = X$; $W = 4X$
3. (e) See Graph 2-3 (f) See Graph 2-4 (h) See Graph 2-5

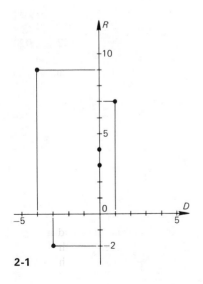

2-1

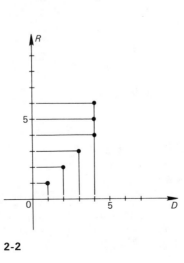

2-2

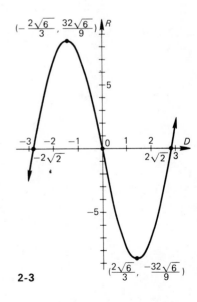

2-3

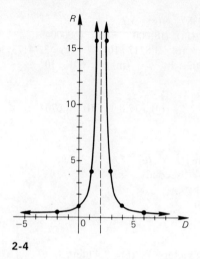

2-4

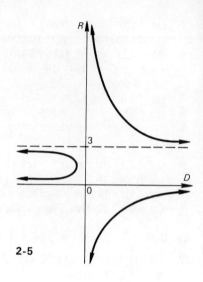

2-5

Set B

4. (a)   Domain = $\mathbb{R}$; range = $\mathbb{R}$
    (c)   Domain = $\{x \mid x \geqslant 4\}$; range = $\{y \mid y \geqslant 0\}$
    (e)   Domain = $\mathbb{R}$; range = $\mathbb{R}$
    (g)   Domain = $\{x \mid x \neq 0\}$; range = $\mathbb{R}$

6.

x	y
1.5	13.055
1.6	13.788
1.7	14.543
1.8	15.320
1.9	16.119
2.0	16.940
2.1	17.783
2.2	18.648
2.3	19.535
2.4	20.444
2.5	21.375

7.

x	y
−3.0	152.14
−2.5	77.53
−2.0	31.15
−1.5	5.35
−1.0	−6.50
−0.5	−9.91
0.0	−9.32
0.5	−8.09
1.0	−8.50
1.5	−11.75
2.0	−17.96
2.5	−26.17
3.0	−34.34

EXERCISES 2-2

Set A

3. (a)   −1   (c) 2   (e) $2\#^2 - 1$ (g) 7   (i) $2x^4 + 4x^2 +$
    1   (k) $10x^2 - 3$ (m) 287   (o) 34   (q) 3
    (s) 289   (u) $^{71}\!/_{32}$ (w) $2x^2 + 5x + 1$ (y) $(2x^2 - 1)/(5x + 2)$,
    $x \neq -\frac{2}{5}$

4. $w = 9x^2$; therefore,

$\{(x, w)\} = \{(-5, 225), (-4, 144), (-3, 81), (-2, 36), (-1, 9), (0, 0), (1, 9),$
$(2, 36), (3, 81), (4, 144), (5, 225)\}$

5. $f[g(x)] = x$; $g[f(x)] = x$; both composites map any domain value into a range value that is equal to the domain value.

Set B

7.

x	y	z
0.0	9.000	99.000000
0.2	7.608	66.683320
0.4	6.264	42.835392
0.6	5.016	27.160512
0.8	3.912	18.487488
1.0	3.000	15.000000
1.2	2.328	14.559168
1.4	1.944	15.118272
1.6	1.896	15.229632
1.8	2.232	14.643648
2.0	3.000	15.000000

8. Selected points:

x	y	z	w
-1.0	-8.000	235.00000	713.00000
-0.8	-8.232	244.85164	742.55492
-0.6	-8.496	256.32403	776.97209
-0.4	-8.744	267.35507	810.06521
-0.2	-8.928	275.69836	835.09508
0.0	-9.000	279.00000	845.00000
0.2	-8.912	274.96748	832.90244
0.4	-8.616	261.63091	792.89273
0.6	-8.064	237.69619	721.08857
0.8	-7.208	202.99052	616.97156
1.0	-6.000	159.00000	485.00000

10. (a) $(f \circ g)(x) = \dfrac{x + 3}{\sqrt{(x + 4)(x + 2)}}$; not valid.

Restriction: $\{x \mid x > -2 \text{ or } x < -4\}$

$(g \circ f)(x) = \dfrac{x}{\sqrt{x^2 - 1}} + 3$; valid.

(c) $(f \circ g)(x) = \dfrac{x + 1}{x}$;   not valid.

Restriction: $\{x \mid x \neq 0 \text{ and } x \geq -1\}$

$(g \circ f)(t) = \sqrt{\dfrac{2t^2 - 1}{t^2 - 1}}$;   not valid.

Restriction: $\left| t \mid t < -1 \text{ or } t > 1 \text{ or } -\dfrac{\sqrt{2}}{2} \leq t \leq \dfrac{\sqrt{2}}{2} \right|$

EXERCISES 2-3

Set A

1. (a) $y = x - 3$

    (c) $y = \sqrt{x - 2} + 1, \; x \geq 2$

    (e) $y = \dfrac{1 + x}{1 - x}, \; x \neq 1$

3. For equation (1): (a) a function;   (b) $y = 2x/5$;
    (c) a function;   (d) $\mathscr{D} = \mathscr{R} = \mathbb{R}$
    For equation (3): (a) a function;   (b) $x^2 = t/6$;   (c) not a
    function;   (e) $x = \sqrt{t/6}, \; t \geq 0$
    For equation (5): (a) a function;   (b) $y = (x - b)/m$;
    (c) a function;   (d) $\mathscr{D} = \mathscr{R} = \mathbb{R}$

4. $f^{-1}(x) = \sqrt{\dfrac{x + 7}{3}}, \; x \geq -7$

Set B

9. Interchanging the domain and range variables results in the same equation.

10. $f^{-1}(x) = \dfrac{dx - b}{a - cx}, \; x \neq a/c$

Set C

11. (b)   Interior of the circle maps into the left half of the w plane.

    (c) $\phi^{-1}(w) = \dfrac{r(1 + w)}{1 - w}, \; w \neq 1$

12. (b) $\phi^{-1}(w) = \dfrac{ri(1 - w)}{1 + w}, \; w \neq -1$

Set A

1. (a) Explicit (c) Implicit; $y = \dfrac{2 \pm 4}{x}$, $x \neq 0$

   (e) Implicit; $y = \dfrac{-x^2 \pm \sqrt{x^4 + 12x}}{2x}$, $x > 0$ or $x < \sqrt[3]{-12}$

   (g) Explicit
2. (a) $F(x, y) = x^2 - 2xy + y^2 - y + 6 = 0$
   (b) Implicit

Set B

3. $\hat{y} = \dfrac{10\hat{x} + 14}{\hat{x}^2 + 3\hat{x} + 2}$, $\hat{x} \neq -2, -1$
4. $V = 2$

7.

t	P	ΔP	$\Delta P/\Delta t$
0.0	0.000		
		1.600	3.200
0.5	1.600		
		0.400	0.800
1.0	2.000		
		−0.154	−0.308
1.5	1.846		
		−0.246	−0.492
2.0	1.600		
		−0.221	−0.442
2.5	1.379		
		−0.179	−0.358
3.0	1.200		
		−0.143	−0.286
3.5	1.057		
		−0.116	−0.232
4.0	0.941		
		−0.094	−0.188
4.5	0.847		
		−0.078	−0.156
5.0	0.769		

A negative value of $\Delta P/\Delta t$ indicates that the rate is decreasing.

8. $y^2(w^2 + 3w - 6) = 8$ and $y^2(w^2 - 1) = 4$
9. (a) $\Delta y/\Delta x = 2x + \Delta x$

10. (a) $\dfrac{\Delta y}{\Delta x} = \dfrac{x^2 - 2xy - x\,\Delta y}{y^2 - 2xy - (y + \Delta y)\Delta x + (2y - 2x + \Delta y)\Delta y}$
  Note that other variations are possible.

EXERCISES 2-5

Set A

2. (a) Even   (c) Odd   (e) Odd

Set B

4. (a) Odd   (c) Neither   (e) Neither
5. (a) Domain $= \mathbb{R}$; range $= \{y \mid 0 \leqslant y < 1\}$
  Symmetry: Even symmetry about the R axis
  (c) Domain $= \mathbb{R}$; range $= \{y \mid -9 \leqslant y \leqslant 3,\ y \neq -3\}$
  Symmetry: Both odd and even symmetry about the lines $x = 2$ and $y = -3$

EXERCISES 3-1

Set A

2. For Figure 3-18, $m = \frac{4}{9}$; for Figure 3-19, $m = -\frac{5}{6}$
4. (a) $m = -2$, R axis intercept: $(0, 4)$
  (c) $m = -\frac{3}{2}$; R axis intercept: $(0, -\frac{3}{4})$
6. (a) $y = 3x/4 + \frac{7}{2}$
  (b) $y = -4x/3 + 16$
7. (a) Straight line passing through points $(0, 7)$ and $(5, 5)$
  (c) Straight line passing through points $(0, 4)$ and $(3, 8)$
  (e) Straight line passing through points $(0, 1)$ and $(3, 5)$
8. (a) $y = 5x/3 - \frac{28}{3}$ (b) $y = -3x/5 - \frac{22}{5}$

Set B

11. $x_m = \frac{7}{2}$, $y_m = \frac{19}{2}$
13. (a) Straight line with intercepts $(0, 31.32)$ and $(9.21, 0)$
  (b) Straight line with intercepts $(0, 0.12)$ and $(-0.043, 0)$

Set C

16. $x = kx_2 + (1 - k)x_1$; $y = ky_2 + (1 - k)y_1$

Set A

1. Constant function: $y = 3$
3. Step function: Discontinuity at $(4, 0)$ of magnitude $+4$
5. Step function: Discontinuity at $(3, -3)$ of magnitude $+4$
7. Ramp function: Ramp beginning at $(2, 0)$ with slope $+1$
9. Ramp function: Ramp beginning at $(5, 0)$ with slope $\frac{2}{5}$
11. Signum function: Discontinuity at $(4, 0)$ of magnitude ± 4

Set B

13. $y = x^2 - 6x + 9$
15. $y = x^3 + 3x^2 + 2x - 1$
17. $y = x^3 + 6x^2 + 9x + 3$

Set C

20. (a) $y = 4U(x + 2) + 5U(x - 5)$
    (c) $y = -6U(x - 1) + 5U(x - 5) - 2U(x - 9) + 3$
21. $T = 420°C$ when $t = 7$ hours
24. $\text{Fare} = 65U(x) + 10U(x) \cdot [\![5x]\!]$

EXERCISES 3-3

Set A

1. $S = [1, \infty)$
3. $S = [\frac{1}{2}, \infty)$
5. $S = (-\infty, \frac{15}{8})$
7. $S = (-\infty, -1) \cup (-\frac{1}{3}, \infty) = \mathbb{R} - [-1, -\frac{1}{3}]$
9. $S = (3, 9)$
11. $S = (-\infty, -\frac{5}{3}] \cup [\frac{7}{3}, \infty) = \mathbb{R} - (-\frac{5}{3}, \frac{7}{3})$
15. See Graph 3-1
17. See Graph 3-2

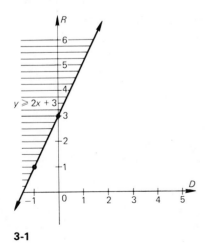

3-1

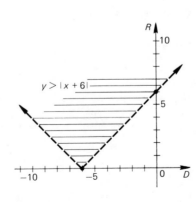

3-2

Set B

21. $S = (-2, -\frac{2}{3})$
23. $S = (-\infty, \frac{7}{3}) \cup (7, \infty) = \mathbb{R} - [\frac{7}{3}, 7]$
25. $S = [-12, -\frac{1}{2}] \cup [\frac{7}{2}, 4] = [-12, 4] - (-\frac{1}{2}, \frac{7}{2})$
27. $S = (\frac{1}{2}, \frac{4}{3})$
29. $S = (-5, 0]$
32. (a) For restriction $x \geq 0$, $f^{-1}(y) = y$
    (c) For restriction $x \geq -3$, $f^{-1}(y) = (y - 6)/2$

Set C

33. $S = (-\infty, -6.4] \cup [3.4, \infty)$
35. $S = [-1.6, 2.7]$
37. $S = (-2, 1) \cup (2, \infty)$

EXERCISES 3-4

Set A

2. (a) $x = -7$, $y = \frac{3}{2}$
   (b) $x = \frac{1}{3}$, $y = \frac{3}{5}$
3. (a) $x = 1$, $y = \frac{5}{3}$, $z = -\frac{2}{3}$

Set B

4. (a) $x = 166$, $y = 67$
6. 5 steers, 20 pigs, 30 chickens
7. (a) To five significant digits, $x = 1.0804$, $y = 8.0196$
   (b) To three significant digits, $x = 0.868$, $y = 2.93$

EXERCISES 4-1

Set A

1. $x = 4 + \sqrt{14}$, $x = 4 - \sqrt{14}$
3. $x = -4$
5. $x = 9$, $x = 3$
7. $x = \dfrac{-1 + \sqrt{37}}{3}$, $x = \dfrac{-1 - \sqrt{37}}{3}$
9. $x = 0$, $x = -\frac{1}{2}$

Set B

11. (a) $(x - 1)^2 + (y - 2)^2 = 9$
    (c) $4(x - \frac{3}{2})^2 - 3(y - 1)^2 = 4$

12.

x	y_1	y_2
5.0	1.697	−1.697
4.0	1.677	−1.677
3.0	1.633	−1.633
2.0	1.500	−1.500
1.0	0.000	0.000
—	—	—
−1.0	0.000	0.000
−2.0	−1.500	1.500
−3.0	−1.633	1.633
−4.0	−1.677	1.677
−5.0	−1.697	1.697

$x \notin (-1, 1)$

Set C

13. Your speed, 16 miles per hour; friend's speed, 30 miles per hour
14. Cost of fencing = $1,161.60
15. (a) $x = 0.1924 + 0.5000i$; $x = 0.1924 - 0.5000i$
    (c) $x = -0.040$; $x = 8.272$
16. (a) $x = y(4y - 3)$

y	x
3.000	24.0000
2.000	10.0000
1.000	1.0000
0.750	0.0000
0.375	−0.5625
0.000	0.0000
−1.000	7.0000
−2.000	22.0000

(c) $xy^2 + x^2y = 0$

x	y_1	y_2
5	0	−5
4	0	−4
3	0	−3
2	0	−2
1	0	−1
0	0	0
−1	0	1
−2	0	2
−3	0	3
−4	0	4
−5	0	5

EXERCISES 4-2

Set A

1. (a) Circle: Center, (0, 0); radius, $r = 2\sqrt{2}$

   (c) Hyperbola, horizontally oriented: Foci, $(\sqrt{5}, 0)$ and $(-\sqrt{5}, 0)$; vertices, (1, 0) and (−1, 0); asymptotes, $y = 2x$, $y = -2x$

   (e) Hyperbola, vertically oriented: Foci, $(0, \sqrt{10})$ and $(0, -\sqrt{10})$; vertices, (0, 2) and (0, −2); asymptotes, $y = \sqrt{6}\,x/3$, $y = -\sqrt{6}\,x/3$

2. (a) Circle: Center, (0, 0); $r = 7$

   (c) Circle: Center, (−3, 2); $r = 5$

3. (a) Parabola, vertically oriented, concave upward: Focus, (0, 2); directrix: $y = -2$; vertex, (0, 0)

   (c) Parabola, vertically oriented concave upward: Focus (0, 0); directrix: $y = -4$; vertex, (0, −2)

4. (a) Ellipse, horizontally oriented: Center, (0, 1); major axis, 14; minor axis, 4

   (c) Ellipse, horizontally oriented: Center, (3, 0); major axis, 4; minor axis, 2

5. (a) Hyperbola, vertically oriented: Center, (−2, 0); vertices: (0, 0) and (0, −4); asymptotes: $y = 2x - 2$, $y = -2x - 2$

   (c) Hyperbola, horizontally oriented: Center = (4, 5); vertices: (−1, 5) and (9, 5); asymptotes: $y - 5 = 5(x - 4)/6$ and $y - 5 = -5(x - 4)/6$

Set B

7. Parabola, vertically oriented, concave upward: Vertex, $(-\frac{1}{6}, -\frac{121}{12})$; focus, $(-\frac{1}{6}, -10)$; directrix: $y = -\frac{61}{6}$

9. Ellipse, vertically oriented: Center, (4, 1); major axis, $2\sqrt{5}$; minor axis, $2\sqrt{3}$

10. (a) $(\frac{5}{2}, 0)$, $(-\frac{5}{2}, 0)$

    (c) $(6 + 2\sqrt{2}, 0)$, $(6 - 2\sqrt{2}, 0)$

Set C

13. $(x - 550)^2/21{,}622{,}500 + y^2/21{,}320{,}000 = 1$

14. $600(y - 600) = -(x - 600)^2$

15. (a) $(d, 0) = (4, 0)$ and $(0, d) = (0, 4)$

    (b) $(h, k) = (1, 1)$

    (c) $x^2 + 2xy + y^2 - 12x + 4y + 4 = 0$

EXERCISES 5-1

Set A

1. (a) 139.23°   (c) 550.61°   (e) 197.10°

(g) 0.471   (i) 0.569
2. (a) 0.88   (c) 17.16
   (e) 9.20   (g) 6.50
3. (a) 1.538 inches   (c) 1.636
   (e) 4.667
4. (a) 3.000 per second   (c) 0.417 inches
   (e) 24.000 per minute
5. (a) 251.05°   (c) 0.0000476
   (e) 7.463   (g) 0.10672
   (i) 914.69°

Set B

7. 2120 miles per hour

Set C

9. (a) 200.10 earth days
   (b) 21.8 miles per second
   (c) $9.4248 \cdot 10^7$ miles per quarter year

EXERCISES 5-2

Set A

1.

	x	y	r	$\sin \theta$	$\cos \theta$	$\tan \theta$	$\cot \theta$	$\sec \theta$	$\csc \theta$
(a)	-3	4	5	$4/5$	$-3/5$	$-4/3$	$-3/4$	$-5/3$	$5/4$
(c)	-15	-8	17	$-8/17$	$-15/17$	$8/15$	$15/8$	$-17/15$	$-17/8$
(e)	9	6	$\sqrt{117}$	$6/\sqrt{117}$	$9/\sqrt{117}$	$2/3$	$3/2$	$\sqrt{117}/9$	$\sqrt{117}/6$

3. (a) $-\sqrt{3}/2$ (c) $\sqrt{3}$ (e) ½   (g) $-\sqrt{2}/2$ (i) 1
   (k) 1

Set B

5. Even functions: cosine, secant
    Odd functions: sine, tangent, cotangent, cosecant

7. (c)   See Graph 5-1

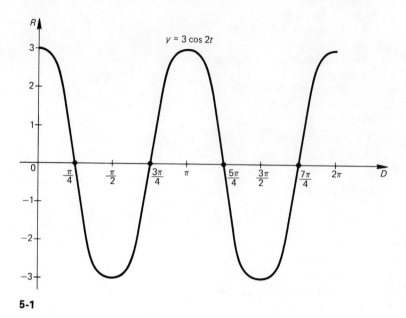

5-1

8. (c)   See Graph 5-2

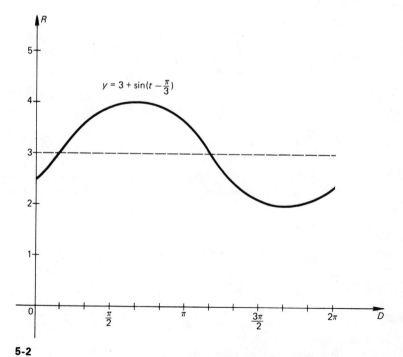

5-2

9. (a) Fundamental period, π. Examples of one-to-one regions are

One-to-one regions	Onto image set
$[-2\pi, -7\pi/4]$	$[0, 2]$
$[-\pi/4, \pi/4]$	$[-2, 2]$
$[3\pi/4, 5\pi/4]$	$[-2, 2]$

(c) Fundamental period, 2π.

One-to-one regions	Onto image set
$[-2\pi, -\pi)$	$[0, \infty)$
$(-\pi, \pi)$	$(-\infty, \infty)$
$(\pi, 2\pi]$	$(-\infty, 0]$

Set C

10. (a) $(f \circ g)(t) = \sin(\cos t)$
    (c) $(f/g)(\pi/3) = \sqrt{3}$
    (e) $(h \circ f)(2\pi/3) = 7/4$
11. (a) Range of $f \circ g$ is $[-\sin 1, \sin 1]$
    (c) Range of $h \circ f$ is $[1, 2]$

EXERCISES 5-3

Set A

1. (a) 0.4617   (c) 0.9596   (e) 0.8949   (g) 0.0300
   (i) 0.9511   (k) 0.6959
2. (a) 0.8632   (c) −0.2910   (e) 0.9537   (g) 1.9626
   (i) 0.4685   (k) −0.3854

Set B

3. (a) 0.9272   (c) 0.9102   (e) 2.4746   (g) −1.4833
   (i) −0.9740
4. (a) 1.9475   (c) 4.2820   (e) 0.3455
5. (a) −2.998   (c) −137.4382

EXERCISES 5-4

Set A

1. 96.02 feet
3. 622.08 feet; 1.41 miles per hour

6. (a) $B = 66°$, $a = 14.23$, $c = 5.79$
   (c) $A = 34.14°$, $B = 100.86°$, $c = 5.04$
   (e) $B = 24.23°$, $C = 117.77°$, $c = 21.56$
   (g) $A = 61.93°$, $B = 90°$, $C = 28.07°$
   (i) $A = 32.94°$, $C = 24.06°$, $b = 35.79$

Set B

8. Position: 1500 miles, N 53.13° E
9. 29.06 feet
11. 107.174 feet (approximately 107 feet)

Set C

13. 723.767 miles
14. $\alpha = 10.2°$, $\beta = 12.8°$; distance saved is 0.535 miles

EXERCISES 6-1

Set A

1. (a) -0.8290 (c) -0.8595 (e) -0.9902 (g) -1.0225
   (i) 0.7660 (k) -1.9170

Set B

8. $\cos 3t = \cos^3 t - 3 \sin^2 t \cos t = 4 \cos^3 t - 3 \cos t$

EXERCISES 6-2

Set A

1. (a) 0.7754 (c) No solution (solution set is empty)   (e) 0.644
   (g) -0.398 (i) No solution (solution set is empty)
2. (a) 0.625 (c) -0.579 (e) No solution (solution set is empty)
   (g) 0

Set B

3. (c) See Graph 6-1

$u = \mathrm{Csc}^{-1} t,\ t \geqslant 1 \text{ or } t \leqslant -1, -\dfrac{\pi}{2} \leqslant u \leqslant \dfrac{\pi}{2},\ u \neq 0$

Chapter 6 **397**

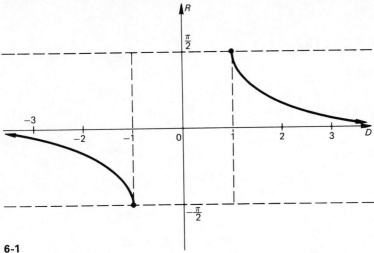

6-1

EXERCISES 6-3

Set A

1. (a) $S = \{\pi/2\}$ (c) $S = \{\pi/8\}$ (e) $S = \{-\pi/6,\ \pi/6\}$
   (g) $S = \{\pi/16\}$
2. (a) $S = \{x \mid x = (4n + 1)\pi/2,\ n \in \mathbb{J}\}$
   (b) $S = \{u \mid u = 2\pi(3n + 1)/3,\ \text{or } u = 2\pi(3n + 2)/3,\ n \in \mathbb{J}\}$
3. (a) $S = \{u \mid u \in \mathbb{R}\}$
   (c) $S = \varnothing$
   (e) $S = \varnothing$

Set B

5. (a) $S = \varnothing$
   (c) $S = \{-2\pi/3,\ 0,\ 2\pi/3\}$
   (e) $S = \{-\pi/2,\ \pi/6,\ 5\pi/6\}$
   (g) $S = \{0\}$
   (i) $S = \{-\pi/2,\ -5\pi/6,\ -\pi/6,\ 0,\ \pi/6,\ \pi/2,\ 5\pi/6,\ \pi\}$
   (k) $S = \{-1.81,\ 0,\ 1.33,\ \pi\}$

Set C

7. (a) $u = \mathrm{Arccos}\ \pi/4 + 2n\pi,\ n \in \mathbb{J}$; or $u = -\mathrm{Arccos}\ \pi/4 + 2n\pi,\ n \in \mathbb{J}$
   (c) No solution
   (e) $u = -0.8415$
9. (a) $x = -\pi/2$ (c) $x = 0.3142$ (note that $x \in [0,\ \pi/8]$)

EXERCISES 7-1

Set A

1. (a) 3   (c) −2   (e) 2   (g) $5/4$ (i) 0   (k) $15/2$
   (m) −1   (o) 12   (q) 1   (s) 8

Set B

5. (a) 0.4 years   (c) 2.1 years
6. (a) b^{2t^2} (c) $x^4 b^{2x^2}$

Set C

9. For selected values of x,

x	$\phi(x)$
−2.0	0.0123457
−1.6	0.0600578
−1.2	0.2055633
−0.8	0.4590428
−0.4	0.8388047
0.0	1.0000000
0.4	0.8388047
0.8	0.4590428
1.2	0.2055633
1.6	0.0600578
2.0	0.0123457

Therefore, ϕ is an even function.

10. (a) Domain of $F \circ G$ is $(-\infty, 0.65]$, where 0.65 is a numerical approximation. Range of $F \circ G$ is $(0, 1]$
11. From the graph, $y = 5$ when $x \approx 0.7$

x	y
0.0	2.000
1.0	6.500
2.0	9.300
3.0	9.900
4.0	9.980
5.0	9.998

Set A

1. 2   3. 4

5. 1   7. $\sqrt[3]{32}$
9. 5   11. 625
13. 9   15. 3
17. 6   19. 36

Set B

21. (b) $A_F = (-\infty, -3) \cup (3, \infty)$
     (c) $B_F = (-\infty, \infty)$
23. (a) $A_F = (-\infty, -7) \cup (0, \infty)$
     (c) $A_G = (4, \infty)$
25. (a) Domain of $F \cdot G$ is $(0, \infty)$
     (c) Domain of $F \cdot G^2$ is $(0, \infty)$

Set C

26. Domain of $F \circ G$ is $[-4, 12)$
     Range of $F \circ G$ is $(-\infty, \log_b 2]$

EXERCISES 7-3

Set A

1. $\log_{10} P = 3 \log_{10} A + \log_{10} B$
3. $\log_3 N = (\log_3 x)/2 + 3 \log_3 y - \log_3 v$
5. $\log_{10} N = \frac{1}{4} [\log_{10} 72.7 + \log_{10} 27.2 + 14.2 \log_{10} 0.0043]$

Set B

7. $N = \dfrac{x^3 y^4}{\sqrt{z}}$

9. $N = \sqrt{\dfrac{6.4}{12 \cdot 8^3}}$

11. $x^3 = \dfrac{(17.4)(1.03)^2}{243^{4/3}}$

EXERCISES 7-4

Set A

1. (a) 1.2405   (c) 4.2405   (e) 5.9921   (g) 0.9504 $-$ 1
    (i) 0.7251 $-$ 1   (k) 0.0253 $-$ 11

2. (a) 451   (c) 2.55   (e) $3.52 \cdot 10^{13}$
   (g) 0.0181   (i) 0.253

Set B

3. (a) 4437   (c) 0.0580   (e) $3.818 \cdot 10^{-9}$
4. (a) 0.0257   (c) 3.8610   (e) $0.6738 - 4$
   (g) $0.7021 - 1$
6. (a) $N = 3.406 \cdot 10^{19}$ (c) $N = 189.8$
   (e) $N = 1.939$ (g) $N = 3.177$
   (i) $N = 3.474 \cdot 10^{11}$

Set C

7.

	x	$\log y$	y
(a)	0.01	3.7311258	$5.384254 \cdot 10^3$
(b)	0.10	1.4373661	$2.737574 \cdot 10^1$
(c)	1.00	$0.5813195 - 1$	$3.813459 \cdot 10^{-1}$
(d)	10.00	$0.6707001 - 2$	$4.684894 \cdot 10^{-2}$
(e)	100.00	$0.1977918 - 2$	$1.576854 \cdot 10^{-2}$

EXERCISES 7-5

Set A

1. 2.8791   3. 3.8964
5. −2.3120   7. −3.8169
9. −8.8774   11. 9.3925
13. −0.7275   15. −4.2815

Set B

17. $y = 2.769 \cdot 10^{-2}$
19. $z = 3.620 \cdot 10^{-6}$
21. $x = 5.554 \cdot 10^{-5}$

Set C

22. (a)

t	i
0.0	0.000
1.0	1.967
2.0	3.161
3.0	3.884
4.0	4.323
5.0	4.590
6.0	4.751
7.0	4.849
8.0	4.908

(b)

t	y
0.0	2000
1.0	1845
2.0	1699
3.0	1563
4.0	1435
5.0	1317
6.0	1206
7.0	1104
8.0	1010

EXERCISES 8-1

Set A

1. (a) $13 - 30i$ (c) $-30 - 45i$ (e) $10 + 23i$
2. (a) $x = 6, y = 18$ (c) $x = 4, y = 10$

Set B

3. (a) 169 (c) $x^2 + y^2$ (e) $2(x^2 + y^2)$

Set C

5. (a) $3e^{-i4t} + 3e^{i4t} = \dfrac{3}{s + i4} + \dfrac{3}{s - i4} = \dfrac{6s}{s^2 + 16}$

   (c) $2t + 4e^{-i3t} - 4e^{i3t} = \dfrac{2}{s^2} + \dfrac{4}{s + i3} - \dfrac{4}{s - i3} = \dfrac{2}{s^2} + \dfrac{-24i}{s^2 + 9} =$

   $\dfrac{2s^2 + 18 - 24s^2 i}{s^4 + 9s^2}$

6. (a) $c^2 + d^2$
   (c) $[a(c + p) + b(d + q)] + [a(d + q) - b(c + p)] i$
8. (a) 1095.14
9. (a) $-38.6032 - 56.4993i$

EXERCISES 8-2

Set A

1. (a) $76.9985 + 36.0032i$
   (e) $-4.8345 - 4.4022i$
   (i) $0.5531 + 1.2337i$
   (m) $86.9834 - 416.0035i$

   (c) $-817.0327 + 743.9641i$
   (g) $86.9834 + 416.0035i$
   (k) $37.7189 + 23.0418i$
   (o) $-170.9943 + 140.0070i$

Set B

4. (c) $z_1 z_2 z_3 = 346.61 - 3099.88i$ (h) $z_3^3 = 2287.0 - 1533.4i$

EXERCISES 8-3

Set A

1. $x = 4$
3. $b = 3$
5. $y = 0.01$
7. $x = (\pi \log_3 e)i$
9. $x = -7$

Set B

11. $x = -4$
13. $x = e$
15. $x = -1$

Set C

16. (a)   See Graph 8-1

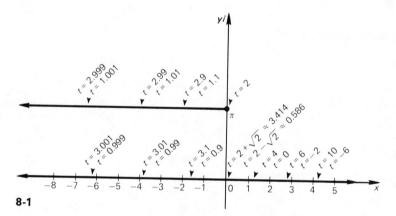

8-1

EXERCISES 9-1

Set A

1. $x = 1$, $x \in (1, 2)$, $x = -2$
3. $x = -4$, $x = 2$, $x \in (-1, 0)$, $x \in (0, 1)$
5. $x = -2$, $x \in (2, 3)$, $x \in (-3, -2)$

7. $x = -2, x = 2$
9. $x \in (0, 1), x \in (1, 2)$
11. $x \in (2, 3)$

Chapter 9 **403**

Set B

13. (a) For testing, $p/q \in \{-2, 1, 3/2\}$
        Rational zeros are $x = -2, x = 1, x = 3/2$
    (c) For testing, $p/q \in \{-4, 2, -1/2, -1/3, -2/3, 1/2, 1/3, 2/3\}$
        Rational zeros are: $x = -4, x = 2, x = -1/2, x = 1/3$
15. The length of the shortest side is $x = 3$

Set C

16. $t = 2, t = 5$
17. $s = -5, s = -3/2, s = -1 + 3i, s = -1 - 3i$

EXERCISES 9-2

Set A

1. (a) $x_2 = 1.25000, x_3 = 1.69230, x_4 = 1.72916, x_5 = 1.73184, x_6 = 1.73203,$
        $x_7 = 1.73204$; hence, $\bar{x} = 1.732$

2. (b) $f(x) = x^2, g(x) = 7 - x, x_{n+1} = \sqrt{7 - x_n}$
        For $\bar{x} \in (-4, -3)$: $x_0 = -3.50000, x_1 = -3.24037, x_2 = -3.20006,$
        $x_3 = -3.19375, x_4 = -3.19276, x_5 = -3.19261.$
        Hence, to three significant digits, $\bar{x} = -3.19.$
        For $\bar{x} \in (2, 3)$: $x_0 = 2.50000, x_1 = 2.12132, x_2 = 2.20877,$
        $x_3 = 2.18889, x_4 = 2.19342, x_5 = 2.19239,$
        $x_6 = 2.19262.$ Hence, to three significant digits,
        $\bar{x} = 2.19.$

3. (a) $x_2 = 3.062500, x_3 = 3.087670, x_4 = 3.097547, x_5 = 3.101384, x_6 =$
        $3.102869, x_7 = 3.103443, x_8 = 3.103664.$
        Hence, to three significant digits, $\bar{x} = 3.10.$

4. (a) $f(x) = x^3, g(x) = 3x^2 + 1, x_{n+1} = \sqrt[3]{3x_n^2 + 1}, x_0 = 4.000000, x_5 =$
        $3.194254, x_{10} = 3.113742, x_{15} = 3.104900, x_{16} = 3.104507.$
        Hence, to three significant digits, $\bar{x} = 3.10.$

Set B

5. $f(x) = 2x^3, g(x) = -5x^2 - 24x - 36, x_{n+1} = \sqrt[3]{\dfrac{-5x_n^2 - 24x_n - 36}{2}}$
    For $\bar{x} \in (-2, -1)$: $x_0 = -2.000000, x_2 = -1.738099$
    $x_4 = -1.700328, x_6 = -1.694035,$
    $x_7 = -1.692232, x_8 = -1.692974.$
    Hence, to two decimal places, $\bar{x} = -1.69.$
7. For $x \in (0, 1), \bar{x} = 0.2413$
    For $x \in (3, 4), \bar{x} = 3.0474$

EXERCISES 9-3

Set A

1. See Graph 9-1

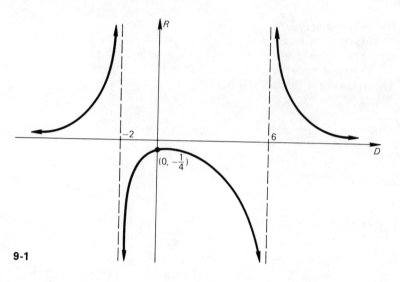

9-1

3. See Graph 9-2

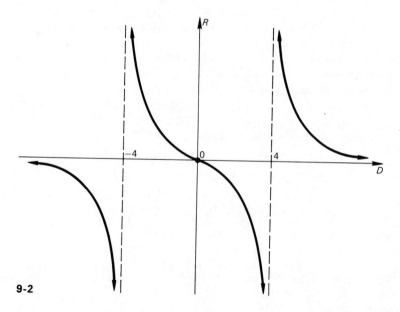

9-2

5. See Graph 9-3

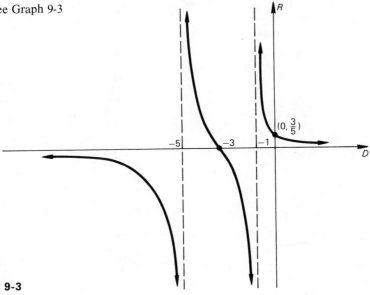

9-3

7. See Graph 9-4

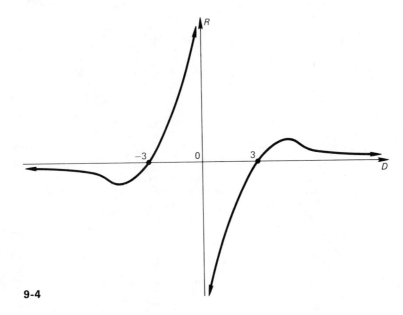

9-4

Set B

9.   See Graph 9-5

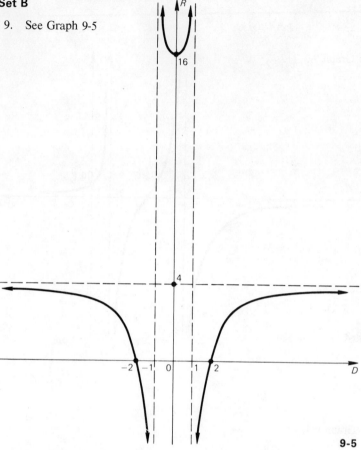

9-5

11.   See Graph 9-6

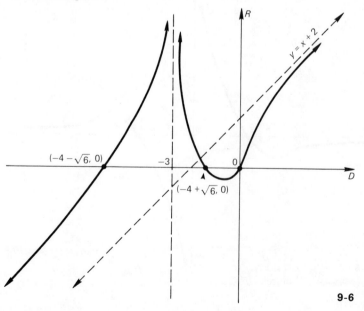

9-6

EXERCISES 10-2

Set A

2. (a) $\{f_k\} = \frac{1}{2},\ \frac{1}{4},\ \frac{1}{6},\ \frac{1}{8},\ \frac{1}{10},\ \frac{1}{12}$
   (c) $\{f_k\} = 0,\ \frac{9}{4},\ \frac{8}{3},\ \frac{45}{16},\ \frac{72}{25},\ \frac{35}{12}$
   (e) $\{f_k\} = -1,\ \frac{3}{4},\ -\frac{5}{9},\ \frac{7}{16},\ -\frac{9}{25},\ \frac{11}{36}$
3. (a) $\frac{137}{120}$
   (c) $\frac{12731}{1200}$
   (e) $-\frac{2621}{3600}$
4. (a) $\{a_k\} = 3,\ 7,\ 11,\ 15,\ 19,\ 23$
   (c) $\{a_k\} = -\frac{1}{3},\ -\frac{5}{3},\ -3,\ -\frac{13}{3},\ -\frac{17}{3},\ -7$
5. (a) $\{b_k\} = 2,\ 4,\ 8,\ 16,\ 32,\ 64$
   (d) $\{b_k\} = -\frac{2}{3},\ \frac{1}{6},\ -\frac{1}{24},\ \frac{1}{96},\ -\frac{1}{384},\ \frac{1}{1536}$
6. (a) 78   (c) −22
7. (a) 126   (d) $-\frac{273}{512}$

Set B

9. (a) $n = 5$ (c) $n = 4$
11. (a) $a_n = 6 + 5(n - 1)/2$
    (c) $b_n = 2^{n-1}$
    (e) $a_n = 16 - (n - 1) = 17 - n$

Set C

16. $a_{k+2} = a_k + a_{k+1}$, for $k \in \mathbb{N}$
18. (a) 10,836   (c) −915   (e) 98,280   (g) −26,183

EXERCISES 10-3

Set A

1. (a) $S = (\frac{2}{3}) \displaystyle\sum_{n=1}^{\infty} (\frac{2}{3})^n$

   (c) $S = \displaystyle\sum_{n=1}^{\infty} \frac{(2n - 1)(2n + 1)}{(2n)(2n + 2)}$

   (e) $S = \displaystyle\sum_{n=1}^{\infty} \frac{1}{n(n + 1)}$
2. (a) $S = 2$ (c) $S = \frac{17}{3}$
3. (a) cos 0.0189 requires 3 terms
       sin 0.0189 requires 2 terms
   (c) cos 0.9314 requires 5 terms
       sin 0.9314 requires 5 terms
   (e) cos 1.439 requires 7 terms
       sin 1.439 requires 7 terms

INDEX

A 7
B 8
C 9
D 0
E 1
F 2
G 3
H 4
I 5
J 6